THE DOCTOR
AND
HIS PATIENT

A *Sociological Interpretation*

By
SAMUEL W. BLOOM, Ph.D.

*This Study was
Supported and Originally Published by
Russell Sage Foundation*

THE FREE PRESS, *New York*
COLLIER-MACMILLAN LIMITED, *London*

PUBLICATIONS OF RUSSELL SAGE FOUNDATION

Russell Sage Foundation was established in 1907 by Mrs. Russell Sage for the improvement of social and living conditions in the United States. In carrying out its purpose the Foundation conducts research under the direction of members of the staff or in close collaboration with other institutions, and supports programs designed to develop and demonstrate productive working relations between social scientists and other professional groups. As an integral part of its operations, the Foundation from time to time publishes books or pamphlets resulting from these activities. Publication under the imprint of the Foundation does not necessarily imply agreement by the Foundation, its Trustees, or its staff with the interpretations or conclusions of the authors.

© 1963, 1965 RUSSELL SAGE FOUNDATION

Printed in the United States of America

All rights reserved. No part of this book may be reproduced or utilized in any form or by any means, electronic or mechanical, including photocopying, recording, or by any information storage and retrieval system, without permission in writing from the Publisher.

For information, address:

THE FREE PRESS
A DIVISION OF THE MACMILLAN COMPANY
60 Fifth Avenue, New York, N.Y. 10011

Collier-Macmillan Canada, Ltd., Toronto, Ontario

Library of Congress Catalog Card Number: 63-20093

FIRST FREE PRESS PAPERBACK EDITION 1965

INTRODUCTION
TO THE PAPERBACK EDITION

IN 1956, when this book was first conceived, sociology appeared to be completing the initial phase of its postwar relationship with medical education. Beginning a decade earlier, the request to sociologists focused on the study of the social behavior surrounding disease and on the study of medical education itself. The challenge to sociology, in effect, was to demonstrate its validity as a science. In the mid-fifties, there was added the request to teach sociology to medical students. The challenge here was to extract from the general field a body of knowledge that was most relevant for the special situation of medical education, and to articulate it effectively for communication to students. This was a trial period for courses in behavioral science, usually in either psychiatry or preventive medicine. Although behavioral science was defined sometimes narrowly as social science and, at other times, much more broadly, sociology was virtually always an important ingredient.

Today, a decade later, still another phase of participation by sociology in medical education appears to be emerging. There are signs that the trial period is almost over, and sociologists are being asked increasingly to join in the common tasks of medical education. The assignment has become less that of the adjunct specialist and more the coequal faculty partner.

At the same time, the place of medical sociology within its parent discipline has undergone an equal if not greater metamorphosis. Much like their medical counterparts, sociologists looked upon medical sociology at first only as a special problem area for research. In time, academic departments of sociology in the university began to teach medical sociology as a legitimate subfield for graduate study. More recently, medical sociology has begun to appear with some regularity as a course in the undergraduate liberal arts curriculum, and sociologists with career activities dominated by research on medical problems have been welcomed to major appointments on sociology faculties.

Thus, two years after the publication of the first edition of this book, the state of the general field for which it was written continues to be active and expanding. In assaying the extent and character of the field's development, there are fortunately a series of very thorough and critical reviews which continue the fine standards of earlier papers by Caudill,[1] Freeman and Reeder,[2] Reader and Goss,[3] and Polgar.[4]

Reader,[5] speaking from the vantage point of a professor of medicine who has collaborated closely with sociologists in both teaching and research for more than a decade, presents an appraisal of medical sociology which finds much solid achievement in the work conducted so far. For the future, he anticipates closer and more stable colleagueship between medicine and sociology. Williams,[6] on the other hand, and Freeman, Levine, and Reeder,[7] place a greater emphasis on the problems which have attended this collaboration. Freidson[8] concentrates on the substance of the sociology of medicine, achieving the best clarification of scientific accomplishments and trends that has yet appeared.

In this book, however, the intention was not to write either a primer on medical sociology or to address a general audience. The specific target was the medical student who, at the time, was most likely to be exposed to sociology in medical school, if at all, in a first- or second-year preclinical course in psychiatry. With reference to this particular educational problem, there is some evidence of changes in the trends described in my earlier introduction. It seems appropriate, therefore, in these brief prefatory remarks, to limit discussion to a closer look at the particular group and educational context for which the book was intended.

There is some reason to believe that, in spite of the significantly increased acceptance of sociology in American medical education, the medical student has less formal contact with sociologists in coursework than he had a few years ago. Preliminary data from a survey currently in progress[9] identifies only twelve medical schools in this country and Canada in which sociologists participate actively as teachers of medical students, including all departments of the medical school. This is a significantly smaller number than the nineteen schools reported by the GAP Survey of 1960.[10] Since the latter survey was restricted to psychiatry departments, the difference is even more striking. At the same time, reports of increased sociological teaching in schools of public health[11] and in psychiatric residency programs,[12] as well as an added emphasis on social science as part of premedical education, indicate that the place of sociology may be shifting from the medical school toward both the broad earlier underpinnings and the more specialized later stages of the total process of educating physicians.

It is sometimes argued, of course, that the introduction into the medical curriculum of basic behavioral sciences such as sociology may best be accomplished by physicians who, by special training or personal effort, become competent in such disciplines. This point of view has proposed that, especially in learning for a practicing profession, it is vital for students to be able to identify with teachers who function as role models of the practitioner. The opposing view argues that the expanding needs of society for more health professionals together with the change in the doctor's role toward partnership in medical teams require a broader educational base for the doctor of tomorrow than today's doctor-educator can achieve alone.

Whoever shall be the teachers, however, sociology and its companion social sciences have survived and grown during two decades of collaboration with medical educators. The hope of the author, in the original writing of this book, was to contribute to this combined effort by serving what was discerned in the classroom to be a need among medical students for an advanced but medically relevant introduction to sociology. This hope persists.

SAMUEL W. BLOOM, PH.D.

May 15, 1965

NOTES

1. Caudill, William, "Applied Anthropology in Medicine" in Kroeber, A. L., editor, *Anthropology Today,* University of Chicago Press, Chicago, 1953, pp. 771–806.

2. Freeman, Howard E., and Leo G. Reeder, "Medical Sociology: A Review of the Literature," *American Sociological Review,* vol. 22, February, 1957, pp. 73–81.

3. Reader, George G., and Mary E. W. Goss, "The Sociology of Medicine" in Merton, Robert K., Leonard Broom, and L. S. Cottrell, Jr., editors, *Sociology Today.* Basic Books, Inc., New York, 1959, pp. 229–246.

4. Polgar, Steven, "Health and Human Behavior: Areas of Interest Common to the Social and Medical Sciences," *Current Anthropology,* vol. 3, April, 1962, pp. 159–205.

5. Reader, George G., "Contributions of Sociology to Medicine" in Freeman, Howard E., Sol Levine, and Leo G. Reeder, editors, *Handbook of Medical Sociology.* Prentice-Hall, Inc., Englewood Cliffs, N. J., 1963, pp. 1–16.

6. Williams, Richard H., "The Strategy of Sociomedical Research" in Freeman, Howard E., and associates, editors, *op. cit.,* pp. 423–448.

7. Freeman, Howard E., Sol Levine, and Leo G. Reeder, "Present Status of Medical Sociology" in Freeman, Howard E., and associates, editors, *op. cit.,* pp. 473–493.

8. Freidson, Eliot, *The Sociology of Medicine.* Basil Blackwell, Oxford, England, 1963.

9. Directed by Peter New, this is a survey of social science teaching and research in medical and public health schools in the United States and Canada. Sponsored by the Section on Medical Sociology of the American Sociological Association, the survey is scheduled for completion in late 1965.

10. Group for the Advancement of Psychiatry (GAP), *The Preclinical Teaching of Psychiatry.* Report No. 54, New York, 1962.

11. See Suchman, Edward A., *Sociology and the Field of Public Health,* Russell Sage Foundation, New York, 1963; and Wellin, Edward, "Uses of Behavioral (Social) Sciences in Public Health," National Institute of Mental Health, July, 1961 (mimeographed).

12. American Psychiatric Association, *Training the Psychiatrist to Meet Changing Needs.* Report of the 1962 Conference on Graduate Psychiatric Education, Washington, D.C., 1963.

CONTENTS

INTRODUCTION TO THE PAPERBACK EDITION	iii
PREFACE BY LESTER J. EVANS, M.D.	7
INTRODUCTION	11
The Baylor Experimental Course in Behavioral Science	11
Some Origins of a Social Science of Medicine	14
The Influence of World War II	17
Sociological Aspects of the Doctor-Patient Relationship	23
Acknowledgments	25

Part One
THE FRAME OF REFERENCE

CHAPTER 1. FROM ART TO SOCIAL SCIENCE	33
The Patient: "Good" or "Bad"	34
A Case Illustration	37
Behavioral Implications of Organic Symptoms	39
Basic Models of the Doctor-Patient Relationship	40
The Influence of Culture	42
A "Home-made" Experiment	44
Time and Responsibility	47
System and the Human Group	48
CHAPTER 2. THE CONCEPTUAL APPROACH	52
The Doctor-Patient Relationship: A Limited View	52
The "Field" of the Doctor-Patient Relationship	58
Culture: A Definition	63
Social Role: A Definition	67
Social System: A Definition	69
The Frame of Reference	72

Part Two
SOCIAL ROLES AND THEIR INSTITUTIONAL CONTEXT

CHAPTER 3. THE MEDICAL PROFESSION: A HISTORICAL DISCUSSION OF THE SOCIAL ORGANIZATION OF MODERN MEDICINE ... 77
Culture: The Significant Sociological Unit ... 79
Medicine in a Plains Indian Tribe ... 81
Dobuan Medicine ... 82
Some Origins of Modern Medicine ... 84
Medicine as a Profession: A Definition ... 87
The Social Role of the Physician ... 91
Summary ... 95

CHAPTER 4. THE ROLE OF THE PATIENT ... 98
The Definition of Illness: I. Across Cultures ... 99
The Definition of Illness: II. Subcultural Differences ... 105
The Sick Role ... 112

CHAPTER 5. THE FAMILY ... 119
The Modern American Family: Its Form and Origins ... 121
The Problem of Illness in the Modern Family ... 123
The Family as the "Field" of the Patient Role ... 127
   The Q- Family ... 128
Discussion ... 135
Summary ... 139

Part Three
THE HOSPITAL AS A SOCIAL INSTITUTION

CHAPTER 6. ORIGINS OF THE TEMPLE OF MEDICAL SCIENCE ... 145
The Hospital: Origins and Development ... 147
The Hospital and the Medical Profession ... 150
The Temple of Medical Science: What God Does It Serve? ... 155
The Trend Toward Personalized Care ... 157
Summary ... 158

CHAPTER 7. THE GENERAL HOSPITAL AS A HUMAN ORGANIZATION ... 160
The Hospital Troika: Three Sources of Authority ... 162
Bureaucracy in the Hospital ... 167
   Case 1. An Example of Functional Adaptation ... 173
   Case 2. An Example of Role Conflict ... 176
Summary ... 181

CONTENTS

CHAPTER 8. SOME EARLY CONTRIBUTIONS TO A SOCIOLOGY OF THE MENTAL HOSPITAL — 184
- The Therapeutic Community: Some Early Examples — 185
- "Moral Treatment": Its Decline and Revival — 194
- The Therapeutic Community: Concept and Program — 201
- Summary — 205

CHAPTER 9. FINDINGS AND CONSEQUENCES OF SOCIAL RESEARCH — 209
- Communication, Duplicity, and Remotivation — 210
- The Human Relations Approach — 211
- The Power-Structure Argument — 219
- Social Remotivation — 224
- Summary — 229

Part Four
THE FRAME OF REFERENCE AT WORK

CHAPTER 10. THE DOCTOR-PATIENT RELATIONSHIP AS A SOCIAL SYSTEM — 235
- Culture and Interaction Process — 236
- The Internal Social Dynamics of the Doctor-Patient Relationship — 247
  - The Case of the Intellectual Woman — 248
- The Full Context of the Doctor-Patient Relationship — 255
- Conclusions — 256

INDEX — 263

PREFACE

It is significant that this book should have been written for students of medicine and other health professions at this critical period in the growth of their educational institutions. By and large a medical student completes his long period of professional education with little understanding of the intricate social complex in which he is to become a leading figure, a complex that is continually being reshaped by the scientific, economic, and human forces that determine the character and function of all social institutions. Such a void in awareness and understanding needs to be filled, and, I believe, *The Doctor and His Patient* will serve that objective.

Medicine is in the midst of a period of transition and challenge not unlike the situation it faced one hundred years ago. In response, it is again reaching outside itself, but now, secure in its century-old partnership with the natural sciences, it seeks the added collaboration of the behavioral sciences.

That this is indeed a critical phase of medical history can be argued from several types of evidence. Perhaps the most striking however, is the emergence of health as a value in itself. Life, of course, has always been precious to man. Yet, now that the expectancy of life's length has been extended so markedly and the fatal threats of infectious, nutritional, and other types of illness reduced so drastically, the general reaction has been to value life more than ever. Instead of being thankful for the respite from death, we have become conscious of and jealous about the gift of life.

The theme has many variations. Disease, most frequently identified by structural change in the body, has been the unrivaled target of medical science; health, conceived as well-being, is now becoming its competitor. Death was the companion of disease and therefore of necessity medicine's overriding preoccupation; but attention has been deflected away from death and toward life. From dying to living patients, from the signals of danger to concern for something more than "the absence of illness" as the criterion of health—these are the directions of modern medicine.

Such alterations in attitude, of course, reflect other underlying changes, including the technology and social organization of medicine. An important purpose of this book is to delineate and describe how these developments have influenced the most basic social relationship in medicine, the doctor and his patient. In the role of the physician himself, one of the most dramatic consequences may be seen. Less and less, the doctor stands alone in his responsibility for treating the patient. As the technology of medical care has expanded, the physician has become more dependent upon a team of collaborating health professions, and upon the hospital as the setting for his work. Both the doctor and his patient may cling to images of each other that are rooted in the past, but the pressure for change is relentless.

Perhaps the most challenging of all, however, are the implications for medical education. How can the human relations of medicine be incorporated as part of the general preparation of the physician? More specifically, how can knowledge derived from the social and psychological sciences be woven into the fabric of medical care itself? These are the major questions of this book.

In his answer, Dr. Bloom seeks to lift the doctor-patient relationship out of the ordinary way of thinking about it. Both the doctor and his patient are shown as the products of the culture and its subgroups. Moreover, the relationship itself is described as a system, in which the elements are interdependent. It is not a static structure, but a system in balance, regulated by the principle of homeostasis, in which no part or function operates independently of all other parts or functions.

The analogy to theories of the physicochemical system is unavoidable and gives hope that the forward thrust which system theory gave to biological science will be matched in the experience of the behavioral sciences. Certainly, it would appear to be more than coincidence that medicine has been forced to seek help from each branch of knowledge at a comparable moment in its history.

Is this part of medicine's recurring tendency to see the whole and not only its parts? The conception of a whole organism and of the patient as a whole human being—are these perhaps ideas that are embedded in the deep-lying logic of medicine, and not simply humanistic hopes? Is it not also a reflection of the fact that health, however perceived and dealt with by man, is increasingly recognized as a major focus of human behavior?

The past fifteen years in medical education have seen a variety of attempts to help future doctors perceive their patients as more than a sum of parts. The effort to bring the patient into focus as a living, feeling, and social human being has been enthusiastic and imaginative. This vigorous enterprise, however, cannot continue to grow and succeed without two related developments, the first, a task of scholarship and the second, a problem of complex organization.

The task for scholars is to sift, arrange, and communicate new areas of knowledge from the behavioral sciences in a form that instills substance and rigor into recent experiments in medical education, comparable to that from the more familiar biological sciences.

The second task is to provide in organized medicine a setting in which the physician, whether a fledgling or a veteran, is encouraged to apply the new attitudes, methods, and knowledge of patients' needs and care to which he has been exposed in recent educational programs.

The challenge—and this is explicit in Dr. Bloom's report—is to build a social science of medicine which, in substance, matches the growing awareness of need for such an added dimension to medicine. There is another challenge equal in importance which, because it is the responsibility of the medical profession, has not been stated in this volume. I refer to the challenge to create the necessary situation, particularly in the hospital but also in the general context of medical care, to enable and foster the practice of comprehensive medicine. Properly conceived, the natural foundation for such an enterprise would be the contributions coming from all fields of knowledge—the natural, physical, and behavioral sciences and the humanities and arts—which contribute to an understanding of the nature and behavior of the human being. That this hope shall become a reality is strongly encouraged by this book, written by a sociologist specifically for the purposes of medical education. In terms that are of immediate relevance but more long-range promise for the physician of tomorrow, *The Doctor and His Patient* is a timely contribution.

LESTER J. EVANS, M.D.
Executive Director
New York State Committee
on Medical Education

INTRODUCTION

THE TEACHING OF "THE BEHAVIORAL SCIENCES"[1] has been an important part of efforts since World War II to improve medical education. The same period witnessed a strong surge of interest in research concerning the social and emotional factors in health and illness. As a result, social scientists, including sociologists, anthropologists, and social psychologists, have been added to the faculties of medical schools for the first time in more than token numbers and with more than token responsibilities.[2]

In retrospect, one finds patterns and trends in this development. Yet each of the innovating programs, for the most part, grew from independent origins. Lacking both precedents and the compelling influence of any single authoritative model, the experience of these newest recruits to medical education was varied. For those asked to teach social science to medical students, however, there was likely to be one way in which the experience was the same: the available publications were not well adapted to the special needs of medical students.[3] The decision to write this book stems from such an experience.

As the first step in this Introduction, we will recount in more detail how and why the book came to be written. Secondly, we will attempt to show its relationships to some of the more general origins of a social science of medicine. Finally, the major subject headings of the book will be reviewed, and their purposes explained.

The Baylor Experimental Course in Behavioral Science

Beginning in 1956 and continuing for five years, the author participated in an experimental course for freshmen students at

Baylor University College of Medicine. The purpose of the course was to introduce the sciences of human behavior, particularly experimental psychology, sociology, anthropology, and the psychology of growth and development. As was true of most comparable efforts to introduce this type of subject matter into the medical curriculum, this course was taught in the Department of Psychiatry.

This is not to say that such courses are limited to any single department. One finds the teaching of similar material and the participation of social scientists in departments of medicine,[4] preventive medicine and public health,[5] and others. Moreover, at the University of Kentucky, a separate Department of Behavioral Science has a major teaching responsibility;[6] and other institutions are at least exploring a similar step.[7] Nevertheless, as a recent survey of the 81 American and 12 Canadian four-year schools has shown, psychiatry has been given a steadily increasing responsibility for teaching in the preclinical as well as the clinical phases of the medical school; and it has interpreted this responsibility broadly to mean that it should introduce medical students to a basic science of normal human behavior. "It is evident," concluded the survey, ". . . that psychiatry, in 1960, had been assigned a significant role in preclinical medical education. . . . Another major trend is a shift in attitude concerning the purpose of preclinical psychiatric education. The traditional orientation was primarily toward specific preparation for clinical psychiatry; the current view explicitly acknowledges that an understanding of human behavior is essential to the functioning of *all* physicians."[8]

At Baylor the shift away from a more narrowly clinical emphasis was initiated in 1954 by Dr. William T. Lhamon immediately after he was appointed chairman of the Department of Psychiatry. At first he gave all thirty-three hours of lecture to the freshmen himself. Within a year, a psychologist joined him, and after another year, the author, as a sociologist, completed the teaching "team."[9]

The author's particular assignment was to select and organize from the main body of modern sociology some concepts that would fit within such a program. It soon became evident that a textbook designed for the special needs of this type of education was needed. Appropriate reading materials in sociology are plentiful, we found, but they are scattered through a wide variety of journals and books.[10] In itself, this would not have caused difficulty if the students had sufficient time and library facilities available. They had neither.

It seemed obvious that this book could not be written as a standard text, either in the sense of being a primer or a comprehensive review of the development of sociology. Not only are there other books devoted to such purposes, but the rather unique teaching situation emphasized what has been called the "problem of relevance." That is, what concepts, theories, and methods in sociology are most directly relevant for medical education, and how can they best be communicated to medical students?[11]

Two separate approaches were taken to this problem, based upon a comparison of the medical student with his peers across the campus who study for the Ph.D. degree. On the one hand, it seemed only appropriate to expect that medical students would have the same kind of interest and seriousness of purpose in learning about the sciences of human behavior as one expects from graduate students in the social sciences. On the other hand, it was only realistic to take account of important differences between the two types of student. One undoubtedly significant difference is in their preparation.

The overwhelming emphasis in premedical studies continues to be in the biological sciences. Even before he reaches medical school, the medical student is taught that the "real payoff," when he becomes responsible for patients, will come from the biological sciences. At least implicitly, the study of the social sciences is downgraded. It was our conclusion, therefore, that even as the medical student should be approached as a relatively mature advanced student, the special circumstances of his preparatory education require also that this approach should be basic and introductory. Moreover, because of the limitations of time and emphasis in the medical curriculum, the illustrative materials should be selected mainly from sociological inquiry on medical problems, rather than from the more complete array of research subjects which are studied by the candidate for a Ph.D. degree.

Sociological research in medicine that can serve to illustrate basic concepts and theory is quite varied and growing rapidly.[12] For purposes of teaching, we chose the doctor-patient relationship as perhaps the most advantageous starting point. Freshman medical students, although still far removed from the role of the doctor, actively think ahead to what it will be like when they become "real doctors." Indeed, such anticipation appears to be important in sustaining them through the "tough" years of preclinical science.[13] Moreover, there are available some excellent materials that treat the doctor-patient relationship primarily in sociological terms.

This, then, became the goal we set in the teaching program at Baylor University College of Medicine and, subsequently, the main objective of this book: *to teach on a graduate but introductory level, basic concepts and theories of sociology, with illustrations derived from an intensive study of the doctor-patient relationship.*

Fortunately, the atmosphere at Baylor was very favorable to the teaching of social science to medical students. Although it was psychiatry that opened the way, other segments of the medical school quickly joined in granting a sympathetic hearing to sociology and its companion sciences of behavior.

Some Origins of a Social Science of Medicine

The place of social science in medical education is by no means an accomplished fact but its imprint is already notable. In its 1960 survey the Group for the Advancement of Psychiatry, for example, made the following statement about social science and psychiatric education: "If the 1940's was an era of psychodynamic and psychoanalytic expansion, the 1950's can be considered the introductory period of the social or behavioral sciences."[14]

Yet twenty years ago, when a similar survey was conducted by Ebaugh and Rymer, virtually no mention was made of a major role for social and behavioral science in either psychiatry or medical education as a whole. Rather, the emphasis was almost entirely on the growth of psychological dynamics as the basic subject matter of psychiatry.[15] By 1951, in the report of the Ithaca

Conference on Psychiatric Education, a new orientation was already evident, favoring the introduction of the study of normal human behavior in the medical curriculum.[16] In the latter report, a special chapter by Norman Cameron entitled "Human Ecology and Personality in the Training of Physicians" proved to be particularly significant.[17]

Cameron's recommended design for a course in human behavior was used as the blueprint for the freshman course in psychiatry at Baylor, and it became evident in the 1960 survey by GAP that psychiatry departments in other medical schools were influenced in a similar way.

In the 1960 survey fully 87 out of 91 departmental chairmen said that social science should be taught both in premedical and in medical education. As many as 20 recommended that a new separate department should be created to teach social science in medical schools; 64 believed that the department of psychiatry should assume this responsibility. These beliefs have already been implemented in 21 departments where sociologists or anthropologists actively teach medical students as part of the psychiatric faculty.

What the GAP survey documents for psychiatric education are the results of a state of unusual ferment and experimentation that has gripped all of medical education since World War II. The mood for change has been so great, and the implications of curriculum revisions such as occurred at Western Reserve University[18] so important, that it has become almost commonplace to draw analogies between the present and the time of the Flexner Report.[19] Perhaps the most significant consequences of events surrounding the Flexner Report was the full wedding of the basic biological sciences to the medical curriculum. In the minds at least of some, we are experiencing today a joining of the sciences of psychological and social behavior to medical education that compares to events a half-century ago.

This was the main idea expressed by George Packer Berry in his 1952 presidential address to the Association of American Medical Colleges. He referred to what he called "provocative experiments . . . aimed at making revisions in our teaching programs which are consistent with a growing knowledge of the whole patient rather than just part of the patient."[20] These experiments were rooted, he asserted, in fundamental changes that had occurred in medical practice. Dramatically increased control of physical illness, he believed, had turned attention to the emotional and social components of patient problems.

The Flexner Report, on the other hand, was based on a different kind of problem. Dr. Henry S. Pritchett, then president of the Carnegie Foundation, stated in the introduction that the Flexner Report grew out of concern for *the relationship between the University and its professional school.* The problem, in other words, was one of social organization. At the time, many medical schools were proprietary, so that medical education was organized largely independent of the university. Room had to be made for laboratory science. The enormous financial burdens of incorporating the rapidly developing technology of biological science had to be assumed. In order to keep its practice in pace with the developments of science, the medical profession had to be motivated to assume this burden. In the end, an argument won out that allied the professional school and the university. The university's academic standards were reasserted in the training of the professional.[21]

Today, however, the basic problem appears to be in the doctor-patient relationship. It is here that a lack, a weakness has asserted itself; and medical education, securely established in the excellence of its scientific standards, is being challenged to provide equally rigorous and effective training for the management of the human relations components of the doctor's job. To meet this problem, the "provocative experiments" described by Berry have emerged.[22]

Merton, in the most detailed treatment of this question yet published, traces what he calls "sources of convergence" in both medicine and sociology that have led to recent collaboration between the two.[23] Merton agrees with Berry's analysis, adding that a commitment to the scientific method led medicine to the attempt to replace "howsoever skilled empiricism by the beginnings of more systematic and rational analysis of the process of education."[24] This kind of motivation on the part of medicine dovetailed with the following kinds of developments in sociology:

1. The marked and cumulating interest in the sociology of professions which includes, as a major component, studies of professional schools;

2. The growing utilization of social science as composing part of the scientific basis for the provision of health care in contemporary society;

3. The considerable recent growth in the empirical study of complex social organizations, among which schools constitute an important special class;

4. The similar growth of interest in the process of adult socialization in general which, in application to the field of medicine, is concerned with the processes by which the neophyte is transformed into one or another kind of medical man; and

5. The recent advances in methods and techniques of social inquiry which make it possible to examine these subjects and problems by means of systematic inquiry.[25]

West proposes that the increased role of social science in medicine is part of a more general movement toward the unification of the sciences.[26] Social science, according to his description, is a latecomer to what he calls "the behavioral science movement." Intellectually, the members of this movement are said to share a conviction in the "necessity to formulate a more scientifically complete picture of the nature of man." The emphasis on *process* in biological science, it is claimed, prepared the way intellectually for behavioral science in medicine.

All of these views focus on intellectual origins of the emergence of social science in medicine. They emphasize the development of science, advances in knowledge that achieve more control over the organic aspects of illness, the growing maturity of social science, and so on—all within the sphere of the history of ideas. However, it was a political and military event, World War II, that triggered medicine's intensified interest in social science.

The Influence of World War II

As one reviews the history of medicine during World War II, two events far removed from social science would appear to dwarf all others. There was first the impact of the antibiotic drugs and their tremendous value not only in the cure of infections but in the prevention of disease. Second to this only in its order of appearance was the break-through of atomic fission. Atomic research immediately had a revolutionary effect upon every clinical and laboratory branch of medical science.[27] Yet when the New York Academy of Medicine organized its Lectures to the Laity in 1946–1947 on the subject of "Medical Experience in the War," it chose for emphasis neither of these outstanding scientific achievements, but instead "Problems of Psychiatry and Human Behavior." As the president of the Academy explained, ". . . the Committee [in its selection] lays pointed emphasis upon the fact that by far the greatest lesson which the war has taught, far greater in its significance for humanity than either atomic energy or the control of the infectious diseases, has been the recent revelation of the magnitude and multiplicity of the disorders of human behavior and their fundamental responsibility for the unhappy state of the modern world."[28]

Particularly significant was the fact that these "problems of human disorder" were not shunted to psychiatry and then forgotten by the rest of medicine. Speaking in what proved to be a prophetic way, the president of the New York Academy of Medicine made it clear that responsibility for the relief of the psychosocial aspects of human disorder must be shared by medicine as a whole in cooperation with the public.

War, of course, is full of irony. The special irony of World War II was that, as its medicine gained victories over disease of truly heroic proportions, the military added to its arsenal a weapon so destructive that these medical gains were puny in comparison. This, it seems to us, is the most direct and simple explanation for the postwar interest by medicine and, indeed, by all society in the so-called "human" factors, the psychological and sociological. In peacetime, medical science, within a short forty-year span, had lengthened life expectancy by one-third. In wartime, a mammoth preventive and curative enterprise had reduced medical fatalities for the first time in history below that caused by battle. The overall death rate was 0.6 per thousand men per year as compared to 16.5 in World War I. Even as these victories over death were consolidated, and battle, so to speak, made safer than ever, mankind watched awe-struck as 80,000 civilians were killed at Hiroshima in a few seconds. In the wake of this awesome event, it must have been obvious to all that the gains of the physical and biological sciences would be neutralized if man could not gain more control over his inner psychological and outer sociological environments.

We use the word "control" because this seems truly the direction in which attention turned. In an age of science, and in the wake of the "age of reason," we seem now to be placing our hopes in the control that is a logical function of knowledge. The control over the physical environment we have gained from natural sciences is no longer disputable. Meanwhile, the age-old controls of faith and morality have served man less well in gaining control over himself. The consequence has been a further shift to the methods of science, which have served him so well in the physical world, only now the focal subject of inquiry is man himself as an actor in society.

This, of course, is the "big picture." There were more specific events in the day-to-day experience of medicine in the war that focused attention upon the psychological and sociological aspects of human disorder. Moreover, these experiences were not only in the military. Civilians were more integrally involved in this war than probably any other before it. Particularly upon children, the emotional effects were critical. As sad as this was, we learned from it.[29]

In our own military establishment, twelve out of every hundred men rejected at induction centers were involved in some personality problem. More startling, 40 per cent of all medical military discharges were due to personality disorders, a total of nearly 400,000. Another 150,000 were discharged without a specific diagnosis of personality disorder but because they "could not fit" into the Army. In short, one out of every seven young men between the ages of eighteen and thirty-seven was adjudged to be ineffective because of an emotional or educational disability.[30]

If these emotional casualties had been primarily cases of breakdown under battle stress, they would probably have caused less interest because it has been our custom, more or less, to think of battlefield psychosis as a danger to which "normal" men are prone. However, more than half of all the psychological cases treated in military hospitals were men who had never been in battle.

In World War I there were 97,578 admissions to neuropsychiatric services in army hospitals. In effect, they were not treated, merely separated from others; their care was not therapeutic in any active sense, only custodial. If they did not recover spontaneously, they were given pensions for life. Our attitude toward these men was one of pity and guilt. They were the awesome residue of war, killed in spirit as surely as those who were dead physically on the battlefield. We did not see them as part of the wounded, but as a group apart, a group for whom we had little hope.

There followed a period between the great wars when psychiatry learned much about mental illness. Therefore, when admissions to neuropsychiatric services in World War II soared to 1,000,000, ten times the figure of World War I, they were treated with hope and with much success. Many of these men were able to return to duty, not a few to combat duty. By 1945, seven out of ten went home rather than to a Veterans Hospital.

Moreover, much of the treatment of these men was given by physicians who had no prewar experience in psychiatry. Under the pressure of war, the crowded neuropsychiatric services were staffed by doctors who either learned at the elbow of a psychiatrist or in brief, highly condensed training courses. In this way, a forced educational process occurred within the medical profession. Doctors learned, in a way that was yet unavailable in most centers of medical learning, about the effective advances psychiatry had already accomplished, and probably, more importantly, many learned to view mental illness in a new frame of reference. The psychotic ceased to be the hopeless, "different" patient, and the neurotic was not just a malingerer or "crock." Instead, emotional disorder came to be recognized as a threat to every individual just as physical illness has been long regarded as a danger to which all are susceptible. Moreover, concepts of prevention were increasingly applied to mental illness.

This view of mental illness was not, in fact, *new* in psychiatry, but only under the conditions of the war did it gain a foothold in the medical profession as a whole.

Another lesson of the war was that "cure" in the sense of removal of symptoms was not required for effective functioning in life situations. This was a way of thinking, of course, which had long been accepted for physical illness; for example, an individual might have a serious chronic illness, like arthritis or diabetes, but continue to work and live "normally" within given limits. The war showed that many personalities thought to be unstable functioned surprisingly well in combat and under other stresses. Also some neurotics gave a good account of themselves in battle, but were unable to stand those aspects of army life that so-called "normals" found less stressful, the regimentation, the discipline, the autocratic organization. In other words, mental sickness was not an absolute, either-or phenomenon. Both psychosis and neurosis came to be seen as the product of a complex set of factors. Among these, the individual's personality was critical but not sufficient in itself. Also significant were elements in his social experience, both in his life history and in his current definition of the social situation.

As can be seen, each of these steps by the medical profession toward better understanding of its own psychiatric branch brought it closer to the social sciences. If a neurotic can function well under some life conditions and poorly under others, obviously his neurotic condition involves not merely a personality but a personality "in interaction with the patterned situation in which the individual behaves."[31] If most "normal" individuals may be assumed to have a "breaking point," then it becomes critical that we understand why, for example, the experience of combat was so much more stressful under certain social conditions and not under others. The spotlight of medical attention changed from a narrow focus on the individual; its circle widened to include the individual in interaction with his social environment.

While interest in the social psychology of the American soldier was emerging in the medical branches, it was already well established in other parts of the military. One of the unique and highly productive intellectual enterprises stimulated by World War II was the work of a group of psychologists and sociologists working in the Research Branch, Information and Education Division of the War Department.[32] From their studies the details of interaction between personality and social environment were charted in ways that were to prove useful to questions of mental health. For example, they found a hitherto unsuspected loyalty and dependence by combat soldiers upon the small group, the squad or platoon that was the primary locus of their participation in the war.[33] Feelings of sharing and belonging to such groups proved to take precedence for many over even their desire for personal survival. Thus soldiers who were evacuated with injuries often showed impatience to "get back to their outfit," even though this meant return to an otherwise dreaded front. Moreover, replacements in such groups found that they must watch out for themselves while the "oldtimers" watched out for each other with fanatical devotion and self-sacrifice. When removed from their original group men not infrequently showed feelings of intense loss, rebelliousness or worse, in spite of the fact that they were placed in situations much less physically dangerous than previously. "In general," a recent retrospective study concluded, "most soldiers required support from their immediate group in order to function effectively. And when their close ties were suddenly severed, many broke down."[34]

Much more could be added concerning the lessons of wartime for both medicine and social science. Here, however, we are concerned only with establishing that the circumstances of World War II accelerated the emergence of a new kind of interest on the part of medicine in the social sciences. Apparently, this was a chain process. Medicine became more interested in its own subbranch, psychiatry. Psychiatry, meanwhile, found itself drawn toward an increasing collaboration with the social sciences. The social sciences themselves were developing methods of investigation and new knowledge that were vital in enabling a convergence of their work with psychiatry and the health professions as a whole. Underlying these events was mankind's sense of frustration at the irony of war. Instead of "making the world safe for democracy," we seemed instead to be achieving maximum physical health only as a preface to atomic obliteration. Obviously, a high-sounding humanitarianism was not enough. It had not prevented man from killing other men with "conventional" weapons; why should it now prevent atomic war. One hope was for science to match its triumphs over man's physicochemical problems with similar advances in explaining his psychosocial problems.

If there was any hesitation about applying these lessons of World War II, they were quickly dispelled in the Korean "police action." As we saw our own men's minds systematically controlled in what was to be popularly termed "brainwashing," we were forced to acknowledge that advances in the social sciences could be used to destroy as well as to heal. There was no longer any escape. The knowledge of social science became as crucial as that of atomic science, for ironically the struggle to heal is thus impelled by the forces of destruction.

Sociological Aspects of the Doctor-Patient Relationship

As we noted earlier, the problem of teaching social science to medical students presents at least two troublesome disparities: first, the students are at the graduate stage of training, but they are, for the most part, not adequately prepared for graduate level study in the social and psychological sciences; and secondly, too little time remains after their tightly scheduled day in the laboratories of the biological sciences for them to work intensively in the library, which is, in an important sense, the "laboratory" where the advanced study of social science should begin.

The special character of this educational problem has been always in mind as this book was written. It is the basis for a decision to emphasize an approach to learning rather than a survey of the field. The major goal has been to teach a frame of reference, to attempt to sensitize students to see the psychosocial aspects of medical problems, and to provide some guidelines for a realistic interpretation of their importance.

The method we have chosen has been to use the doctor-patient relationship as the unifying theme of a sociology of medicine. This seemed doubly appropriate, for on the one hand, it was out of a new awareness of the social psychology of the doctor-patient relationship that medical education invited the sociologist to share its task; and, from the student's point of view, it is a highly relevant subject for the testing of this type of knowledge.

The discussion begins with a critical evaluation of one view of this relationship that, we believe, is very common but inadequate. It is that conception in which the doctor and his patient are seen essentially as a dyad, interacting according to forces that derive mainly from the adjustment of two separate personalities, drawn together out of the compelling needs set off by illness. The very excellent contributions of this limited view of the doctor-patient relationship are not, in our view, to be dropped or discredited. Rather, we believe they are incomplete. Their full value can be realized only if the relationship is seen against a more complete background. The "field of forces" includes, at the very least, the influence of the major reference groups of each participant: for the doctor, his profession, and for the patient, his family. These, in turn, are derived from culture.

As we build a sketch of the relationship, each of the picture's details is fully described and its place in a larger social system is explained. To be more precise, after defining the major concepts of the approach in Chapters 1 and 2, Chapter 3 is devoted to a description of the physician's role and its roots in the history and organization of the medical profession. Chapter 4 shifts to the patient in the sketch. After a detailed representation of the patient role, the variations of the sick role across cultures and within American society are explained and illustrated. This is followed by a chapter devoted to the family as the single most important social institution from which the patient role is defined and learned.

The major thesis of Chapter 5 is that developments in the evolution of the modern family and technological developments in modern medicine have converged to remove much of the treatment of illness from the home into specialized health-care agencies. Among such agencies, the modern hospital is the outstanding example.

Because of its greatly increased importance in medicine, the hospital is the subject of four chapters. Chapter 6 reviews the history of the hospital, and the variety of forces which have shaped its character. It is a story of an institution originally a refuge for the sick and friendless, once dominated by the authority of the church, and which today has become "the temple of medical science." Chapter 7 studies the general hospital, focusing on the development of its present-day bureaucratic form of organization. The development of team medicine and its effects upon the doctor's role are discussed thoroughly as two of the most significant facets of hospital social organization. Chapter 8 reviews aspects in the history of the mental hospital which have contributed to the development of the program of patient care called "The Therapeutic Community," and Chapter 9 describes and interprets the major theoretical contributions of research on the mental hospital.

In Chapter 10 we return to the perspective of the physician and attempt to show how the approach that has been described can be put to work. For this purpose, case illustrations from the earlier chapters are reviewed, and one additional example is inserted in full detail.

Acknowledgments

It is always difficult to place in their proper order the sources that make the writing of a book possible. In this instance, however, the greatest debt is, without any question, to Russell Sage Foundation. When the Foundation learned of the efforts at Baylor University College of Medicine to develop the teaching of sociology to medical students, it volunteered valuable advice, encouragement, and financial support. At a time when commercial publishers were uncertain or dubious about this type of book, the Foundation urged and facilitated its writing. Particularly, my gratitude is extended to Drs. Donald Young, Leonard S. Cottrell, Jr., Esther Lucile Brown, and Eleanor Bernert Sheldon.

In preliminary mimeographed draft, this book has been used over a period of two years by freshman medical students at Baylor in their first course in psychiatry. Similarly, it has been assigned for reading in lecture courses to psychiatry residents. With the help of funds from Russell Sage Foundation, detailed questionnaire studies and interviews were used to test the responses of these students to the manuscript. They supplied the most vital ingredient to the writing.

Among the students who were particularly helpful were Drs. Jonathan Malev and Russell Martin. They became the first students at Baylor to earn the M.S. degree in behavioral science, and during their special work contributed most significantly to my thinking about the book.

I am especially indebted to Dr. William T. Lhamon, then chairman of the Department of Psychiatry at Baylor and now the chairman of the Department of Psychiatry at Payne Whitney Psychiatric Clinic, Cornell Medical Center. He initiated the teaching program from which this book was conceived, and gave it his generous support. Among my other colleagues at Baylor, I would like to thank particularly Drs. Neil Burch and Howard Kaplan, who were my closest associates in this and other efforts. The interest and support of Dean Stanley W. Olson is acknowledged with deepest appreciation.

It was my good fortune to be introduced to the sociological study of medicine by Professor Robert K. Merton of Columbia University. The experience under his direction was invaluable preparation for my later work as a medical educator.

From the period of my association with the Columbia University Bureau of Applied Social Research, there are many others whom, in gratitude, I would like to recall: particularly, Dr. John McK. Mitchell, then dean of the University of Pennsylvania School of Medicine; Drs. Lester J. Evans, John Eberhart, and Charles Warren, of the Commonwealth Fund; Dr. George G. Reader, professor of medicine at Cornell Medical College; and the research team at the Bureau, including Dr. Patricia L. Kendall, Mary Jean Huntington Cornish, William Martin, William Nichols, David Nasitir, and Drs. David Caplovitz, Renée Fox, Mary E. W. Goss, Gene Levine, Alan Meyer, and Natalie Rogoff Ramsoy.

Among my assistants and secretaries, several were of special help with this manuscript, particularly Carol Summy, Marianne Rose, Margot Palmer, and Marcella Bernstein.

And finally, my family, whose intimate involvement in this work transcends adequate acknowledgment, has agreed that the book should be dedicated to my son Jonathan and to his and my friend, Irwin Barg.

S. W. B.

NOTES TO INTRODUCTION

1. As the term is used currently, behavioral science (or, synonymously, "the behavioral sciences") is hardly more than a decade old. It represents, according to a recent published statement, an attempt to integrate several older areas of scientific inquiry within a more comprehensive and up-to-date approach to the study of man. There are two distinct definitions in use: "One is a comprehensive view including an array of biological, psychological, and social sciences in collaborative inquiry concerning the behavior of man. The other is an interdisciplinary view in a much more limited sense, restricted primarily to collaboration among the fields of sociology, anthropology and social psychology." See Group for the Advancement of Psychiatry (GAP), *The Preclinical Teaching of Psychiatry*, Report No. 54, New York, 1962, pp. 39–43.

2. The exception to this statement is psychology. As early as 1913, a majority of medical schools expressed a desire to establish the teaching of psychology as the basic science of clinical neurology and psychiatry. (See Franz, Sheppard Ivory, "On Psychology and Medical Education," *Science*, vol. 38, 1913, pp. 555–566.) The content that was strongly favored for such courses, however, was "purely objective," or, in other words, only that part of psychology which closely paralleled the natural sciences. (See Watson, John B., "Content of a Course in Psychology for Medical Students," *Journal of the American Medical Association*, vol. 58, March 30, 1912, pp. 916–918.) Approval to teach in terms that more fully expressed the complete range of content in psychology was held back largely until after World War II. It was at this more recent period that sociologists and anthropologists also were brought into medical education. For a thorough discussion of both the history and current status of these behavioral sciences in medicine, see GAP Report No. 54, pp. 9–19.

3. This may be interpreted from the series of books that have been written or are in preparation by the early participants in these educational experiments. Some examples are the following, all published by Russell Sage Foundation: Simmons, Leo W., and Harold G. Wolff, *Social Science in Medicine*, 1954; Saunders, Lyle, *Cultural Difference and Medical Care*, 1954; Paul, Benjamin D., editor, *Health, Culture, and Community*, 1955; Macgregor, Frances Cooke, *Social Science in Nursing*, 1960; and King, Stanley H., *Perceptions of Illness and Medical Practice*, 1962. Also, Jaco, E. Gartly, editor, *Patients, Physicians and Illness*, The Free Press, Glencoe, Ill., 1958.

In preparation are textbooks by Herbert Weiner, a psychiatrist at Albert Einstein Medical College, and another by Bernard Kutner, an anthropologist at the same institution. These, of course, include only such works as the author is aware of. Rodger Badgley, of the University of Saskatchewan Medical College, and Robert Straus, University of Kentucky College of Medicine, have both written detailed course outlines that may by this time have grown into planned publications.

4. An example is the Cornell Comprehensive Care and Teaching Program. See Reader, George G., "The Cornell Comprehensive Care and Teaching Program" in Merton, Robert K., George G. Reader, and Patricia L. Kendall, editors, *The Student-Physician:* Introductory Studies in the Sociology of Medical Education, Harvard University Press (for the Commonwealth Fund), Cambridge, Mass., 1957, pp. 81–101.

5. The examples of this type are more numerous than in medicine. Some of the best known, all social scientists who are teaching members of departments of

preventive medicine and public health, are Lyle Saunders at the University of Colorado, Leo G. Reeder, University of California at Los Angeles, Bernard Kutner, Albert Einstein, and Andie L. Knutson, University of California at Berkeley.

6. See Straus, Robert, "A Department of Behavioral Science," *Journal of Medical Education*, vol. 34, July, 1959, pp. 662–666.

7. See GAP Report No. 54, pp. 37 ff.

8. *Ibid.*, p. 37.

9. This program and its history are described in detail in Bloom, Samuel W., "The Role of the Sociologist in Medical Education," *Journal of Medical Education*, vol. 34, July, 1959, pp. 667–673.

10. This statement (and the book) limits itself to sociology only because this is the author's major field. It is equally true that existing sourcebooks in the other sciences of human behavior do not readily fit the requirements of medical education.

11. Stainbrook, Edward, and Murray Wexler, "The Place of the Behavioral Sciences in the Medical School," *Psychiatry*, vol. 19, August, 1956, pp. 263–269.

12. Several excellent review papers have kept pace with this development over the last decade. See Caudill, William, "Applied Anthropology in Medicine" in Kroeber, A. L., editor, *Anthropology Today*, University of Chicago Press, Chicago, 1953, pp. 771–806; Clausen, John A., *Sociology and the Field of Mental Health*, Russell Sage Foundation, New York, 1956; Freeman, Howard E., and Leo G. Reeder, "Medical Sociology: A Review of the Literature," *American Sociological Review*, vol. 22, February, 1957, pp. 73–81; Reader, George G., and Mary E. W. Goss, "The Sociology of Medicine" in Robert K. Merton, Leonard Broom, and L. S. Cottrell, Jr., editors, *Sociology Today*, Basic Books, Inc., New York, 1959, pp. 229–246.

13. See Huntington, Mary Jean, "The Development of a Professional Self-Image" in Merton, Reader, and Kendall, *op. cit.*, pp. 179–187; and Merton, Robert K., Samuel Bloom, and Natalie Rogoff, "Studies in the Sociology of Medical Education," *Journal of Medical Education*, vol. 31, August, 1956, pp. 552–565. Another study takes the different view that medical students become so absorbed in the demands of their work as students that they do not think of much else. See Becker, Howard S., Blanche Geer, Everett C. Hughes, and Anselm L. Strauss, *Boys in White:* Student Culture in Medical School, University of Chicago Press, Chicago, 1961.

14. GAP Report No. 54, p. 16.

15. Ebaugh, Franklin G., and Charles A. Rymer, *Psychiatry in Medical Education*. Oxford University Press (for the Commonwealth Fund), New York, 1942.

16. *Psychiatry and Medical Education:* Report of the 1951 Conference on Psychiatric Education. American Psychiatric Association, Washington, 1952, pp. 62–97.

17. *Ibid.*, pp. 64–66.

18. See "Reports on Experiments in Medical Education," *Journal of Medical Education*, vol. 31, August, 1956, pp. 515–565.

19. Flexner, Abraham, *Medical Education in the United States and Canada:* A Report to the Carnegie Foundation for the Advancement of Teaching. Bulletin Number Four, New York, 1910.

20. Berry, George Packer, "Medical Education in Transition," *Journal of Medical Education*, vol. 28, March, 1953, pp. 17–42.

21. The history of this development is very succinctly sketched in Brown, Esther Lucile, *Physicians and Medical Care*, Russell Sage Foundation, New York, 1937, pp. 10–37.

22. For a more detailed comparison of the events surrounding the Flexner Report and those of today, see Bloom, S. W., "Changing Perspectives in Medical Education: From the View of the Sociology of Knowledge," *The Pharos*, vol. 21, July, 1958, pp. 3–10.

23. Merton, Robert K., "Some Preliminaries to a Sociology of Medical Education" in Merton, Reader, and Kendall, *op. cit.*, pp. 3–79.

24. *Ibid.*, p. 36.

25. *Ibid.*, p. 52.

26. West, Louis Jolyon, "Behavioral Sciences in the Medical School Curriculum," *Journal of Medical Education*, vol. 34, November, 1959, pp. 1070–1076.

27. New York Academy of Medicine, *Medicine in the Postwar World:* The March of Medicine, 1947, Number XII of the New York Academy of Medicine Lectures to the Laity. Columbia University Press, New York, 1947, p. v.

28. *Ibid.*, p. vi.

29. See Freud, Anna, and Dorothy T. Burlingham, *War and Children*, Medical War Books, International Universities Press, New York, 1944; Freud and Burlingham, *Infants Without Families*, Medical War Books, International Universities Press, 1944; Wolf, Katherine M., "Evacuation of Children in Wartime: A Survey of the Literature with Bibliography," *The Psychoanalytic Study of the Child*, vol. 1, 1945, pp. 389–404. The last reference lists 229 references concerned in general with the problems of civilians in wartime, and with particular thoroughness on the problems observed when Great Britain evacuated 734,883 of its children.

30. Ginzberg, Eli, J. B. Miner, J. K. Anderson, Sol W. Ginsburg, John L. Herma, *The Ineffective Soldier:* Breakdown and Recovery. Columbia University Press, New York, 1959.

31. Merton, Reader, and Kendall, editors, *The Student-Physician*, p. 62. Merton's full statement of this problem is as follows: ". . . the distinctly sociological matter that behavior is not merely a result of the individual's personal qualities but a resultant of these in interaction with the patterned situation in which the individual behaves."

32. Stouffer, Samuel A., and associates, *The American Soldier: Adjustment During Army Life; The American Soldier: Combat and Its Aftermath*, vols. 1 and 2, of Studies in Social Psychology in World War II. Princeton University Press, Princeton, N. J., 1949.

33. Moreover, the soldiers of the enemy, as different as their ideology appeared to be, reacted much the same. Their loyalties were less to the Nazi regime, it would seem, than to each other. See Shils, Edward A., and Morris Janowitz, "Cohesion and Disintegration in the Wehrmacht in World War II," *Public Opinion Quarterly*, vol. 12, no. 2, 1948, pp. 280–315.

34. Ginzberg, Eli, and others, *op. cit.*, p. 9.

PART ONE
THE FRAME OF REFERENCE

Chapter I

FROM ART TO SOCIAL SCIENCE

ART AND SCIENCE march hand in hand through the history of medicine, each taking turns at the lead. A century or more ago science became the dominant partner and has remained so ever since. The art of medicine meanwhile, like an honored but neglected wife, walked behind, passive and obedient to call at those odd moments when the master needed a change of pace.

Recently a change has appeared in the conception of medicine's art-science dualism. Like the ancient mind-body controversy, it is argued that the two are falsely divided. The art of medicine after all is but a name for the human relations of medicine, and is not this the subject of the social sciences just as the human organism is the subject of the biological sciences? Science, the argument continues, is above all a method and its disciplined, systematic approach is as applicable to the study of human relations as to any other subject matter.

In this book the basic assumption is that a body of knowledge is available, sufficient to guide human beings toward more rational and effective relationships with each other. For the physician this is taken to mean that special understanding and skill concerned with the emotional and social aspects of his relationships with patients may be added to what he calls his "armamentarium" of diagnostic and treatment tools. It means that insofar as possible the psychosocial aspects of medicine are *not* left to chance, but are fitted into a systematic approach to the totality of a patient's problems. In other words, as an eminent historian of medicine has written:

> Medicine, in the ordinary sense, represents a group of biological sciences, but . . . medicine as an art is closely related to the social

sciences. This is true, at least, if one may employ the term "art" in the rather broad sense of including both medical practice and the social relations which this involves.[1]

The Patient: "Good" or "Bad"

The first step toward science is a step away from value-judgment. A science of human behavior must be based on the description of human behavior as it is and not as we want it to be.

The intervention of values in the development of knowledge is a constant problem in all the sciences. The history of anatomy offers but one example. For almost fifteen hundred years following Galen, anatomists saw in their dissection only what they were told to look for by Galen. When they found structures that were different from or missing in the descriptions by the master, they called them "abnormal." In effect, the cadavers that did not confirm their expectations were judged to be "bad" cadavers. Not until the sixteenth century, in the work of Vesalius, was anatomy established as a science in which observation took precedence over authority. Only when the dissector began to look at the structure of the human body as it is, and not as he believed it should be, was he able to correct such Galenic errors (resulting from the projection of pig, monkey, or dog anatomy into the human body) as the five-lobed liver, the seven-segmented sternum, the mandible consisting of two parts, the double-bile duct and the horned uterus.[2]

Galileo provides another example. Barely 300 years ago Galileo was jailed for arguing that the earth revolves about the sun. Not only was his mathematical demonstration of the Copernican hypothesis rejected by the authorities of his time, but he was branded a criminal for his refutation of Ptolemaic theory.[3]

Moreover, the order in which one belief system is followed by another is not necessarily logical. There was, for example, great enthusiasm for the application of biological science to medicine in the seventeenth century, but it was short-lived. John Locke wrote at the time about the great promise he saw in the medical sciences. Locke, whom we know today mainly as a philosopher, was also a physician. Together with eminent physician-scientists like Leibnitz and Descartes, Locke believed that medical science would continue steadily along the path broken by physics and chemistry, and that medical practice would follow closely after. Then, as the story is told, "a strange and tragic thing happened. Strange, because at first glance it seemed inexplicable; tragic, because it was fraught with such dire consequences for human health and happiness. Medicine at first faltered, and then fell behind . . ."; medical practice failed to keep up with science.[4]

Medicine fell behind biological science at this juncture of history because a reaction against science occurred in the medical profession. The result in the case of such concrete discoveries as microscopy and the clinical thermometer was indeed unfortunate:

> The rare enthusiasm displayed by seventeenth-century experimenters was succeeded by a strange indifference, by a curious lag in the employment of their improved means of observation and measurement. . . . Galilei (had measured) the pulse and temperature; and about two generations later, Leeuwenhoek had so improved his lenses as to discover protozoa and bacteria. It is even possible that he used, in this connection, the dark-field method of illumination. Yet Leeuwenhoek lived to see his methods almost ignored; and neither pulse-counting nor temperature-taking was generally practiced during the eighteenth century or the first half of the nineteenth century. Texts used in English-speaking countries as late as 1830 spoke of microscopy as an "art now almost forsaken." An eminent surgeon has testified that there were probably not half a dozen clinical thermometers employed in the largest Union army throughout the American Civil War. And this was some two hundred and fifty years after their first introduction![5]

Such long delay between discovery and application, it has been argued, can only be explained by the rejection *in belief* of the principles underlying technological and scientific advancement. "Apparently the reaction against the mechanical and mathematical schools involved a rejection of quantitative procedures as such."[6]

The significance of belief-systems, or values, in both medical science and practice continues today, though in different forms. Thus, whereas the disease concept was rejected a century ago, it grew to dominate medicine to what some now contend is an extreme and damaging degree. In both instances it was not so much *what was known* that guided the profession, but rather *what was believed*.

When one considers how pre-scientific conceptions of physics and of biology have been so resistant to the application of scientific method, it is perhaps more understandable why, even today, it is not easy for man to yield his own social behavior to the uncompromising scrutiny of scientific inquiry.[7] Four centuries ago Francis Bacon pointed out how man is reluctant to study objectively *what men do*, but very willing to judge what men *ought* to do. In spite of the development of modern social science, man's preference when dealing with human behavior continues to be to *moralize* rather than to *understand*.[8]

In medicine this is exemplified by the common tendency to judge patients on a moralistic basis. That is, rather than perceiving patients as they are, the doctor (or nurse) views the patient according to preconceived attitudes of how "good" patients should behave. Apparently, this practice begins early in the medical career. For example, a class of freshman students at a leading medical school recently were asked on an examination to discuss the role of the patient in the doctor-patient relationship. Seven out of ten students answered with descriptions of "good" patients and "bad" patients cast in highly moralistic tones. Quite common were firm statements about how patients "should" behave. Moreover, recent studies of medical students suggest that the tendency to judge patients on a moralistic or utilitarian basis is more likely to intensify than to reverse with progress through medical school.[9] The "crock" is a special medical designation for the uncooperative ("bad") patient; it is a term the neophyte quickly learns in the hospital.

Yet, if we are to understand the social relations of medicine, if some systematic order is to be achieved in the analysis of human behavior, this tendency toward moralistic judgment in preference to understanding based on fact and reason will block the path. Such danger to the development of a social science of medicine is always present, intruding itself when least expected.

In dealing with this problem, we do not propose to try to eliminate values from the doctor-patient relationship. That is not possible or even desirable. Insight into the influence of values, however, is a first step toward the discipline of knowledge.

Thus we try to learn about values, how they are acquired and then used in structuring social relationships. We will dissect out some of the patterned values that define the situation between the doctor and patient. We will show how this pattern, although it is only in the minds of the participants, has all the properties of morphology. Values are the building blocks of social structure. If we can describe them and their sources in culture, and follow this with evidence about how they guide the dynamic process of human interaction, we will be at least launched toward a social science of medicine.

A Case Illustration

In a teaching conference at a university hospital in a large eastern city, the following case was presented recently. The medical problem is a common one.

The patient is Mrs. Tomasetti,* 55 years old, who emigrated to this country from southern Italy about forty years ago. Her present admission was an emergency diagnosed as congestive heart failure, associated with diabetes mellitus, which the patient has had for a period of years. She is a familiar figure at this clinic where a careful and complete workup has been done. There is no mystery about her physical condition, or the requirements for the management of her illness. She tolerates well the insulin she needs, and is faithful about taking medication. However, a major additional requirement in her type of diabetes is that she follow a carefully controlled diet in which carbohydrates and fats are eaten sparingly.

At this conference, a now familiar pattern is repeated with Mrs. Tomasetti. Upon questioning, she readily reveals that she ate a large dinner the night before her present attack. The menu? Her doctor winces as Mrs. Tomasetti describes a spicy combination of Italian-American foods heavy in carbohydrates which obviously violates the prescribed diet. "Yes," she replies, "I know you told me not to eat these foods, but there was company at the house, old friends, and well, I thought just this once." Her doctor,

* The name is fictitious, as will be all names used in case illustrations in this book.

a resident in internal medicine, listens with impatience. He has been through this with Mrs. Tomasetti before.

The doctor has explained to Mrs. Tomasetti the nature of her illness, and she seems to understand. He has warned her of the danger if the medication is not taken or the diet neglected. Each time this occurs, the patient appears to accept the doctor's recommendations and agrees to cooperate, but she does not carry out the doctor's orders after she leaves the hospital.

Following this conference, however, an interesting change occurred in the case of Mrs. Tomasetti. As part of an experimental teaching program, she was placed under the care of a fourth-year medical student. Although the supervision of the case remained in the hands of senior attending physicians and residents, Mrs. Tomasetti now had a new "doctor," whom she would be encouraged to consult on an outpatient basis after her release from the hospital.

Three months later, this case was again presented at the same weekly teaching conference. Mrs. Tomasetti had, in the meantime, made several visits to the outpatient clinic on appointment with her student-doctor, and he, in turn, had made a number of visits to her home. Mrs. Tomasetti was maintaining her prescribed medication and diet well, and reducing her visits to the clinic. For the first time in her long history at the clinic, a feeling of confidence seemed justified that she would continue with the requirements for her medical problem.

The discussion at the conference, as one might expect, was spirited. What had happened to change the direction of this case? In their usual order, the several dimensions of the problem were considered.

First, there were the physical findings. These were unchanged. The diagnosis was unquestioned. The medical management was sound, as indeed was demonstrated by the fact that the treatment proved successful when the patient followed the prescribed regimen.

Secondly, the psychological aspects of the case were discussed. The patient, in her known history, had never shown any evidence of psychic distress. She discussed herself and her symptoms accurately, without exaggeration. She perceived her situation clearly and evidently understood the explanations her physicians gave concerning her illness and its treatment. Obviously, her behavior in violating the requirements of her illness were self-destructive. However, the sources of this behavior were elusive. No evidence of significant unhappy personal experience could be found. The patient, to all appearances, had been happily married for many years. With grown children and grandchildren, she continued to maintain a central role of importance in her family; the extended family organization typical of her European background had been maintained.

The discussion then turned to the sociological aspects of the case. What was happening in the interaction between the patient and her physicians? Here, it was noted, the only known change had occurred that might explain the course of the patient's behavior. That is, her doctor had been changed. Her drugs were the same. Her diet was the same. Her home life was the same. The only new ingredient in the case was the doctor.

Reviewing the details of the patient's relationship with her first clinic doctor, the conference noted that, in the beginning, the relationship had appeared cordial enough. The doctor had explained the medical problem in straightforward, simplified terms, and when this proved inadequate, the doctor appealed to her reason. Next, he emphasized the danger to her life. Finally, he tried threats, cajoling, and appeals to "good sense." In time, there came despair: Mrs. Tomasetti was relegated to the heap of "uncooperative patients," the "problem-patients," with whom nothing could be done.

Yet Mrs. Tomasetti did ultimately change. Why was her early treatment so ineffective, and what happened to change her behavior?

Behavioral Implications of Organic Symptoms

The major illness itself, diabetes mellitus, has certain special characteristics that are likely to influence the situation of the doctor-patient relationship. It has been observed that the response to an illness is likely to be related to the symptoms. Pain, for example, often serves as a reminder to the patient that he is ill, and consequently motivates him to follow treatment which he either knows or believes will help to cure or assuage the illness. The symptoms of diabetes mellitus, except in emergency states, are not severe. With treatment, the diabetic can be relatively symptom-free. As a consequence, the patient's motivation for prolonged, usually life-long treatment is not supported by the symptoms of the illness. As long as the diabetic is faithful to his treatment, he usually does not feel sick, nor indeed does he show any signs to reveal to others that he is sick.

It is required, however, that the diabetic patient participate in the treatment of his disease to an unusual extent. Although treatment methods are usually effective, it is necessary for the patient to be a willing, active partner in his own treatment.[10]

When one considers that treatment is normally so hopeful, it seems paradoxical that a majority of diabetic patients do *not* achieve the major objective of treatment, normoglycemia. Commenting on this fact, a psychiatrist and an internist recently asserted that technical problems—regulation of insulin dosage, diet, and so on—probably account for only a small number of failures. "This suggests," they continued, "that the patient's attitude, the physician's approach and the interaction of physician and patient should be carefully scrutinized to determine their part in this problem."[11]

In other words, the effect of this disease upon the human organism (the patient's symptoms), plus the known requirements for treatment (the application of the physician's technological skill and knowledge), produce a situation that, in turn, has requirements of its own. This situation determines to a large extent how the physician and the patient must act toward each other. In this case, for example, the patient is required to be active. He must participate with his physician, or his relationship with his physician will deteriorate and with it the medical treatment and his health. With another kind of illness, a different basic situation would be created, varying what we will speak of as the role requirements of the doctor-patient relationship.

Basic Models of the Doctor-Patient Relationship

Three types of doctor-patient relationship that are directly related to the organic symptoms of illness have been described by

Szasz and Hollender: (a) activity-passivity, (b) guidance-cooperation, and (c) mutual participation:

> 1. ACTIVITY-PASSIVITY. Here the orientation is one in which the physician is active and the patient is passive. It has originated in, and is entirely appropriate for, emergencies (severe injuries, marked blood loss, delirium or coma). The patient is more or less completely helpless and the physician *does* something to him. Treatment takes place regardless of the patient's contribution. The relationship of the doctor to the patient is similar to that of the parent to the helpless infant.
>
> 2. GUIDANCE-COOPERATION. This model usually underlies the doctor-patient relationship when the circumstances are less desperate than those described above. It applies to most acute disorders and especially to those of an infectious type. Although the patient is ill, he is still keenly aware of what is going on, and he is capable of following directions and of exercising some judgment. Moreover, when the approach is geared at this level, the patient is expected to look up to his physician and to obey him. In essence, the patient says: "You know what is best for me. That is why I come to you. Tell me what to do and I will follow your directions." This model has its prototype in the relationship of the parent and his child (or adolescent).
>
> 3. MUTUAL PARTICIPATION. This approach is often useful for the management of chronic illnesses in which the treatment program is carried out by the patient with only occasional consultation with a physician (i.e., diabetes mellitus, myasthenia gravis, psoriasis, etc.). According to this model, the physician *helps the patient* to *help himself*. Since it requires a complex psychological and social organization on the part of the patient, it is rarely appropriate for children or for people who are mentally deficient, very poorly educated or profoundly immature. Its prototype is the relationship of adult to adult (with one having specialized knowledge that the other needs).

As the authors of these models add, "It would be inaccurate and misleading to maintain that one model is better than another. It is rather a question of which model is more appropriate for (or works better in) a given situation."[12]

Looking again at the case of Mrs. Tomasetti, one finds that the model used in her earlier treatment was, by and large, the most common model for clinical practice: guidance-cooperation. However, in the opinion of the physicians who conceived of these models, guidance-cooperation is appropriate mainly for acute processes in which suffering provides the motivation. There are many pitfalls when this approach is applied to chronic illnesses:

> Both physician and patient regard the treatment program as imposed by the physician (which is actually so). This creates the danger that the physician rather than the illness will be viewed as the frustrator and restrictor. Thus instead of being an ally, the physician may be regarded as someone who is pitted against the patient, and a power struggle may ensue. In this way, an internal conflict about following a plan of treatment is externalized, and a battle is waged against the physician with seemingly little awareness of the self-destructive consequences. . . . The *emphasis here is on being a good or a bad patient* and *not on maintaining the best possible health*.[13]

Was this danger an actual one in the Tomasetti case? To some extent, it would seem so at least from the view of her first physician. The resort to a moral judgment on his part is unmistakable. He sees Mrs. Tomasetti as a "bad" patient.

Yet this alone does not suffice to explain the course of the relationship. Why, for example, does Mrs. Tomasetti show little or no difficulty in following the quite complex requirements of her medication, which would seem to pose at least as much difficulty as her diet? The doctor's approach along the model of guidance-cooperation worked well in one aspect of the problem; why not in the other?

The Influence of Culture

One of the participants at the conference raised a question about Mrs. Tomasetti's cultural background. Would there be anything in a southern Italian cultural upbringing that might help to explain her problem in conforming to the prescribed diet? In the discussion that followed, someone pointed out that food is highly valued in Italian and other Mediterranean cultures as a symbol of hospitality and well-being. Eating is regarded as a solace, and health itself is sometimes equated with heaviness. The conference at this point became animated, even jubilant. The participants had uncovered what seemed *the* answer to a difficult treatment problem. "Under such cultural conditions," one student added, "no wonder a restrictive diet is difficult for the patient to maintain. If one is taught from childhood to eat for pleasure and to gain weight for health, it is certainly understandable that it would be difficult to restrict eating and limit the variety and amount of food in order to lose weight. Moreover, if one's home is saturated with an atmosphere conducive to eating and drinking, in which food is a symbol of health and happiness, would it not be difficult to maintain a solitary course, distinctive from the rest of the family?"

A word of caution must be injected, however. Culture is a concept that we will discuss at length as a valuable tool in problems of health and illness, but it is complex. Although on occasion it will appear to present *the* answer, interpretation should be conservative.[14] In Italy, for example, attitudes toward food are by no means invariable. Particularly in the northern part, the women are noted (and greatly admired) for their svelte figures. The southern provinces are very poor, a factor that influences attitudes toward health; in general, Italians in those provinces place a high value on food, much as described at the conference on Mrs. Tomasetti. However, is this a sufficient explanation of why she was not able to follow her diet?

Undoubtedly Mrs. Tomasetti's cultural background is important both in her response to her illness and in her relationship with her physicians. Moreover, the importance of culture is evidently increased by her first physician's unrealistic assumption that the desire for health by the patient will necessarily supersede any other considerations on her part. In other words, the doctor is assuming that certain values related to health and illness which he has learned in his own cultural background are shared by this patient, whereas her cultural value orientation is, in fact, decisively different.

This assertion, however, does not explain how culture functions in this relationship. How does culture fit into the total dynamics of the interaction? Unless we can go further in the specification of its influence—as we shall attempt to do in later chapters—the awareness of culture as a determinant is useful only as a very general common sense type of observation.[15]

A "Home-made" Experiment

The question remains: Why did the student-physician succeed where his more highly trained colleague had failed? What was there about the relationship between Mrs. Tomasetti and her student-physician that achieved the mutual participation lacking with her prior physician? This was the question to which the case conference now devoted its full attention. What, specifically, it was asked, was done with the patient?

In summary, the student-doctor reported the following. He began in the manner required for all students with a newly assigned patient: he performed a complete physical examination and took a history. He found Mrs. Tomasetti friendly, compliant to the hospital requirements, and, as far as one could tell, aware of the meaning of her illness and the danger if she failed to follow the recommendations for both medicine and diet. He was alerted, of course, by the experience of his predecessor to the fact that the appearance of understanding and compliance on the part of the patient was not reliable.

In his regular visits with Mrs. Tomasetti in the hospital, he noted that her family visited her whenever possible, including her husband, two daughters, and a son. Her children were all married and had children of their own. They came usually in groups of two or three, including in-laws, and gathered about Mrs. Tomasetti with voluble warmth and concern. As he watched the family, the student-doctor decided he would visit her at home as soon as possible after discharge from the hospital. Up to this point, he could see no progress in the case beyond that enjoyed previously. To prevent the same type of relapse that had occurred repeatedly in the past, he would seek the problem at its source, in the Tomasetti home.

In the meantime, he did little more than listen during his visits to Mrs. Tomasetti in the hospital, urging her to talk about herself and her life, alert to any clue she might give to explain her repeated failure to follow her diet.

His first home visit was made during the week following Mrs. Tomasetti's discharge. He arrived in the early evening, and found Mrs. Tomasetti in a small but comfortable apartment with her husband, daughter, son-in-law, and infant grandchild.

He was aware from the patient's history that this daughter's small family lived with Mr. and Mrs. Tomasetti, and that the daughter continued to hold a full-time job. Only now, however, did he begin to appreciate some of the implications of this arrangement. For example, during the visit, Mrs. Tomasetti's other two children dropped in, as well as a neighbor. As each one entered, it was Mrs. Tomasetti who took charge, offering coffee and something to eat.

Obviously, Mrs. Tomasetti retained her central place in this family. Everyone else was dependent on her for the running of the household—a warm, friendly household in which food played a part of very great importance. This meant that the entire burden of keeping her own special diet fell on Mrs. Tomasetti alone, plus the responsibility for the diet of her household.

As he became thus more fully aware of the situation from his patient's point of view, the student-doctor sought a new approach to her problem. For help, he consulted with the medical clinic's social worker.[16]

As they reviewed the case together, some of the additional meanings that food might possess for the patient began to emerge. The diet was a threat to the patient's full and spontaneous sharing of an important family activity. Furthermore, it might easily disturb her conception of herself and her role in the family, and become, in effect, a symbol of separation from the pattern of life in which she was so deeply embedded.

The social worker suggested that perhaps, in these circumstances, the patient's family should be brought more actively into the problem. Why not invite their help, informing them in the meantime of his speculations about how the diet might seem for Mrs. Tomasetti a threat to her place in the family. The critical question for the family seemed to be: "Why place this responsibility so completely on your mother? Isn't there some way to watch and supervise her diet, just as she has always done for the family?" The social worker also suggested consultation with a public health nurse.

The public health nurse attached to the clinic concurred with their appraisal of the case. She added the opinion that Mrs. Tomasetti might need some guidance in the practical problems of her diet; she offered to visit the patient at her home to instruct her in the details of the dietary management of her illness.[17]

The student-doctor arranged his next home visit at the home of the older daughter, with only the children and their spouses present. They seemed to respond well to the explanation of the problem. However, even as the family gained a fuller understanding of the realities of Mrs. Tomasetti's illness, it was not easy for them to fashion an effective solution. For one thing, they pointed out, Mrs. Tomasetti would not readily yield her position as matron of the family—and particularly it was "her" kitchen. Indeed, it was agreed that, in any steps to be taken, it was important to avoid giving any impression to Mrs. Tomasetti that she was going to be "replaced" in anyway. They decided that she might be receptive to or even eager for help in the household, but that she would not like a reduction of her activity. If such help came from her own daughters, they decided, she would be most likely to accept it.

The most likely candidate was the daughter who lived in the same house; but she and her husband were dependent on her continuing, at least for a time, as a full-time wage earner.

At this time, which was about one month after discharge from the hospital, the student-doctor and the family together agreed on a plan they would try, at least on a tentative basis. It was decided that the whole family should join in specific steps to see that Mrs. Tomasetti would not be alone in the responsibility for the family's meals. Since the two other children lived in the neighborhood, a sister and a sister-in-law could share this task with the youngest daughter. More importantly, they were not to make Mrs. Tomasetti feel that she was being "replaced," but only that the family were alert to her special dietary needs, and that they believed in the diet and wanted her to follow it. In order to help her, in effect they were going to share with her the responsibility of adhering to the diet, and at the same time were reassuring her that the family's characteristic mode of life and her place in it was not being changed in the process.

The public health nurse would help launch this plan, making daytime visits both to educate the family on the details of Mrs. Tomasetti's treatment, and to support them in carrying it out.

Needless to say, the experience with this plan was not to be without its difficulties for all concerned. Nevertheless, in his visits to the Tomasetti home, the student-doctor found that the general plan was being continued, so that he was able to reduce his weekly home visits to one a month. He now plans to see the patient only in the clinic. The public health nurse meanwhile has terminated her visits because the family are managing so well on their own.

Time and Responsibility

The response of the conference to this story was mixed. On the one hand, there was admiration for the sensitivity, ingenuity, and persistence of the student-doctor in his handling of the case. On the other hand, there was a sense of dismay at what appeared to be overwhelming demands upon the doctor's time and what might be the overreaching of proper boundaries of responsibility. As one student expressed it: "Even if it did work in this case, how can a busy doctor take on so much? Where does the doctor's job end, anyway?"

"Weren't we in error," another student asked, "when we observed earlier in the conference that the only change of ingredients between the first and second approaches to the patient was the change of doctors? What about the social worker? Indeed, isn't the second doctor taking on responsibilities that are more appropriate to the social worker? Why couldn't he just turn over the case to her, instead of doing it all himself?"

At this point the professor of medicine who was in charge of the conference made the following statement: "These questions are unquestionably important and relevant. However, do they touch on the most basic problem illustrated by this case? After all, if the problem here had involved a surgical question, and a surgeon therefore were called in consultation, would it ever occur to us to turn over the responsibility to the surgeon without at the same time attempting to know everything possible about the nature of the patient's illness? Indeed, even after a surgeon or another kind of specialist is called in on a case, does the referring physician step out? What if the consultant of choice is not available, does the doctor's responsibility cease because he is not a surgeon himself, or any other type of specialist?"

Once again, the conference reacted with mixed feelings. In spite of differences of opinion, however, there was consensus that the physician's responsibility included the effort to understand everything possible that contributed to the welfare of his patient. In the case before it, therefore, the basic question remained unanswered: what was it that had changed the course of Mrs. Tomasetti's illness? It was not enough to say that consultants had been added, or that the patient's family had been drawn into participation in the treatment. Nor was it enough to find in the disparity of cultural orientation between the first doctor and Mrs. Tomasetti a plausible explanation for his failure to achieve her cooperation in the treatment. To perceive what is wrong in one approach is not necessarily to explain what is correct in another. Therefore, the conference agreed that it needed to understand more specifically what the underlying dynamics were in this case example.

System and the Human Group

Perhaps the most striking fact about the foregoing illustration is the use that was made of the most time-honored of all diagnostic instruments: the doctor's senses applied in the most rigorous possible observation. Just as doctors have learned routinely to palpate, to percuss, and to auscultate the body of patients, so the student-doctor in this case used his eyes and ears to probe for all the details of personal and family behavior that might bear on the health problem.

However, no instrument in itself is useful without knowledge about how to use it. There is no magic in the stethoscope as such; but in the ability to differentiate the sounds it conveys, the skill of diagnosis is greatly enhanced. Similarly, there is no magic in the acceptance of the relevance of social and emotional variables in illness unless one can go on to understand the differential significance of the facts one observes about these variables.

The remainder of this book is devoted to such a task. It will describe a framework that has a twofold general purpose. First, it attempts to free the physician from some of the distortion that is implicit in a moralistic approach to the study of human behavior. Second, it seeks to add the discipline of the scientific method in the study of human behavior.

Quite obviously, we are not finished with the case of Mrs. Tomasetti. Before continuing to probe its specific details, however, we have chosen to fill in the details of an approach to the type of problems of which her case is but one example. Later in the book, in the final chapter, the case will be reviewed in more detail.

One could at this point add a series of cautions and qualifications. It will be obvious to the reader that we have chosen to emphasize certain aspects of the case illustration and to underplay others. This is done deliberately in the service of the book's major purpose; that is, to describe a sociological approach to the study of human behavior in terms that are relevant to medicine. We do not thereby, however, intend in any way to discount the validity and significance of other possible approaches.[18] In the final analysis, as we will attempt to demonstrate, it is only by a comprehensive approach that human behavior can be most effectively understood. Each of the various social and psychological sciences as well as the biological sciences offers separate but complementary approaches to this end.

Hollender, for example, emphasizes the dynamics that come from within the personality to explain the type of problem presented by Mrs. Tomasetti. In his discussion of obesity in its relationship to diabetes, he asserts that strong cravings for food or oral gratification often represent an expression of profound psychological disorder. He wrote:

> These people often eat to relieve feelings of anxiety or in an effort to satisfy intense longings for love. In some instances the imposition of a strict diet will lead to one of several unfortunate results: (a) failure, (b) a serious breach in the doctor-patient relationship or (c) a neurotic or psychotic depression. When obesity is rooted in deep-seated personality problems, psychotherapy may be necessary. If the patient is unwilling or unable to undertake psychiatric treatment, your approach will have to be more flexible if there is to be hope of even limited success.[19]

The possibility would certainly have to be considered that Mrs. Tomasetti is responding to her student-physician because he has provided, as in psychotherapy, relief for her anxiety or need for affection. Even if this were true, it does not mean that the various sociocultural factors we have introduced are irrelevant. Moreover, it will be contended here that to view this case mainly as a problem of the individuals involved, studied separately, is to grasp no more than a segment of the whole. One must study the groups, each one a social system in itself.

The first doctor and Mrs. Tomasetti constituted a human group that can be conceived of as a social system.[20] When this doctor gave up the case, a new group was formed between the patient and the student-doctor. The patient's family is another group that is obviously a salient feature of the total health problem. Both the intragroup dynamics and the intergroup relations of these three social entities must be studied to gain a full view of the actual course of Mrs. Tomasetti's illness. This we will attempt to do, following the dictum proposed at the beginning of the chapter; namely, that the "art of medicine" can be translated, in important respects, into a social science of medicine, which, in turn, provides the substantive basis of a skill in human relations that can be taught as part of medical education.

NOTES TO CHAPTER I

1. Shryock, Richard H., *The Development of Modern Medicine*. Rev. ed. Alfred A. Knopf, Inc., New York, 1947, p. 38.
2. Ackerknecht, Erwin H., *A Short History of Medicine*. The Ronald Press Co., New York, 1955, p. 94.
3. Moore, George Foot, *History of Religions*. Charles Scribner's Sons, New York, 1949, vol. 2, pp. 372–373. The famous sentence of the Inquisitors stated: "That the Sun is in the centre of the universe and motionless is a proposition absurd and false in philosophy, and formally heretical, because it is in express contradiction to Holy Scripture. That the earth is not the centre of the universe, and not motionless, but has also a diurnal motion, is likewise a proposition absurd and false in philosophy, and, theologically considered, at least erroneous in matter of faith." It was not until 1835 that the Catholic Church explicitly rescinded the prohibition of Copernican teachings.
4. Shryock, Richard H., *op. cit.*, p. 17.
5. *Ibid.*, p. 23.
6. *Ibid.*, p. 24.
7. Argyris recently expressed this thought in the following way: "Being aware of ourselves is not an easy or necessarily a pleasant task. It is much easier to study *others* than to study ourselves. One student of science points out that those sciences that developed first required the least amount of self-study among men. Man tends to shun the behavioral sciences because they ultimately will coerce him to take a closer look at himself." Argyris, Chris, *Personality and Organization*. Harper and Bros., New York, 1957, p. 6.

8. See Henderson, Lawrence J., "The Patient and Physician as a Social System," *New England Journal of Medicine*, vol. 212, May, 1935, pp. 819–823.

9. Gee, Helen Hofer, and Robert J. Glaser, editors, *The Ecology of the Medical Student*, Association of American Medical Colleges, Evanston, Ill., 1958. See particularly Eron, Leonard D., "The Effect of Medical Education on Attitude: A Follow-Up Study," pp. 25–33; and Christie, Richard, and Robert K. Merton, "Procedures for the Sociological Study of the Value Climate of Medical Schools," pp. 125–153.

10. Hollender, Marc H., and Leonard A. Stine, "The Medical Patient" in Hollender, M. H., *The Psychology of Medical Practice*. W. B. Saunders Co., Philadelphia, 1958, pp. 35–88.

11. *Ibid.*, p. 59.

12. Szasz, T. S., and M. H. Hollender, "A Contribution to the Philosophy of Medicine: The Basic Models of the Doctor-Patient Relationship," *A.M.A. Archives of Internal Medicine*, vol. 97, May, 1956, p. 585; cited in Hollender, Marc H., *op. cit.*, pp. 6–7.

13. Hollender, Marc H., *The Psychology of Medical Practice*, p. 60.

14. For an interesting discussion of this problem with case examples, see Macgregor, Frances Cooke, *Social Science in Nursing*, Russell Sage Foundation, New York, 1960, pp. 255 ff.

15. See the discussion of this problem as it relates to both the Italian and Jewish cultures in Zborowski, Mark, "Cultural Components in Responses to Pain," *Journal of Social Issues*, vol. 8, no. 4, 1952, pp. 16–30, reprinted in Jaco, E. Gartly, editor, *Patients, Physicians and Illness*. The Free Press, Glencoe, Ill., 1958, pp. 256–268.

16. For an excellent discussion of the medical social worker, see King, Stanley H., *Perceptions of Illness and Medical Practice*, Russell Sage Foundation, New York, 1962, pp. 279–306; also see Committee on Medical Care Teaching of the Association of Teachers of Preventive Medicine, *Readings in Medical Care*, University of North Carolina Press, Chapel Hill, N. C., 1958, pp. 244–250.

17. See Rossman, I. J., and Doris R. Schwartz, *The Family Handbook of Home Nursing and Medical Care*, Random House, New York, 1958.

18. A recently published study is that by Stanley H. King, *op. cit.*, in which very similar goals are approached with an emphasis that is more psychological than that of this book. Two works that emphasize anthropological concepts and illustrations are a casebook edited by Benjamin D. Paul, *Health, Culture, and Community*, Russell Sage Foundation, New York, 1955, and Lyle Saunders' *Cultural Difference and Medical Care*, Russell Sage Foundation, 1954. Several other books published by Russell Sage Foundation represent in general the social science of medicine, but, taken separately, each approaches the task with different points of emphasis. These include: Brown, Esther Lucile, *Newer Dimensions of Patient Care*, Part I, The Use of the Physical and Social Environment of the General Hospital for Therapeutic Purposes, 1961, and Part II, Improving Staff Motivation and Competence in the General Hospital, 1962; Freidson, Eliot, *Patients' Views of Medical Practice:* A Study of the Subscribers to a Prepaid Medical Plan in The Bronx, New York, 1961; and Simmons, Leo W., and Harold G. Wolff, *Social Science in Medicine*, 1954.

19. Hollender, Marc H., *The Psychology of Medical Practice*, pp. 66–67.

20. See Parsons, Talcott, *The Social System*, The Free Press, Glencoe, Ill., 1951 especially chap. 10, pp. 428–479.

Chapter 2

THE CONCEPTUAL APPROACH

THE DOCTOR-PATIENT RELATIONSHIP, we have said, is a social situation that may be used to exemplify the primary concepts of knowledge and theories about social interaction. Having briefly introduced some of these concepts as they applied to the case of Mrs. Tomasetti, we shall attempt now to give them more precise definition. We shall also try to show how these concepts may be integrated into a unified frame of reference for the study of the doctor-patient relationship.

The Doctor-Patient Relationship: A Limited View

The doctor-patient relationship is often conceived of as an interaction essentially limited to two persons. The important elements of the relationship are similarly limited to two: (x) the personalities of the participants, upon which the "rapport" is dependent, and (y) the skill of the physician as a "medical scientist." Abstracted in diagrammatic terms, such a relationship may be conceived of as presented in Figure 1.

This view of the doctor-patient relationship reminds one of early conceptions by psychologists of the perceptual act. We refer to interpretations of perception that were limited to the properties of the stimulus and the respondent.[1] The deficiencies of early stimulus-response theory were demonstrated in several classic experiments conducted more than a generation ago by the Gestalt school of psychology. The latter made the assertion that perception must be interpreted according to the *field* in which the stimulus and response exist. The polemical exchange between the Gestaltists and the elementaristic theories of the physiologist Hering provide an excellent example.[2]

[Figure 1: The Interaction Model — an oval enclosing two circles labeled "Doctor (A)" and "Patient (B)", with arrows between them labeled "(x) Human Interaction" above and "Objective Application of Medical Science (y)" below.]

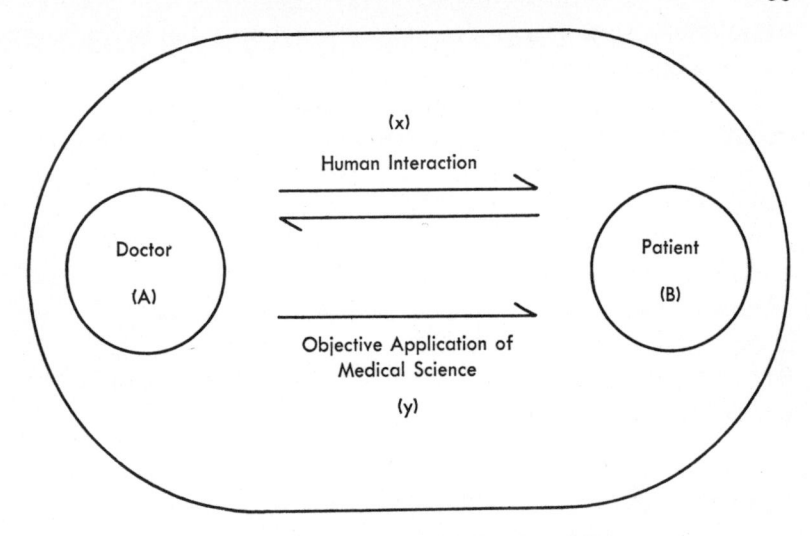

FIGURE 1. THE INTERACTION MODEL

Hering explained visual perception in terms of *direct retinal stimulation*. Consider the question: How do we tell that a line is vertical, horizontal, or tilted to a given degree? Hering's answer was that a line may be said to consist of points; if the image of the points on the retina is vertical, we see the line as upright. The retina was thus described as a "coordinate system." This offered a simple explanation of the perception of direction in space.

The Gestaltists added one condition, the enclosure of the line within a variable framework. In one experiment by Asch and Witkin,[3] the line or rod was placed at the back of a small wooden room, open in the front. This room was tilted 22 degrees. The observer in the experiment was asked to stand on a level ground in front of the tilted room. He then was instructed to state, as the rod was moved, when it reached the objective vertical. Under these conditions, it was found that most people see the line as tilted when it is objectively vertical, that is, parallel to the walls of the building and to his own body.

The conclusion drawn from this simple experiment was that the perceived direction of the lines is a function of the surrounding framework and does not depend solely on the stimulation of the retina produced by the line alone. "We can keep the retinal stimulation constant and alter its perceived direction by varying the surrounding field."

The doctor-patient interaction is similarly dependent upon the "field" in which it occurs. The significant conditions, however, are not physical (for example, a tilted room); they are psychosocial. The difference may be illustrated with another very simple but compelling experiment, conceived by Solomon Asch.[4]

The Asch experiment is a study of what he calls "the social and personal conditions that induce individuals to resist or to yield to group pressures when the latter are perceived to be contrary to fact."[5] The experimenter himself describes the basic conditions of the experiment as follows:

> We employed the procedure of placing an individual in a relation of radical conflict with all the other members of a group, of measuring its effect upon him in quantitative terms, and of describing its psychological consequences. A group of eight individuals was instructed to judge a series of simple, clearly structured perceptual relations—to match the length of a given line with one of three unequal lines. Each member of the group announced his judgments publicly. In the midst of this monotonous "test" one individual found himself suddenly contradicted by the entire group, and this contradiction was repeated again and again in the course of the experiment. The group in question had, with the exception of one member, previously met with the experimenter and received instructions to respond at certain points with wrong—and unanimous—judgments. The errors of the majority were large (ranging between $\frac{1}{2}''$ and $1\frac{3}{4}''$) and of an order not encountered under control conditions. The outstanding person—the critical subject—whom we had placed in the position of a *minority of one* in the midst of a *unanimous majority*—was the object of investigation. He faced, possibly for the first time in his life, a situation in which a group unanimously contradicted the evidence of his senses.[6]

As can be seen, the model of the Asch experiment is analogous to the tilted-room experiment. Again, an experimental attempt is made to alter perception by varying the "field." The new factor is the unanimous evidence of a group of equals which contradicts the evidence of the subject's own experience of a clearly perceived relation. Although the majority was concretely present, surrounding the subject physically, the most salient variable is social; that is, the subject is forced to reconcile the evidence of his own senses against the contradictory evidence of a group of his peers.

In the results of the Asch experiment, there was "a marked movement toward the majority." One-third of all the estimates by the uninstructed subjects (Asch calls them the "critical" subjects) were errors identical with or in the direction of the distorted estimates of the majority. However, the effect of the majority was "far from complete." Fully two-thirds of the estimates of the critical subjects were correct despite the pressure of the majority.

In his interpretation of these results, Asch describes three types of independent subjects substantially as follows:

> (a) independence with confidence in one's perceptions and experience; (b) independence accompanied by an emotional withdrawal, and assertion of explicit principles about the necessity of being an individual; and (c) independence accompanied by considerable tension and doubt with adherence to judgments on the basis of a felt necessity to deal adequately with the task.

> He also describes three major forms of yielding: (a) distortion of perception, (b) distortion of judgment, and (c) distortion of action.

Unlike the tilted-room experiment, where the variation of the stimulus physical field produced virtually unanimous variation of response, response to the Asch experiment is not unanimous. As Asch interpreted the experiment, "The results . . . are clearly a joint function of two broadly different sets of conditions. They are determined first by the specific external conditions, by the particular character of the relation between social evidence and one's own experience. Second, the presence of pronounced individual differences points to the important role of personal factors, or factors connected with the individual's character structure. We reasoned that there are group conditions which would produce independence in all subjects, and that there probably are group conditions which would induce intensified yielding in many, though not in all. . . . We deemed it reasonable to assume that behavior under the experimental social pressure is significantly related to certain characteristics of the individual."[7]

Asch continued his experiment by systematically varying the social conditions of the critical subject. For example, *two* naive critical subjects were placed in the midst of the instructed majority. The result was to provide the individual with a partner against the majority. It was found that this disturbance of the unanimity of the majority markedly increased the independence of critical subjects.

A next step was to withdraw the partner. That is, the critical subject started with a partner who responded correctly. The partner was a member of the majority who had been instructed to respond correctly and to "desert" to the majority in the middle of the experiment. The withdrawal of the partner produced a powerful effect. It was also unexpected, as Asch reports:

> We had assumed that the critical subject, having gone through the experience of opposing the majority with a minimum of support, would maintain his independence when alone. Contrary to this expectation, we found that the experience of having had and then lost a partner restored the majority effect to its full force, the proportion of errors rising to 28.5 per cent of all judgments, in contrast to the preceding level of 5.5 per cent.[8]

This basic experiment was elaborated in a variety of admirably simple logical designs which tested the elements of social influence upon individual judgments. The conclusions were that independence and yielding are a joint function of the following major factors:

> (1) The character of the stimulus situation. Variations in structural clarity have a decisive effect: with diminishing clarity of the stimulus-condition the majority effect increases.
>
> (2) The character of the group forces. Individuals are highly sensitive to the structural qualities of group opposition. In particular, . . . [the experiment] demonstrated the great importance of the factor of unanimity. Also, the majority effect is a function of the size of group opposition.
>
> (3) The character of the individual. There were wide and indeed, striking differences among individuals within the same experimental situation.[9]

Before we discuss the specific implications of the Asch experiment for the study of the doctor-patient relationship, a description of one further experiment in the field of social perception is added. This research commands our interest because it uses the experimental model of Asch, but changes and adds several conditions. Most important, there are added a variety of types of stimuli, including complex tasks such as estimates of the opinions of others and the expression of personal preferences. Thus, by analogy, the findings of the Asch experiment are brought closer to a natural life situation like the doctor-patient relationship.

As reported by Crutchfield,[10] one hundred subjects participated in a series of experiments similar to those of Asch. The subjects were a special group of business and professional leaders. About half the men served as controls. By an ingenious apparatus, all of these men were able to be studied as critical subjects within the basic design of the Asch experiment.[11]

On a simple perceptual task like that used by Asch, virtually identical results were found. That is, about one-third of the total group yielded to the majority, with the remainder, in various ways, retaining the independence of their judgments in spite of the pressure from the majority.

Dealing with a factual judgment, however, there was as high as 79 per cent of conformity to a spurious group consensus upon an arbitrarily chosen and irrational answer. With ambiguous stimuli, confirming the findings of Asch and others, even more striking influence effects were achieved.

When, however, individuals were asked to express preferences for artistic drawings, virtually no yielding occurred to the influence of the majority. Opinion statements, in contrast, evoked considerable influence by the majority.

For example, an expression of agreement or disagreement was called for on the following statement of opinion: "Free speech being a privilege rather than a right, it is proper for a society to suspend free speech whenever it feels itself threatened." Among control subjects (40 men responding to the stimulus *without* exposure to contradiction of their judgments by a majority) only 19 per cent expressed agreement. When, however, the experimental subjects were confronted with a unanimous group consensus agreeing with the statement, 58 per cent expressed agreement.

Another item was phrased as follows: "Which one of the following do you feel is the most important problem facing our country today?" The following five alternatives were offered:

> Economic recession
> Educational facilities
> Subversive activities
> Mental health
> Crime and corruption

Among control subjects, only 12 per cent chose "Subversive activities" as the most important. But when exposed to a spurious group consensus which unanimously chose "Subversive activities" as the most important, 48 per cent of the experimental subjects expressed this same choice.

The Crutchfield experiment took one further step in the attempt to see whether the power of the group to influence the judgments of the individual may be even more greatly reinforced. With another group of subjects, the investigators told half the subjects that "in order to see how well they were doing during the procedure, the experimenter would inform the group immediately after the judgments what the correct answer was." This was done only for those stimuli in which there was a conceivably correct answer, namely, unambiguous perceptions (what Asch calls, "objectively verifiable stimuli"), logical solutions, and so on.

The experimenter here again deceived the subjects, choosing as "correct" answers only those which agreed with the false group consensus. "In short," writes Crutchfield, "the external authority of the experimenter was later added on as reinforcement to the group consensus."[12]

The effect of this "correction" method is reported as "striking." As the series of judgments goes on, subjects express greater and greater conformity to the group pressure.

The "Field" of the Doctor-Patient Relationship

Returning now to the doctor-patient relationship and to the diagram at the beginning of this chapter, it is obvious that one must calculate more than *rapport* and *skill* in order to understand the processes of interaction. One must see the doctor and the patient within a "field" whose elements include more than "personality" and technical skill.

To illustrate the importance of the full social context of the doctor-patient relationship, imagine a hypothetical situation in which a doctor has just received laboratory confirmation of a malignancy. The patient has entered his office, and the doctor must decide how to proceed.[13]

The doctor could, in this situation, simply tell the patient that he has a carcinoma. This is the most direct—some would call it the most "honest"—action possible. Yet it is a rare individual who could take such action without a searching consideration of its probable concomitants. Some of these have been described by Henderson:

> . . . Consider this statement, "This is a carcinoma." . . . We may regard the statement as a stimulus applied to the patient. This stimulus will produce a response and the response, together with the mechanism that is involved in its production, is an extremely complex one. . . . For instance, there are likely to be circulatory and respiratory changes accompanying many complex changes in the central and peripheral nervous system. With the cognition there is a correlated fear. There will probably be concern for the economic interests . . . of wife and children. All those intricate processes constitute a response to the stimulus made up of the four words, "This is a carcinoma."[14]

This is a description of some of the complex aspects of the expected patient response. The stimulus itself, however, has complex roots.

The stimulus-statement may be a result of the fact that diagnosis is the overriding concern of the physician. Perhaps, in his view, the disease is the thing, whereby his patient is now "this carcinoma," more than "this patient." Much has been said recently among physicians and medical educators concerning "seeing the patient as a disease-entity," and the alternate, "seeing the patient as a whole person." What determines the view a physician will take, one may ask?

Probably the first answer that should be considered is the influence of individual differences. As it was in the Asch experiment, the predisposition of individual character structure is a factor in how the physician perceives his patient. As was also indicated by the Asch experiment, the influence of predisposing individual differences varies according to the total situation or field in which the individual acts. Every physician, for example, is exposed in his professional education to a set of values and norms for behavior in the doctor's role. There is, moreover, the continuous representation of these professional values in the professional groups which he joins after medical school, and in the colleagues whom he chooses as "models." It is important to note that such professional value-systems are not short-range, *ad hoc* creations; they are the consequences of a long historical development.

For example, the percept "disease-entity" is a product of the disease concept which itself is quite young, and by no means universal in the modern world. According to this concept, illness is a natural event; that is, it is caused by forces within nature. Although in American society today this is a most commonplace idea, it was not so a brief century ago. At that time, illness was regarded mainly as a consequence of supernatural actions or forces, just as it still is in a large number of societies in the world today (and indeed still is among subgroups of our own society).

If we now reconsider the diagram presented on page 61, our subsequent discussion suggests that the representation of the doctor-patient relationship should be expanded to include three elements instead of only two. Considered from the physician's point of view, these include:

(A) the individual predispositions of the physician;
(A') the standards of professional behavior which have been internalized in the physician;
(B) the specific stimulus complex provided by the patient, perceived as a "medical problem."

The diagram now appears as follows:

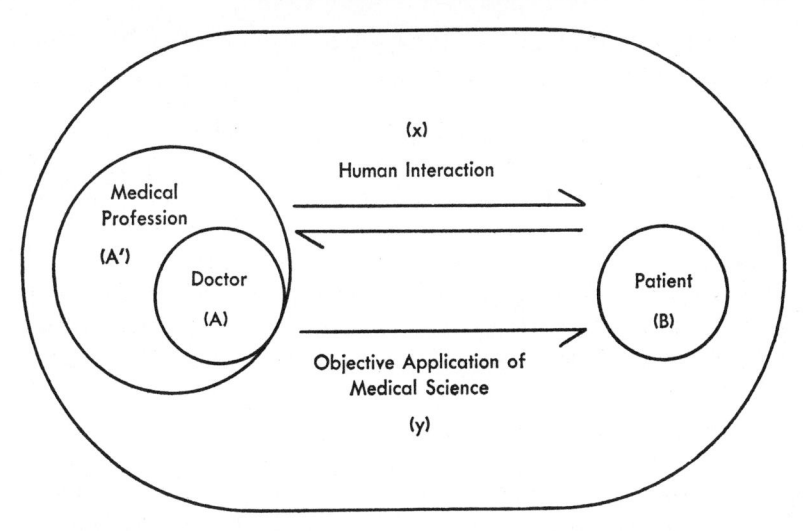

FIGURE 2. THE DOCTOR'S VIEW: A LIMITED SYSTEM

(Diagram: an outer oval contains an inner oval labeled "Medical Profession (A')" which contains a circle "Doctor (A)". A separate circle "Patient (B)" is on the right. Arrows between Doctor and Patient are labeled "(x) Human Interaction" (bidirectional, above) and "(y) Objective Application of Medical Science" (below).)

This revision of the picture of the doctor-patient relationship is intended both to add and to subtract from the previous diagram. We take away the assumption that the physician, operating in a field of forces approximately as shown in the diagram above, acts primarily as *a rational professional man,* choosing from his armamentarium of professional knowledge and skill those that are best fitted to the problems of his patient. In place of this assumption, it is asserted that the personal attributes which the physician brings to the situation determine *un*consciously much of what he will perceive and do. These subjective attributes are not necessarily adaptable to the rational requirements of the situation. Similarly, the social norms, in this case the professional standards and values, that influence the behavior of the physician, may or may *not* fit the rational requirements of the situation.

The tendency to assume that human behavior is dominated by rational, problem-solving motives is strong in the culture of the United States. As one would expect, this applies to the patient as well as to the doctor. The sick are, quite logically, expected to want to get well, to seek the most skilled help, and to cooperate in treatment. However, especially when the nature of illness is serious or uncertain, the patient is not likely, in fact, to think or to act rationally. Henderson emphasizes this point as he elaborates the problems of communication between doctor and patient:

> A patient sitting in your office facing you, is rarely in a favorable state of mind to appreciate the precise significance of a logical statement, and it is in general not merely difficult but quite impossible for him to perceive the precise meaning of a train of thought. It is also out of the question that the physician should convey what he desires to convey to the patient if he follows the practice of blurting out just what comes into his mind. The patient is moved by fears and by many other sentiments, and these, together with reason, are being modified by the doctor's words and phrases, by his manner and expression.[15]

Like the physician, the patient is moved by the situation as well as by the subjective attributes which distinguish him as an individual. Moreover, just as the doctor is guided in his behavior in this particular life situation by his membership in the medical profession, so also the patient's behavior in the sick role is modified by his membership in selected social institutions. The most important social influence on the patient, by and large, is his family.

The family itself, however—and the same must be said of the medical profession—sensitively reflects the prevailing currents in the culture at large. In our own society, for example, processes of industrialization and urbanization have had a revolutionary impact upon the size, the structure, and the values which characterize the American family. Among the results has been the delegation of functions which it once performed to other organs of society. It is obvious, therefore, that the individual patient's participation in other primary social institutions, the school being but one example, affects the way he will behave in response to illness. Although we contend that the family remains the most significant socializing agency for behavior in the patient role, it is important to add that we mean the family as an integral part of the culture, or "sociocultural matrix," and not as an independent unit.

Our graphic model of the doctor-patient relationship now appears as follows:

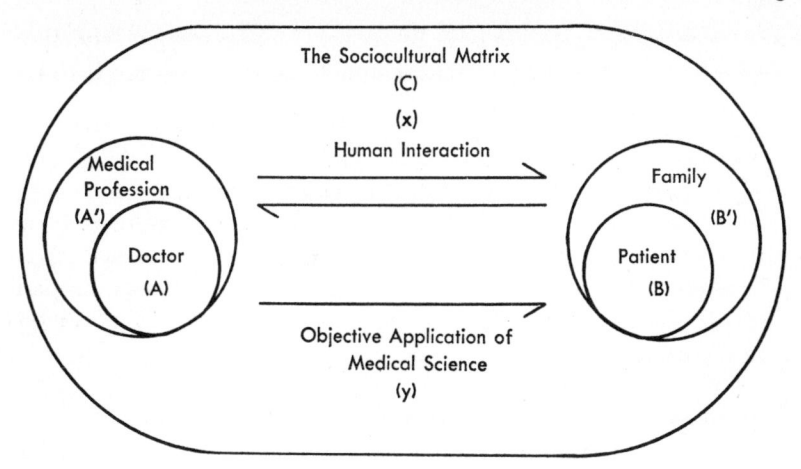

FIGURE 3. THE DOCTOR-PATIENT RELATIONSHIP AS A SOCIAL SYSTEM

The model, however, presents only a framework from which to begin the interpretation of the doctor-patient relationship. Rejecting a limited view that would overemphasize the rational and the individual, we have done no more than assert and, to some extent, attempt to show why the total situation (or "field") underlying the doctor-patient relationship is significant to its understanding. There remains the task of filling in the elements of this framework: culture, social role, and social system.

Culture: A Definition

Medicine is conceived of as a social institution which is an integral part of culture. These terms have a distinctive, technical meaning in social science, and it is in this specialized sense that they are used here. The words themselves, however, have more general and multiple connotations so that some clarification of their intended meaning is required.

Culture, as used in anthropology and sociology, means "the total way of life of a people, the social legacy the individual acquires from his group. Or culture can be regarded as that part of the environment that is the creation of man."[16]

"In ordinary speech," Kluckhohn has pointed out, "a man of culture is a man who can speak languages other than his own, who is familiar with history, literature, philosophy, or the fine arts. . . . To the anthropologist, however, to be human is to be cultured."

> There is culture in general, and then there are the specific cultures such as Russian, American, British, Hottentot, Inca. The general abstract notion serves to remind us that we cannot explain acts solely in terms of the biological properties of the people concerned, their individual past experience, and the immediate situation. The past experience of other men in the form of culture enters into almost every event.[17]

The most important aspect of this concept, as we will use it, is summarized in the phrase, "Each specific culture constitutes a kind of blueprint for all of life's activities,"[18] relatively standardized prescriptions as to what must be done, ought to be done, should be done, may be done, and must not be done.[19]

Man is said to vary in two fundamental ways: in physical form and in social heritage. The cataloging of mankind according to bodily structure and physiological characteristics has been the task of physical anthropology. "But," as Malinowski has written, "man varies also in an entirely different aspect. A pure blooded [African] Negro infant, transported to France and brought up there, would differ profoundly from what he would have been if reared in the jungle of his native land. He would have been given a different social heritage: a different language, different habits, ideals and beliefs; he would have been incorporated into a different social organization and cultural setting. This social heritage . . . is usually called culture in modern anthropology and social science."[20]

What culture *is* may be classified by what it is *not*. "Culture is not a disembodied force. It is created and transmitted by people. However, culture, like well-known concepts of the physical sciences, is a convenient abstraction. One never sees gravity. One sees bodies falling in regular ways. One never sees an electromagnetic field. Yet certain happenings that can be seen may be given a neat abstract formulation by assuming that the electromagnetic field exists. Similarly, one never sees culture as such. What is seen are regularities in the behavior or artifacts of a group that has adhered to a common tradition. The regularities in style and technique of ancient Inca tapestries or stone axes from Melanesian islands are due to the existence of mental blueprints for the group."[21]

Another common misunderstanding about culture is that one must be aware of cultural factors in order to be influenced by them. As Williams states, "Nothing could be further from the truth. Participants in social groups are seldom fully aware of what determines their behavior, or of what results from it. Usually we do not fully know what we are doing until after we have done it, and often we remain unaware of causes and consequences even then. Probably no individual ever 'knows' the total culture in which he is immersed. Most American parents, for example, certainly do not usually think of themselves as doing anything so formidable as 'transmitting culture' when they deal with their children. They 'just act.' But their actions constitute, in fact, an important part of the transmission of culture. When little Johnny is told that 'it's not polite' to hit the guest over the head with his baseball bat, or is admonished 'don't be a bully,' he is being introduced to the norms of his culture. Thousands of specific experiences with specific persons in particular situations comprise the 'socialization' process. The individual eventually absorbs a complex and fairly standardized system of rules, perspectives, and valuations common to many other individuals in the society."[22]

The term "norm," as used above, has a rather precise technical meaning. It will appear repeatedly throughout the book, used very much according to the definition by Williams:

> It has been emphasized that culture includes definitions of events, objects, or behaviors as "good" or "bad"; it marks off the things to be sought or avoided. . . . The core of any culture consists of those values and ideal-patterns widely regarded as obligatory. The term "cultural norm" refers to a specific prescription of the course that action *should* (is supposed to) follow in a given situation. Cultural norms, therefore, include both cultural *goals* and the approved *means* for reaching those goals. To be *cultural*, the norms have only to be acquired by learning and to be shared by individuals.[23]

There are, of course, many complicated shadings and types of norms. Williams describes the almost purely technical or cognitive norms (how to boil an egg, the most effective way to manufacture certain products) and, on a very different level, "moral" norms (thou shalt not kill). Some norms *proscribe* what should not be done. Others *pre*scribe what should or must be done.[24]

Social institutions, in ordinary common usage, usually refer to definite types of social groups such as the family, the school, and the church which are organized to take care of universally important life problems. Birth, marriage, and death, for example, are life events that are shared by all men, no matter what their culture. However, each culture attaches quite different values to the various ways in which people may behave in the face of these universal events, and through its institutions, each society regulates such behavior.

More technically, institutions are a *set* of norms that cluster around these critical events. "American society," writes Williams, ". . . like any other, must somehow deal with sexual activity, the care of dependent children, and the social relations established by sexual unions and the birth of children. The institutional norms concerned with these matters constitute the *familial* or *kinship institutions* of the society. Similarly, there is in every society a set of functional problems centering around the coercion of some individuals by others. The problem of power is a central fact of political life, and it is convenient to group together the norms regulating power as the *political institutions* of the society."[25]

Medicine, we have said, is a social institution. In all societies, diagnosis of illness and the treatment of illness are fitted with particular orientations and methods of practice. The use of these methods is delegated to a special group. As the society grows more complex, the healing institution within it becomes more specialized. Thus the British anthropologist W. H. R. Rivers, himself a physician, wrote after extended field investigations of primitive cultures:

> Medicine is a social institution. It comprises a set of beliefs and practices which only become possible when held and carried out by members of an organized society, among whom a high degree of the division of labour and specialization of the social function has come into being. Any principles and methods found to be of value in the study of social institutions in general cannot be ignored by the historian of medicine.[26]

From culture, therefore, institutional norms develop which prescribe and proscribe behavior in illness. In every society, patterns of expected behavior form into definite social roles associated with the healer and the sick. By means of culture, these roles persist and are transmitted from generation to generation.

Social Role: A Definition

A social role is a pattern of expected behavior. Such patterns are regulated by cultural norms or rules of behavior, and organized into rights and obligations which have general acceptance within a group. We shall use the term in two distinct ways: (1) to refer to "normative" patterns of expectation, based on the cultural system, and (2) to describe behavior which is patterned within small-scale groups and based on actual experience in the group. The former meaning is the more common and is explained at this point; the latter will be postponed until later in the discussion.

For example, the social role of the physician, as we shall describe it, includes the privilege of confidential access to extraordinary intimacies of his patient's physical and social experience. A doctor who as an individual is a complete stranger is allowed to examine parts of his patient's body which no other stranger is allowed even to see. This privilege is granted him as *Dr.* John Smith, whereas it would not be granted to *Mr.* John Smith. Moreover, it is a privilege which the doctor expects from his patient just as a doctor expects to be held responsible himself for holding in confidence the knowledge which results from this privilege. Because these are normative patterns of expected behavior, the doctor does not have to instruct each patient concerning his privileges and obligations as a physician; his patient has learned about the doctor's social role as part of his general participation in a society and his indoctrination into its culture.

Similarly, the patient has learned what his society "normally expects" from "a patient." As he assumes the role of patient, his behavior is guided accordingly.

A social role, in the classic definition of Ralph Linton, is always associated with a status.[27] Societies, in order to function, organize behavior into reciprocal patterns. The doctor, for example, behaves in relationship to other persons. His behavior is not determined in a social vacuum, according to the specific tasks he can perform. His behavior is always conceived with reference to the pattern of someone else's behavior. This "reciprocity" of behavior pattern is an essential feature of the organization of human behavior. Within such organization, each individual is assigned a position or *status*.

Inherent in a status is a set of *rights* and *duties*, which are distinct from the persons who express them. That is, it is not just Mrs. Tomasetti who is obligated to seek medical help and to be motivated to get well; these obligations are part of the patient's position in an organized network of human relations in a particular society. Only when Mrs. Tomasetti becomes a patient does she become so obligated, just as others in the same status or position are.

A *role* is "the dynamic aspect of a status," and, moreover, is perhaps the most important of the concepts which will be developed as our discussion proceeds. An extended quotation from Linton will, it is hoped, serve to clarify its meaning, together with that of status:

> . . . We . . . pointed out that the functioning of societies depends upon the presence of patterns for reciprocal behavior between individuals or groups of individuals. The polar positions in such patterns of reciprocal behavior are technically known as *statuses*. The term *status*, like the term *culture*, has come to be used with a double significance. A *status*, in the abstract, is a position in a particular pattern. It is thus quite correct to speak of each individual as having many statuses, since each individual participates in the expression of a number of patterns. However, unless the term is qualified in some way, *the status* of any individual means the sum total of all the statuses which he occupies. . . . Thus the status of Mr. Jones as a member of his community derives from a combination of all the statuses which he holds as a citizen, as an attorney, as a Mason, as a Methodist, as Mrs. Jones's husband, and so on.
>
> A status, as distinct from the individual who may occupy it, is simply a collection of rights and duties. Since these rights and duties can find expression only through the medium of individuals, it is extremely hard for us to maintain a distinction in our thinking between statuses and the people who hold them and exercise the rights

and duties which constitute them. The relation between any individual and any status he holds is somewhat like that between the driver of an automobile and the driver's place in the machine. The driver's seat with its steering wheel, accelerator, and other controls is a constant with ever-present potentialities for action and control, while the driver may be any member of the family and may exercise these potentialities very well or very badly.

A *rôle* represents the dynamic aspect of a status. The individual is socially assigned to a status and occupies it with relation to other statuses. When he puts the rights and duties which constitute the status into effect, he is performing a rôle. Rôle and status are quite inseparable, and the distinction between them is of only academic interest. There are no rôles without statuses and no statuses without rôles. Just as in the case of *status*, the term *rôle* is used with a double significance. Every individual has a series of rôles deriving from the various patterns in which he participates and at the same time *a rôle*, general, which represents the sum total of these rôles and determines what he does for his society and what he can expect from it.*[28]

Social System: A Definition

The social system concept has roots at least half a century old in both American and European sociology. As the concept is described here, however, the writing of Lawrence J. Henderson is the most important source.[29] Henderson was himself a physician, who became interested in sociology in the latter part of his life after he was already established as a physiological chemist and as a clinician. This unusual combination of interests undoubtedly contributed to Henderson's concern for the application of social science to medicine, and to his ability to build intellectual bridges toward this goal.[30]

The direction of Henderson's sociological thinking might have been predicted from the nature of his major scientific contributions in biological chemistry. As his friend Dr. Bock wrote at his death, in 1942:

> His formulation in 1908 of the acid-base equilibrium has had far-reaching significance. . . . The second great contribution made by Dr. Henderson was in furtherance of Claude Bernard's insistence

* From: *The Study of Man* by Ralph Linton, pp. 133 ff. Copyright, 1936, D. Appleton-Century Company, Inc., New York. Reprinted by permission of the publisher.

upon the necessity for synthesis of physiological systems. By simple mathematical methods Henderson was able to demonstrate for the first time the quantitative relationship in eight variables in the blood. His thinking concerning the equilibrium in the body had long been influenced by Willard Gibbs' study, "On the Equilibrium of Substances," and is best exemplified in his book, *Blood—A Study in General Physiology*, published in 1928.[31]

Following the model of his work on the synthesis of physiological systems, Henderson formulated concepts of social equilibria. His description of the social system concept is directly analogous to Willard Gibbs' generalized description of a physicochemical system.

Stated in brief summary, any system is conceived to be a unified whole composed of interdependent parts. Its unity is based upon the functional quality of the relations within the whole. Thus any change in one part of the system sets off simultaneous variations throughout the whole of the system. When one speaks of the structure of a system, he is referring essentially to the pattern of relationships. The key features of a system, therefore, are the patterned interdependence of its parts, and their functional interrelationships. The system is conceived of as a structure in dynamic balance, rather than in static construction.

In theories of biological systems, particularly of the human organism, an important assumption is that a state of balance is characteristic of the system, which, when disturbed, reacts toward reestablishing the "normal" condition. This process is called *homeostasis*.

A social system consists of two or more individuals interacting according to stable social roles. In the case described earlier, for example, three groups were described, representing two types of social system. The groups included (1) Mrs. Tomasetti and her first clinic doctor, (2) Mrs. Tomasetti and her second clinic doctor, and (3) the Tomasetti family. The types of social system were (a) the doctor-patient relationship and (b) the family.

According to system theory, Mrs. Tomasetti and her doctor are not simply two unique human individuals spontaneously interacting together. Each plays a social role, more particularly the *patient role*, on the one hand, and the *doctor's role*, on the other. Such roles are patterns of expected behavior which are derived from both culture and individual experience. Thus, Mrs. Tomasetti brings to each experience that she has with *a* doctor a set of expectations about how he will behave. These expectations (at the outset) have nothing to do with the particular doctor in question; they are expectations about how doctors in general are supposed to behave.

The doctor, in turn, enters the relationship with Mrs. Tomasetti with a set of expectations about how a patient should behave. Furthermore, each member of this group has a stable image of himself and how he should behave in this particular group. This is not a generalized conception of the self. It is particular to the group situation; that is, Mrs. Tomasetti has learned a pattern of related behaviors which she associates with being a patient. Similarly, the doctor has a self-concept of how he, *as a doctor*, is supposed to behave. Even though actual behavior may not conform to these role expectations, they are always there and exert a significant force upon the social system.

The relationship between Mrs. Tomasetti and her first doctor developed what is commonly called disharmony. In the terms of system theory, it is a group that is out of balance; the complementarity of the relations between parts of the system has been disrupted. The effort by the doctor to restore equilibrium does not work, thereby increasing his frustration and compounding the strain on the system. Similar to organic problems of homeostasis in biological systems, some balance between the essential organs must be restored or the system (organism) will be destroyed. In this case, the group does not survive. The doctor gives up his efforts and begins to withdraw behind the rationalization that this is an uncooperative patient and "there is nothing more that a doctor can do." The patient becomes sicker.

Henderson, in his use of the doctor-patient illustration, called attention to the fact that the full range of patient responses (sentiments) is often not calculated by the physician. The doctor, by virtue of the emphasis on his technical competence, is constrained to think along highly concrete, logical, rational channels. The patient, on the other hand, is peculiarly vulnerable to misperceptions, fears, and emotional interferences with direct and reasonable response to the stimuli provided by the words of the physician. There is, in other words, an almost built-in disharmony to this system, based upon the incompatibility of the "sentiments" of the doctor and patient, unless of course, appropriate corrections are made.

As the social system concept is developed more fully in later chapters, we will follow recent sociological formulations that favor status and role as the units of the social system in place of Henderson's "sentiments." Henderson's work, however, continues to have more than historical value; and those who are currently using the social system concept most actively[33] share his belief that just as Gibbs' conception clarified, directed, and economized the thoughts of all chemists, so the system concept will make more possible this scientific ordering of the complex phenomena of social behavior.

The Frame of Reference

These are the elements of the frame of reference that will guide this book's discussion: culture, social institution, social role, and social system. The doctor-patient relationship is conceived of as a system of social roles, derived from culture, and learned and controlled by two major social institutions, the medical profession and the family.

We turn now to the filling in of the details of this framework. First, the medical profession is studied as the major source of reference for the doctor's role. Second, the family is described as the primary reference group for the behavior of the patient. Finally, all of these concepts, structures, and forces are fitted to the analysis of the hospital which is the single most important institution in modern medicine.

NOTES TO CHAPTER 2

1. For a discussion of this development in the history of psychology, see Koffka, Kurt, *Principles of Gestalt Psychology*, Harcourt, Brace and Co., New York, 1935.
2. See Asch, Solomon E., *Social Psychology*, Prentice-Hall, Inc., New York, 1952.

3. Asch, Solomon E., and H. A. Witkin, "Studies in Space Orientation: I. Perception of the Upright with Displaced Visual Fields," *Journal of Experimental Psychology*, vol. 38, June, 1948, pp. 325–337; also "Studies in Space Orientation: II. Perception of the Upright with Displaced Visual Fields and with Body Tilted," *Journal of Experimental Psychology*, vol. 38, August, 1948, pp. 455–477.

4. Asch, Solomon E., "Effects of Group Pressure Upon the Modification and Distortion of Judgments" in Maccoby, Eleanor E., Theodore M. Newcomb, and Eugene L. Hartley, editors, *Readings in Social Psychology*, 3d ed., Henry Holt and Co., New York, 1958, pp. 174–183.

5. *Ibid.*, p. 174.

6. *Ibid.*, p. 175.

7. *Ibid.*, pp. 178–179.

8. *Ibid.*, p. 180.

9. *Ibid.*, pp. 182–183.

10. Crutchfield, Richard S., "Conformity and Character," *American Psychologist*, vol. 10, May, 1955, pp. 191–198.

11. *Ibid.*, pp. 191–192. The reader with special interest in the application of experimental methods to the study of social psychological problems will almost certainly find the details of design in this experiment intriguing.

12. *Ibid.*, p. 198.

13. The author acknowledges a special debt to L. J. Henderson who used a similar illustration in what may be called a classic paper on this subject. See Henderson, Lawrence J., "Physician and Patient as a Social System," *New England Journal of Medicine*, vol. 212, May, 1935, pp. 819–823.

14. *Ibid.*, p. 822.

15. *Ibid.*, p. 821.

16. Kluckhohn, Clyde, *Mirror for Man*. Fawcett Publications, Greenwich, Conn., 1957, p. 20. (Originally published by McGraw-Hill Book Co., New York, 1949.)

17. *Ibid.*, pp. 20–21.

18. *Ibid.*, p. 21.

19. Williams, Robin M., Jr., *American Society:* A Sociological Interpretation. 2d ed. Alfred A. Knopf, Inc., New York, 1961, pp. 22–25.

20. Malinowski, Bronislaw, "Culture" in *Encyclopaedia of the Social Sciences*. Macmillan Co., New York, 1931, vol. 4, p. 621.

21. Kluckhohn, Clyde, *op. cit.*, p. 24.

22. Williams, Robin M., *op. cit.*, pp. 24–25.

23. *Ibid.*, p. 25.

24. For a more complete but succinct definition of "cultural norm," see Williams, Robin M., *ibid.*, pp. 25–30.

25. *Ibid.*, pp. 31–32.

26. Rivers, W. H. R., *Medicine, Magic, and Religion*. Harcourt, Brace and Co., New York, 1924.

27. Linton, Ralph, *The Study of Man:* An Introduction. Appleton-Century Co., New York, 1936, pp. 113 ff.

28. *Ibid.*, pp. 113–114.

29. In addition to the paper cited in note 13, see Henderson, Lawrence J., *Pareto's General Sociology:* A Physiologist's Interpretation, Harvard University Press, Cambridge, Mass., 1935; "The Practice of Medicine as Applied Sociology," *Transactions of the Association of American Physicians*, vol. 51, 1936, pp. 8–22; "The Study of Man," *Science*, vol. 94, July 4, 1941, pp. 1–10.

30. Henderson's interest in sociology, moreover, was not narrowed to its application in medicine. During the last decade of his career at Harvard, he taught and influenced a distinguished group of social scientists, including George Homans, Henry Murray, Talcott Parsons, and Robert Merton.

31. Bock, Arlie V., "Lawrence Joseph Henderson, 1878–1942," *Transactions of the Association of American Physicians*, vol. 57, 1942, pp. 17–19.

32. Henderson, Lawrence J., "Physician and Patient as a Social System," 1935, p. 823.

33. The most detailed statement of the social system idea did not make claim to a theory. See Parsons, Talcott, and Edward A. Shils, *Toward a General Theory of Action*, Harvard University Press, Cambridge, Mass., 1951.

PART TWO
SOCIAL ROLES AND THEIR INSTITUTIONAL CONTEXT

Chapter 3

THE MEDICAL PROFESSION:
A HISTORICAL DISCUSSION OF THE SOCIAL ORGANIZATION OF MODERN MEDICINE

> *The characteristic features of the medical profession are determined to a large extent by the attitude of society towards the human body and by the valuation of health and disease. The scope of medicine was always the same: to cure disease and eventually to prevent it. Medicine always meant service: therefore at all times certain qualities were required of the physician—readiness to help, knowledge concerning the nature of disease, and skill in curing the sick man. However, the medical ideal was a very different one in different periods of history, determined by the structure of the society of the time and by its general conception of the world.*
>
> HENRY E. SIGERIST, M.D.,
> *The Physician's Profession Through the Ages*[1]

THE MODERN DOCTOR has been described as one of the last of the American entrepreneurs, a persistently rugged individual in a corporate age. It is estimated that at least 70 per cent of the physicians in the United States remain independent practitioners.[2] Through the American Medical Association, the physicians of this country have vigorously defended the rights of physicians as individuals against anything more than a minimum of regulation from outside the profession.[3]

To be unusually free from legal and other types of formal regulation, however, does not necessarily provide the doctor with independence of thought or behavior. Actually, the physician is a member—as physicians in our society have been since medieval times—of a highly organized and tightly knit occupational group: the community commonly referred to as "the medical profession." Each physician has been carefully trained not only in the skills and knowledge of his profession, but also in its values and attitudes. His profession is ever present within his life-space, ready to enforce, to reward, and to punish its members according to the rules, both spoken and unspoken, that prevail in the group.

This high degree of integration of the doctor in his profession, and his consequent dependence on the professional group is not in itself unique. All individuals, it is our assumption, are more or less dependent upon group memberships for the guidance of their behavior. In their choice of the alternatives of life experience, individuals can never be entirely *in*dependent. They are always influenced by the norms—the patterns of prescribed (accepted) behavior which they have learned. The teaching of such norms of behavior is a major function of social institutions, such as the family, the church, and the school. The medical profession is this type of social institution. Its norms for the guidance of the behavior of members of the profession are conveyed and controlled through the medical school, the hospital, the American Medical Association, and, more recently, through the increasing and more powerful specialty boards and associations.

Basic to an understanding of medicine as a social institution is its status as a "profession." In this chapter we will describe medicine according to the special meanings that have come to be ascribed to a profession, and attempt to show how medicine is rooted in culture. Medicine has not always been a "profession," however. Professionalism has been a distinguishing feature of medicine only in our own society, and may be dated to medieval times. As a brief preface, therefore, we will look at medicine as a major social institution in other, less-developed societies than our own. Such societies have different conceptions of life's most important forces, including the causes of illness and the role of the healer.

Culture: The Significant Sociological Unit

The major social institutions evolve around important aspects of life, such as getting a living (economic institution), regulating the relations between the sexes (marriage), dealing with the supernatural (religious institution), and exercising control over group living through rules, regulations, and laws (government). Appropriate ways of acting also become crystallized around special occasions such as childbirth, weddings, death, and sickness. Medicine develops for the treatment of sickness. Its character and dynamism depend upon the cultural pattern within which it is a part. "The significant sociological unit," Ruth Benedict has written, "is not the institution but the cultural configuration."[4]

Studies of primitive medicine provide excellent examples of both the unity of culture and the differences among cultures. For a long time primitive culture was regarded as simply a stage in the evolution of society. All of primitive medicine tended, therefore, to be lumped together under a general description of healing art, dominated by assumptions of supernatural etiology and magical treatment. Like their parent cultures, such institutions of medicine were considered not only "primitive" but ignorant. Social evolution itself was conceived of as a linear process of growth, guided toward progressively higher stages by increases of knowledge.

As we have learned more about primitive societies, however, this view of social evolution has been discredited. "Measuring everything with our everyday standards," writes an outstanding historian of medicine, "we will never understand either the past or the future. Primitive medicine is not a queer collection of errors and superstitions, but a number of living unities in living cultural patterns, quite able to function through the centuries in spite of their fundamental differences from our pattern."[5]

If ignorance were the critical factor which differentiates primitive society from the modern, the problem of social change would be relatively simple. It would be a matter mainly of education, of reducing the wide gap of knowledge. Simple ignorance, in other words, may be expected to yield to the enlightenment of knowledge. However, the experience of public health workers both among the primitive and the more modern but underdeveloped societies has demonstrated that social change is more complicated.

People in other societies think differently. They are able to learn new ideas only when these ideas are made compatible with their cultural frame of reference, or by actually changing their frame of reference. Thus sometimes modern medical methods can be introduced in other cultures quite successfully if properly disguised. In some cases where the societies in question were dominated by magical conceptions of disease, it was required that science be disguised as magic. (In our own science-dominated society, it has been said that magic must be disguised as science.)[6]

A magico-religious frame of reference is not a function of ignorance. For the primitive whose culture is dominated by a magico-religious view, illness, like other significant aspects of his experience, is seen and interpreted within this framework. Like Koffka's tilted room which, as the field of perception, made a tilted line appear vertical, the magico-religious frame of reference dominates the primitive perception.

We in contemporary western society have learned to think of illness as a natural event. For the primitive, however, illness, like death or an accident, is not regarded as a natural event, but as the consequence of supernatural actions or forces. Mystical object-intrusion, breach of taboo, and witchcraft are regarded as the most common causes of illness. Such beliefs can only occur in a world quite different from ours,

> . . . in a magical world where the natural is supernatural but the supernatural quite natural, where causality in our sense does not exist but things, animals and plants are tied together by mystical participations and moved by occult forces. Primitive causality is not afraid of contradictions and looks for the cause of a material effect in another supernatural dimension or vice versa, because it sees no limits between the two realms.[7]

Primitive medicine can be shown to be intricately woven from the *fabric of its culture*. It is *not* a contrivance of *quacks*, as so often concluded by observers from a quite different culture. Out of deep-lying cultural beliefs in causes of disease, methods of diagnosis and treatment which to us appear exotic and irrational are for the primitive needed and used. Every kind of divination, trance, astrology, and dream is used for diagnosis. Dances, soul-hunts, exorcism, and purification are common methods of treatment.

The *healer* in primitive medicine is often compared to the modern doctor. In nineteenth-century evolutionary theories, such as that of Spencer, "the medicine man is the forefather of the modern physician."[8] The validity of this evolutional analogy has been effectively refuted.[9] However, the medicine man is, in a certain sense, the primitive counterpart of the doctor; he is the person who is responsible for diagnosing and treating illness.

The important point here is that primitive medicine is integrated with culture and not primarily to be explained by a universal theory of social evolution. There is, in fact, no *one* kind of primitive medicine; there are many. By way of very brief inquiry into this hypothesis, the following descriptions of a Plains Indian tribe and a Melanesian society provide culture case examples.[10]

Medicine in a Plains Indian Tribe

The Cheyenne Indians are found to be little concerned about disease. Their ceremonies are seldom concerned with illness. This may be contrasted with the Navahos who spend one-fourth to one-third of their productive hours in religious activities involving 35 principal ceremonies, a majority of which are concerned with disease. With the Cherokees also, the chief necessity for religion is found in the existence of disease and its eradication is the responsibility of the culture's principal office.

The Cheyennes *are* a religious people. In fact, their whole life is full of little ceremonial acts. Their ceremonies, as one expects, cluster around the activities that are most important to the pulse of life in the tribe; but illness is not one of these. Warfare, on the other hand, is the activity that for Cheyenne culture has the highest value. Consequently, "counting the coup" is their outstanding ritual act. This means literally "touching the enemy." Neither killing nor scalping the enemy is so important as counting a coup, and the recitation to the tribe by a brave on how he "counted a coup."

Hunting is another vital aspect of the culture. Traditionally, hunting is the basic occupation of the Cheyenne male. Elaborate ceremonials are provided in the culture to accompany hunting.

The medicine man is an important figure in Cheyenne society, but his major function is to protect the hunting and warfare. He is not a healer.

Cheyenne medicine is essentially a minor institution in Cheyenne life. This is appropriate to the cultural matrix. The conception of disease, methods of treatment, and the role of the office of the healer fit the cultural attitudes toward illness. This conclusion is supported both by a study of Cheyenne medicine itself and by comparison with the medicine of other Plains Indian tribes and with less closely related American Indian tribes that are in a comparable state of social development.

Dobuan Medicine

A quite different type of medicine from the Cheyenne is found in Dobuan culture. The Dobuans are a Melanesian people who live on a small volcanic island, north of eastern New Guinea. The major occupation is the cultivation of yams.

Dobuan culture has fascinated anthropologists precisely because it is so different from our own. It is indeed unique by any standard.

Pervading all of Dobu life is the incantation. The power of a secret charm, and the defense against the secret charms of others, preoccupy all Dobuans. The contest that results is between people, not with the forces of nature. When one's yam garden prospers, it is because the strength of one's charms are greater than his neighbor's. It is assumed that one's neighbor is a witch or sorcerer who will "do you in" if he can—through sorcery, of course. Not even from his own spouse does the Dobuan feel safe.

Disease pervades Dobu life as a weapon of sorcery. It is a principal magical weapon. An example is the following incantation for causing gangosa, a horrible disease that eats away the flesh much like the hornbill, the animal patron from which the disease is named, eats the tree trunks with its great rending beak:

Hornbill dweller of Sigasiga
in the lowana tree top,
he cuts, he cuts,
he rends open,
from the nose,
from the temples,
from the throat,
from the hip,
from the root of the tongue,
from the back of the neck,
from the navel,
from the small of the back,
from the kidneys,
from the entrails,
he rends open,
he rends standing.
Hornbill dweller of Tokuku,
in the lowana tree top,
he [the victim] crouches bent up,
he crouches holding his back,
he crouches arms twined in front of him,
he crouches hands over his kidneys,
he crouches head bent in arms twined about it,
he crouches double twined.
Wailing, shrieking,
it [the immaterial power of the charm] flies hither,
quickly it flies hither.[11]

Such incantations are believed by the Dobuan to cause disease. Thus, when he finds himself the victim of disease, he must, in order to get well, depend upon the person who has put the disease upon him. No one else can help him, for incantations are secret, and privately owned. Only the sorcerer whose incantation caused a disease knows the corresponding exorcism.

It is interesting that diseases introduced by contact with white civilization, such as tuberculosis, measles, influenza, and dysentery, have no incantations, in spite of the fact that they have been known in Dobu for almost three-quarters of a century. It is not permissible to create new incantations; they are passed on from individuals to appropriate kin and only at certain times and under given conditions. Thus the Dobuan assumes that the white man's diseases have incantations that are the secret possessions of those who brought the diseases to the island. The Dobuan accepts the idea that only from the white man can the appropriate incantation be learned. That no such incantation is forthcoming does not surprise the Dobuan. He guards the incantations of his own diseases just as zealously.

Since everybody fights against everybody else in Dobu and knows disease incantations, and since the sorcerer is necessarily also the healer, there is no special medicine man and no special medical department. Disease is everywhere. Even as the Cheyennes fled disease by arranging to die in battle a hero's death, so similarly the Dobu make it impossible to escape disease All illness, disease and death are attributed to jealousy and used as the basis of recrimination and revenge.

As Ackerknecht writes: "The unity of Dobuan culture cannot be denied, sinister as it may seem to us. . . . Nowhere else than in Dobu do [supernatural beliefs] seem to have attained such forms which almost defeat the purpose [to enforce lawful behavior toward neighbors]. Nowhere is every evil attributed with such consequence to human agency. . . . Dobuan medicine owes its special features to its perfect integration with the pattern. In Dobu there is only one cause of disease, witchcraft or sorcery. There is no possible intervention of supernaturals, independent from human agency, imposing a more impersonal sanction . . . no influence of ghosts, no taboo infraction as elsewhere in Melanesia. . . . Dobuan 'medicine' needs no special practitioners; it is generalized, and its outstanding feature is that disease-making counts more than disease-healing."[12]

Some Origins of Modern Medicine

The heritage of modern western medicine appears to be derived from two quite divergent sources: ancient Greece and medieval Europe. Our knowledge concerning the distant fourth century B.C., of course, is very incomplete, just as the contemporary western culture is perhaps too near and too complex for a clear view. Nevertheless, it is instructive to speculate on the order of the historical development of medicine.

The strides that ancient Greece made in medicine were truly remarkable. Hippocrates and his school at Cos developed an advanced clinical case method. A school at Cnidus devoted itself to the study we now call physiology. Herophilus and Erasistratus in Alexandria established the foundations of human anatomy. All of these developments were in the fourth century B.C.

It is not by accident, however, that these so-called "schools" were named after particular individuals like Hippocrates or Herophilus, while the famous medical schools of the late Middle Ages were the Universities of Montpellier, Paris, Salerno, Bologna, Oxford, and Padua, all the names of cities. In ancient Greece the physician was a craftsman. He was trained not in a school but through apprenticeship to an individual master. Outstanding master craftsmen established centers for such training, but the result was not a "doctor" similar to that of today. His emphasis was on prognosis. He was concerned not with disease but the patient, the patient as a whole.

This emphasis in Greek medicine on seeing the patient as a whole person was based not so much on a particular philosophy of medical care as it was on the peculiar, unprotected social position of the Greek physician. "He was a traveling craftsman, and had to gain the public's confidence through marvelous prognoses. . . . He could not afford failure."[13] Failure, in fact, sometimes led to the severe punishment of the Greek physician. Consequently, it was of the utmost importance to him to know whether or not he should accept treatment of a patient—and sometimes whether and when he should leave town. Under these circumstances he needed to learn everything possible about the patient, including, but not limited to, his current complaint.

We tend to look back at Greek medicine through the distorting lens of legend. Consequently, as Sigerist has written, "We do not like the idea of a Greek physician being a craftsman, going from one city to another, knocking at the doors, and offering his services as a shoemaker or a blacksmith would. And yet there is no doubt that that was the case. Several Hippocratic treatises give us very enlightening accounts of such occurrences. There was very little privacy in the relations between doctor and patient. The doctor's shop, the *iatreion*, like other craftsmen's shops, was open to everybody, and medical questions were discussed publicly in the market place. When it happened that two doctors came to the same town at the same time, a wild competition was the result of such a coincidence. Again, the Hippocratic writings tell us how many doctors tried to attract the patients' attention by dressing extravagantly, being profusely perfumed, and by displaying showy instruments. Dr. Ludwig Edelstein has demonstrated very convincingly that the art of prognostic developed in Greek medicine to such an extent chiefly on account of these peculiar conditions in medical practice. The doctor who came to a small city generally was unknown to the population. The best way to secure a good reputation was by making correct prognoses and by telling the patient right away what his disease was without even asking questions."[14]

It was in the medieval university that the present title of "doctor" was created. With the title went a status in society, a proper education, and important affiliations in organizations, such as the universities, colleges, and guilds. Medical laws were enacted in the West during the twelfth century, making provisions for curriculum, state examinations and licenses, a fee schedule, a regulation of the practice of apothecaries, and control of city hygiene. Such legislation spread gradually from Sicily, to Spain, and then to Germany.

The paradox is that ancient Greece possessed a mode of thought, an intellectual frame of reference which was much closer to that of modern medicine than was true of the late Middle Ages. At its high point, Greek medicine was rational, empirical, experimental. Human dissection was practiced as a method of inquiry in Alexandria, and not as the illustrative exercise which it became in the late Middle Ages:

> . . . After the 13th Century, dissections were practiced on an increasing scale. . . . Doctors supervised dissections, but they did not actually observe what was being dissected; rather they saw what they were supposed to see according to Galen. . . . The two hundred years of fruitless dissection in the late Middle Ages only confirm what has been observed among primitives, Egyptians, Babylonians, and Mexicans. *The mere technique of dissection could not advance the knowledge of anatomy. What was needed was a new approach*—an approach which was not found in the Middle Ages.[15]

On the other hand, the social organization of medicine during the late Middle Ages closely approximated that of today.

It would appear that two quite separate factors are part of the complex known as modern medicine. The first is the ideology that is the essential underpinning of rational empirical science. The second is a form of social organization that provides the physician with a social role sufficiently stable and protected to develop methods of applying the knowledge of science to the treatment of illness. As is demonstrated by the Greek and medieval examples, neither one of these factors without the other is sufficient for the medical profession today.

In ancient Greece the mode of thought that dominated medicine was conducive to the development of a rational science, but the physician was handicapped by the place he was given in society, by the role that was prescribed for him in the total scheme of Greek culture. In the late Middle Ages, on the other hand, the doctor attained a high and secure status socially; but he was not able to break out of the boundaries of thought typical of the time, a mode of thought that was decidedly antithetical to rational science. It might have been hoped, for example, that the horrible witch-burning craze that prevailed at this time would be opposed by the university-trained doctors. It was not. The doctors, by and large, gave witch-burning official support. Only when the mode of thought basic to rational science was coordinated with the social status that was institutionalized in the professions was it possible for modern medicine to develop.

Medicine as a Profession: A Definition

Out of the medieval guilds and universities, the professions developed. The earliest use of the term "profession" recorded by the *Oxford English Dictionary* dates from 1541. There is no corresponding term in any language of the ancient world.[16] Yet doctors, clergymen, and lawyers were part of earlier societies. What, more precisely, distinguishes these and other professions as we know them today?

One method of discerning the distinction is to observe the principal differences between these endeavors in ancient and medieval times. "In Greece the lawyer," as Carr-Saunders and Wilson have noted, "was not a specially trained advocate practicing before a specially trained judge who decided the case according to law; he was the litigant's friend speaking on his behalf before the litigant's peers, who decided the issue on all the merits of the case as they saw them. Again the physician, though in some cases more of a specialist, did not receive any formal training; at the best he was the pupil of some eminent practitioner. In the Roman Empire the position of the lawyer was much the same as in Greece; the physician on the other hand was generally a slave attached to a rich man's household, while the accountant, the architect, and the engineer were usually salaried administrators in the employment of the state. It appears that in ancient times there were no training schools where those who followed the vocations which we call professions received instruction, that the practitioners seldom or never formed distinct social groups, and that they were not infrequently in a dependent position. Moreover they did not form vocational associations of the kind familiar to us."[17]

The extended formal training which the medieval doctor, lawyer, or priest received and which his ancient counterpart did not receive, remains today one of the core characteristics of the professions. A second basic attribute of a profession is an orientation toward service to the community. Thus a profession is "a vocation in which a professed knowledge of some department of learning or science is used in its application to the affairs of others or in the practice of an art founded upon it."[18]

There are two other characteristics that have long been associated with the professions. First, their practitioners form a distinct social group, classified as such both by the practitioners themselves and by the society in which they operate. The basis of this social group is in their professional activity and not some other social or economic attribute. Secondly, the social group itself is organized into an association which establishes formal rules and informal practices of behavior. The association disciplines its own members, maintaining an ethical standard by its own means, and thus preserving the independence of its members in the practice of the profession.

However, "an industrializing society is a professionalizing society."[19] Two indices of this relationship in the American experience have been described: "One is an increase in the proportion of the labor force in the white-collar occupations generally, and the professions and semi-professions specifically. The other is the increase in the number of occupations trying to acquire the symbols of professional status, following a program of action spearheaded by their formal associations, which might lead to recognition as professions."[20]

With increasing professionalization, the descriptive definition of a profession like modern medicine becomes more complex. At the core remains the two primary characteristics: (a) a prolonged specialized training in a body of abstract knowledge, and (b) a service orientation. As an occupation becomes more professionalized, it acquires a number of features that appear to be derivative from the two just noted. In a recent discussion of this process, the following traits were listed:

1. The profession determines its own standards of education and training.
2. The student professional goes through a more far-reaching adult socialization experience than the learner in other occupations.
3. Professional practice is often legally recognized by some form of licensure.
4. Licensing and admission boards are manned by members of the profession.
5. Most legislation concerned with the profession is shaped by that profession.
6. The occupation gains in income, power, and prestige ranking, and can demand higher caliber students.
7. The practitioner is relatively free of lay evaluation and control.
8. The norms of practice enforced by the profession are more stringent than legal controls.
9. Members are more strongly identified and affiliated with the profession than are members of other occupations with theirs.
10. The profession is more likely to be a terminal occupation. Members do not care to leave it, and a higher proportion assert that if they had it to do over again, they would again choose that type of work.[21]

"These characteristics," Goode states, "are closely interdependent. More important, they are all *social* relationships; they assert obligations and rights between client and professional, professional and colleague, or professional and some formal agency. Consequently, an important part of the process by which an occupation becomes a profession is the gradual institutionalization of various role relationships between itself and other parts of the society. These clients or agencies, or the society generally, will concede autonomy to the profession only if its members are able and willing to police themselves; will grant higher fees or prestige only when both its competence and its area of competence seem to merit them; or will grant an effective monopoly to the profession through licensure boards only when it has persuasively shown that it is the sole master of its special craft, and that its decisions are not to be reviewed by other professions."[22]

The main distinction between a profession and other similar occupations, according to Flexner, is the existence of "unequal responsibility" for the application of intellectual knowledge in science to the community. Pharmacy, for example, contains most of the qualities which are the marks of a profession, but it does not include original or primary responsibility. "The physician thinks, decides, and orders; the pharmacist obeys—obeys, of course, with discretion, intelligence, and skill—yet, in the end, obeys and does not originate. Pharmacy therefore is an arm added to the medical profession, a specially and distinctly higher form of handicraft, not a profession. . . . The physician's function is overwhelmingly intellectual in quality and his responsibility absolutely personal. He utilizes various instruments—physical and human: microscope, stethoscope, sphygmograph, orderly, pharmacist, dietitian, nurse. But his is the commanding intelligence that brings these resources to bear; his is the responsibility of decision as to the problem and how it is to be solved. There are, of course, physicians in abundance to whose processes the word intellectual cannot be properly applied—routineers, to whom a few obvious signs indicate this or that procedure, by law of mechanical association; but these poorly trained and ill-equipped medical men have no place in modern medicine. They are already obsolete—mere survivals destined soon to pass away."[23] Flexner wrote these words in 1914, but they remain pertinent.

The Social Role of the Physician

To make generalizations about any aspect of social behavior in our complex contemporary western culture is a difficult task. However, just as we have tried to construct generalizations about the past in spite of the handicaps of distance and inadequate information, so the attempt may be made to find some order among the very complicated demands made upon the modern physician. With this word of caution, we turn to a description of the patterns of expectation that may be discerned in our society concerning the behavior of the doctor.

The two most important characteristics of a profession, as we have defined it, are an extended period of formal training and an orientation toward service to the community. The various professions are by no means equal on these criteria. Nursing, for example, thinks of itself today as a profession, and its right to do so is widely accepted. It qualifies more than other professions in its orientation toward service, but less than the major professions, (medicine, law, the ministry) in its requirements for a prolonged specialized training in a body of abstract knowledge.

The image which others have of the nurse is influenced by these criteria. That is, there is a generalized expectation that the nurse will *care for* rather than *treat* the sick. A common conception of her role is more that of one who comforts than of one who applies scientific knowledge.

Under the impact of changes in the requirements of medical care, the role of the nurse is changing. Modern medicine has become increasingly technical and hospital-centered. The physician has become more dependent upon skilled helpers to do his job well. This is the age of what is called "team medicine," including not only the nurse, but the hospital administrator, the social worker, and the laboratory technician.

Moreover, the nurse together with the other members of the health "team" do not think of themselves primarily as doctors' helpers; all of them insist that they have an area of competence quite distinct from what they may do as medical assistants.

In the meantime, the professionalization of these groups has been stepped up considerably by the technological revolution in the hospital. Responsibilities have diversified and increased, and the needs for training have been extended accordingly. It is not surprising that each of these groups appears to see itself more than ever as qualified to join the front ranks of the professions. Public acceptance of these claims, however, seems to lag behind.[24]

Society's image of the physician, on the other hand, generally ranks him at the very top of the scale on all the basic and secondary criteria of professionalism. His education is considered to be exacting intellectually and demanding of skill. It is as long or longer than any other professional qualification. Also demanded is that he should be oriented, above all, toward service to others.

The unique characteristics of the social role of the physician can only be understood when one calculates the special meanings which society places upon behavior in the professions. It is not uncommon, for example, for laymen to criticize physicians and their organizations for what they call excessive financial self-interest. As the Fabian Society is reported to have said in England in 1927: "Whenever you see a statement on public policy by the British Medical Association you always know that they are considering the private pockets of the doctors who are their members, and are never in the least degree interested in public welfare. I do not think that there is a single exception where for a quarter or half a second the British Medical Association has ever put aside the pecuniary interests of its members for the sake of improvement in public health."[25] Are such charges likely to be made against a chamber of commerce, or association of manufacturers? They are not, simply because it is taken for granted in manufacturing and trade that profit is the major motive and "let the buyer beware." (*Caveat emptor.*) In the professions, on the other hand, and in the medical profession in particular, service to the community is expected as a basic orientation. Any suspected violation of this orientation is subject to severe criticism by the public.

Does it follow, therefore, that physicians must be unusually altruistic people, more interested in serving others than they are in gain for self? Many have concluded that they are. Parsons has reviewed studies of the professions and found what he calls a tendency to characterize professional behavior as *a*typical in terms of its motivation. That is, the society as a whole is seen as business-centered and thus as an "acquisitive" society, with "self-interest" and "profit" as the dominant, motivating forces. By contrast with business in this interpretation, the professions are marked by altruism. It is asserted that the service aspect of professional behavior, particularly in medicine, is stronger than is self-interest.[26]

This kind of analysis weights the influence on motives for behavior. It attributes to one part of society, business and industry, one type of motive, "the profit motive"; it attributes to another part of society, the professions, a different type of motive, a service motive. It says, in effect, that these two groups are propelled, one by egoistic motives and the other by altruistic motives.[27]

Parsons disagrees. The difference between the professions and business, he says, is not mainly a difference of typical motive at all, but one of situation in which the commonly human motives operate. In other words, the situation which is faced by the doctor typically in his work is different from that faced by the businessman or the industrialist.

What then is the situation of the physician?

The summary description given by Parsons is: "Modern medical practice is organized about the application of scientific knowledge to the problems of illness and health and to the control of disease." The physician's role (that is, the pattern of expected behavior) is functionally specific. This means that he is expected to apply a high degree of achieved skill and knowledge to problems of illness. He is not a generalized sage or wise man. He is a technical specialist in health and disease, a specialist by virtue of his own attainments in a rigorous scientific training, not by virtue of special appointment. Thus the status which society attaches to his position is regarded as an achieved status, not an ascribed status.

In association with this particular role attribute (which Parsons calls "functional specificity"), the physician also is given certain unusual privileges. He may, for example, examine his patients physically, and also may inquire into the most intimate areas of both physical and personal life. This privilege, it is argued, is legitimized not because the physician is regarded as fundamentally more honorable than other men, but because his job, the application of his specific technical skills, requires the privilege of such intimacy.

A second important attribute of the physician's role is called by Parsons "affective-neutrality." This means that the physician is expected to be objective and emotionally detached. There is a subtle balance required in this particular aspect of his role. The doctor is expected to have concern for his patient, to be sympathetic and understanding. On the other hand, in the special privileges given him with the patient's body and life history, he is expected to be neutral in judgment and controlled emotionally.

There is considerable strain on the physician in his effort to maintain "affective neutrality." As a member of the society at large and as a person with special subgroup affiliations, the individual physician necessarily has personal values. Thus when he learns from a patient about conduct that contradicts his personal value-system, he will be under special stress in maintaining value-neutrality as a physician. Similarly, he is, as an individual, susceptible to spontaneous emotional responses which, as a physician, he must control.

It may be readily seen that both of these attributes of the physician's role are derived from the nature of the situation between physician and patient. They are *not* necessary derivatives of a special motivational system. In similar terms, it is the situation of the physician that influences him to treat his patient primarily according to the health requirements of the community rather than according to the doctor's own needs. It is the "welfare of the patient" which dominates the situation, not the advancement of self. In the words of Parsons, this third role attribute of the physician is "orientation to the collectivity" as opposed to "self-orientation."

A fourth role requirement is that the physician is subject to universal rules of his profession primarily and not the requirements of a unique particular relationship. Euthanasia offers an illustration. A professional rule about euthanasia is the guidepost of a physician's behavior in treating painful terminal illness. This protects the physician from the tremendous strain that would be on him if he were expected to make his own personal decision in such cases. It also protects patients from possible malpractice associated with the power over life and death.

As a member of the medical profession, then, the physician is expected to apply highly specialized technical skills based on scientific training to problems of illness and health and to the control of disease. He is expected to treat his patients with sympathy but also with value-neutrality and with well-controlled emotions. He is oriented to the welfare of his patient as a representative of the community as opposed to his own self-interest; and he is expected to be guided by rules of professional behavior that are universally binding to medical practice, rather than by the requirements particular to each medical situation.

In broad terms, this role description is incorporated in all of us as part of the basis from which we make the decision to enter a relationship with a doctor.

Summary

Medicine, as one of society's major social institutions, is "nowhere independent and following its own motivations." This is the major proposition of this chapter. "The significant sociological unit . . . is not the institution . . . but the cultural configuration."[28] Its character and dynamism depend on the cultural pattern within which it is part.[29]

In our own modern culture, medicine may be distinguished from other historical periods and other cultures by two criteria: (a) its social organization as a profession, and (b) by the high level of its application of rational experimental science to the practice of diagnosis and treatment.

The role of the doctor in our society entails a stable set of general obligations and privileges. Thus the doctor achieves his position by learning an elaborate complex of skills and knowledge. There follows a general expectation from the society that he will be highly skilled in a specific way. In his application of these skills, society grants him unusual rights that are believed to be necessary for him to be effective; for example, he has complete confidential access to his patient's personal and physical history. At the same time, he is obligated to treat such confidences with both emotional and moral restraint. He is, moreover, obligated to treat all patients without regard to his self-interest, emphasizing the welfare of the patient and the community.

Such attributes represent the broad general expectations of the society. Each member of the society is taught this type of generalized image of the physician. That this general image is represented among individuals with great variation, of course, is self-evident. Nevertheless, the general conception of the role of the doctor has significant force, guiding the methods of the profession for policing its own conduct, and orienting the patient in the broad realities of what he can expect when he initiates a relationship with a physician.

Such role expectations are the foundation of the doctor-patient relationship. However, our description is, at this point, one-sided. Becoming a patient is not an automatic process. The society also prescribes a set of obligations and privileges for the "sick role." In the next chapter the social role of the patient is the subject of inquiry.

NOTES TO CHAPTER 3

1. Sigerist, Henry E., "The Physician's Profession Through the Ages" in Marti-Ibanez, Felix, editor, *Henry E. Sigerist on the History of Medicine*. MD Publications, New York, 1960, p. 3.
2. Nagan, Peter S., *Medical Almanac 1961–62*. W. B. Saunders Co., Philadelphia, 1962, p. 298.
3. Garceau, Oliver, *The Political Life of the American Medical Association*. Harvard University Press, Cambridge, Mass., 1941.
4. Benedict, Ruth, *Patterns of Culture*. A Mentor Book published by The New American Library, New York, 1946 (1960 printing), p. 213. (Originally published by Houghton Mifflin Co., Boston, 1934.)
5. Ackerknecht, Erwin H., "Problems of Primitive Medicine," *Bulletin of the History of Medicine*, vol. 11, May, 1942, p. 503.
6. Caudill, William, "Applied Anthropology in Medicine" in Kroeber, A. L., editor, *Anthropology Today*. University of Chicago Press, Chicago, 1953, pp. 771–806.
7. Ackerknecht, Erwin H., *op. cit.*, p. 505.
8. *Ibid.*, p. 508.
9. See Sigerist, Henry E., *A History of Medicine*, vol. 1, Primitive and Archaic Medicine, Oxford University Press, New York, 1951; see also Ackerknecht, Erwin H., *op. cit.*

10. These case descriptions are brief abstracts from Ackerknecht, Erwin H., "Primitive Medicine and Culture Pattern," *Bulletin of the History of Medicine*, vol. 12, November, 1942, pp. 545–574.

11. Benedict, Ruth, *op. cit.*, pp. 136–137.

12. Ackerknecht, Erwin H., *op. cit.*, pp. 563–564.

13. Ackerknecht, Erwin H., *A Short History of Medicine*. The Ronald Press Co., New York, 1955, p. 54.

14. Sigerist, Henry E., *Sigerist on the History of Medicine*, 1960, p. 6.

15. Ackerknecht, Erwin H., *A Short History of Medicine*, 1955, pp. 82–83. (Italics added.)

16. Carr-Saunders, A. M., and P. A. Wilson, *The Professions*, Oxford University Press, London, 1933; for a brief summary see the article by the same authors, "Professions" in *Encyclopaedia of the Social Sciences*, vol. 12, 1934, pp. 476–480.

17. *Ibid.*, p. 476.

18. The Oxford English Dictionary, Unabridged, 1933.

19. Goode, William J., "Encroachment, Charlatanism, and the Emerging Profession: Psychology, Sociology, and Medicine," *American Sociological Review*, vol. 25, December, 1960, p. 902.

20. *Ibid.*

21. *Ibid.*, p. 903.

22. *Ibid.*

23. Flexner, Abraham, "Is Social Work a Profession?" *School and Society*, vol. 1, 1915, p. 905.

24. It should be added, however, that such a general observation does not tell about important variations in the public's image of these occupations. The image of the nurse, for example, is low among upper-middle class and upper class groups "not only because of the length and nature of training but because nurses are predominantly women and few of them are above the median line of the middle class. Many lower class patients, on the other hand, have an exalted picture of nurses; and in some rural areas, they are more highly regarded than are doctors." We are indebted to Esther Lucile Brown for these comments, quoted from a personal communication.

25. Carr-Saunders, A. M., and P. A. Wilson, *The Professions*, 1933, p. 101.

26. Parsons, Talcott, "The Professions and Social Structure" in *Essays in Sociological Theory*. Rev. ed. The Free Press, Glencoe, Ill., 1954.

27. "The *profit motive* is supposed to be drastically excluded from the medical world. This attitude is, of course, shared with the other professions, but it is perhaps more pronounced in the medical case than in any single one except perhaps the clergy." Parsons, Talcott, *The Social System*. The Free Press, Glencoe, Ill., 1951, p. 435.

28. Benedict, Ruth, *op. cit.*, p. 213.

29. Ackerknecht, Erwin H., *op. cit.*, 1942, p. 546.

Chapter 4

THE ROLE OF THE PATIENT

We all live in a specific rhythm, determined by nature, culture, and habit. Day and night alternate in an unending ebb and flow, and we ourselves conform to this rhythm with waking and sleeping, with work and rest. . . . An undisturbed rhythm means health. . . . Disease . . . strikes abruptly into this structure.

HENRY E. SIGERIST, M.D.
"The Special Position of the Sick"[1]

THE ROLE OF THE SICK possesses at least one universal quality: sickness forces an individual to live differently from what is customary in his own life or what prevails in his society. The rhythm of existence is broken sharply: "Night comes, and other men sleep. But sleep eludes the sick man. Mealtime arrives, but the stomach of the sick person refuses food altogether or makes strange demands at odd hours.[2] Sickness, however, is not simply a "natural phenomenon," with no relationship to human motives.[3] To be sure, an important proportion of sickness is based upon "natural" processes over which we have little or no control; but an equally important proportion is influenced by motives that, in turn, are the product of such factors as culture, a variety of social variables, and personal history.

Each illness, in theory, has a clinical unity: it is describable according to identifying signs as one illness or a cluster of illnesses. But the *meaning* of illness, from the view of the patient, is more variable. It is not capricious, but it is complex. People perceive illness in different ways. The pattern of these perceptions or definitions of illness vary according to culture and within culture.

Once illness is perceived, it is followed by patterns of behavior that are, to a significant extent, socially determined. These two parts of the process of illness are discussed separately below: (a) the definition of illness, and (b) the patterns of behavior in the sick role.

The Definition of Illness: I. Across Cultures

What is for one society an obvious and fearsome illness may not, in another society, be regarded as an illness at all. We have selected several types of cases to illustrate this proposition: (a) a primitive society that regards as "normal" what is to other societies an obvious form of disease; (b) a rural-agrarian community based upon a religious sect, living alongside contemporary American communities of the Midwest, which appears to have virtually no mental illness; and (c) a modern small town where the accepted definition of certain types of illness was found to be quite different from that of a visiting team of medical experts.

The Kuba of Sumatra are the first example. The Kuba are described as "a generally intelligent people who carry on a difficult way of life in the primeval forest close to nature. Skin diseases and injuries to the skin occur frequently among them—so often that they do not find such conditions at all abnormal. The person suffering from such a condition is not considered a sick man among the Kuba. He lives as do the rest of his fellow tribesmen."[4]

A very comparable problem existed in whole areas of North Africa where, earlier in this century, hookworm was regarded as a normal condition. The endemic character of this disease was accepted to such an extent by local populations that public health measures to correct it were violently opposed.[5]

Many similar examples may be cited of endemic diseases among modern peoples, as well as primitive and historic cases. To mention briefly only one, there is the problem of dental caries in contemporary United States, which we tend not to define as "illness." The condition, no matter how pathological in medical terms, does not interrupt the normal rhythm of life. Consequently, the tendency of the cultural group is to view it as a normal state and not a disease.

This does not mean that the concept of *normality* is used here in essentially statistical terms. Redlich, for example, states: "There are diseases such as caries, athlete's foot, or, in certain areas, malaria or endemic syphilis which are extremely frequent (or 'normal') in the statistical sense, and yet abnormal in the individual from a clinical viewpoint."[6] We agree with Redlich and with Kubie's statement that statistical frequency has nothing to do with health. "Common colds," as Kubie added, "are illnesses no matter how many people suffer from them."[7]

We do differentiate, however, between the social definition and the clinical definition of illness. If a society accepts endemic syphilis as a condition that is within the normal range of expected life events, it will not, therefore, think of the syphilitic as "sick," and will not assign to him the privileges and the obligations of the sick role.

A second type of example is found in the Hutterites, the Anabaptist religious sect that is currently living in small but thriving agricultural villages in the Dakotas and central Canada. They are not primitive people. They are civilized, Christian, and speak English. That they are distinctive from surrounding populations is based upon their common adherence to an unusual ideology that dominates their way of life.

The Hutterites have a longstanding reputation for being virtually free of mental illness. Moreover, as recently as 1947, an official government report to the Manitoba Provincial Legislature referred to "a complete absence of mental illness" among the Hutterites. More than fifty medical doctors from neighboring communities who regularly treat their illnesses concurred with the government report.

This generally accepted observation was put to a careful test a decade ago by a research team that conducted a mental health survey of the entire community of Hutterites.[8] After their study, both in the United States and in Canada (the total census of Hutterites numbered 8,542 in 1950), the team, composed of a sociologist, psychiatrist, and two psychologists, found that some cases of both psychoses and psychoneuroses did exist. Although the rate of incidence was relatively low compared with other cultures, it was not among the lowest known rates by any means.

However, schizophrenia was extremely rare, and no diagnosis of psychopathic personality was found. The manic-depressive symptomatology was most frequent. This distribution of symptoms is unusual and suggests the strong influence of cultural factors.

For the purposes at hand, however, the most striking datum concerning mental health among the Hutterites is that virtually no cases were hospitalized. What happened to them? Where and how were they treated? The non-Hutterite physicians who were regularly consulted about other forms of illness were virtually never called upon to treat mental illness.

The answer, at least in part, to these questions would appear to be that the definition of such illnesses by the Hutterites is different from that in our own society. When the symptoms of mental illness appear, the Hutterites do not take them as cues to stop the normal rhythm of the sick individual's life. Rather, "the onset of a symptom serves as a signal to the entire community to demonstrate support and love for the patient. Hutterites do not approve of the removal of any member to a 'strange' hospital. . . . All patients are looked after by the immediate family. . . . They are encouraged to participate in the normal life of their family and community, and most are able to do some useful work. . . . No permanent stigma is attached to patients after recovery. The traumatic social consequences which a mental disorder usually brings to the patient, his family and sometimes his community are kept to a minimum by the patience and tolerance with which most Hutterites regard these conditions."[9]

Our third illustration of the importance of "definitions of illness" is again a contemporary community from the same fertile northern plains where the Hutterites live. Unlike the Hutterites, however, whose unusual way of life sets them sharply apart from the main stream of the surrounding culture, this illustration is a small Canadian town with a population of 1,350 that can be matched in general type by many communities of midwestern Canada and the United States.

Prairie Town, as this community is called in a recent book by John and Elaine Cumming, was the subject of an experiment designed to change popular attitudes toward the mentally ill.[10]

The plan was "to develop a program of education that would give people in the community a better understanding of mental illness. ... In the long run," it was hoped, "such an educational program might possibly decrease the incidence of mental illness."[11] At the very least, it was the hope of the sponsors of the educational experiment that more complete and scientifically accurate knowledge about mental illness would encourage a more tolerant popular attitude toward those who had been in mental institutions, and thereby speed the process of psychiatric rehabilitation and lower the high relapse and readmission rate.

The experiment, however, was a failure. The people of Prairie Town, after at first welcoming the physician and social scientist who directed the educational program, soon withdrew their cooperation. At the end of six months, they displayed "outright antagonism" and it was no longer possible to continue the effort effectively. Moreover, there was objective evidence to show that the concerted efforts to bring about a measurable change in attitude toward the mentally ill had been fruitless: interview and questionnaire data, collected at the beginning of the intensive campaign and again at the end showed that no significant change in attitudes had occurred.

The final published report of the Prairie Town experiment became, in effect, a study of failure. It concluded that the educational campaign failed "to account for the function of popular beliefs in the community." What exactly does this mean?

At the very beginning, it had been anticipated by the directors of the project that the conception of mental illness by the people of Prairie Town would be quite different from professional psychiatrists and their co-workers. This proved to be correct. However, the actual details of the conceptual differences, in significant measure, were not as anticipated.

For example, the educational campaign attempted to convey the idea that so-called "odd" behavior was not necessarily a sign of mental illness; or, in other words, it was taught that "normal" behavior covers a very wide range. It was discovered, however, that the people of Prairie Town already accepted as normal an even wider range of behavior than most psychiatrists would accept.

The most trouble apparently was caused by the educators' attempt "to make people more accepting of the mentally ill and more willing to act toward them as they did toward 'normal' people. It was precisely this result that the people of Prairie Town seemed determined to prevent."[12]

The Cummings were finally to report that the people of Prairie Town differentiated sharply between "normal" and abnormal. On the one hand, Prairie Town accepted a very wide range of behavior as "normal." However, once a person was definitely classified as "mentally ill," usually because he had been hospitalized, people's attitudes sharply reversed themselves. Instead of saying in effect, "He's just about like everyone else," Prairie Town people would say, "He's very different from everyone else and must be separated from normal people." The attitude questionnaire showed that people wished to avoid close contact with the mentally ill. It also showed a considerable fear of disturbed persons, along with a tendency to be ashamed of that fear.[13]

When the Cummings discovered this conflict between the goals of their educational campaign and such unyielding ideas, they came to the conclusion that neither view was, in any absolute sense, more true than the other. "Their [the Prairie Towners'] ideas about mental illness and the mentally ill appeared inconsistent and often illogical when judged in terms of our ideas; but looked at in their own terms they were consistent, even reasonable and necessary. The whole set of ideas, beliefs, and attitudes about mental illness held by the people of Prairie Town was a response not to considerations of empirical truth, but rather to the needs of the community. For the community of Prairie Town, it was far less important to know the detached 'truth' about mental illness than to have some workable way to handle the difficult problem of mental illness. A crucial element in their method of handling this problem was belief in a black-and-white difference between the sane and the insane, and the concomitant conviction that the mentally ill must be removed from the community. These popular ideas were diametrically opposed to those our educational program sought to teach. As we worked to undermine them and replace them with 'correct' ideas, people became increasingly upset and angry. Why should this be so?"[14]

The people of Prairie Town, from their own point of view rather than from a scientific or clinical standpoint, formed their ideas concerning the nature, cause, and treatment of mental illness in a consistent pattern, which the Cummings called the "pattern of denial and isolation." Briefly, this pattern was described as follows: "People tend to deny the existence of abnormal behavior for as long as they possibly can. When behavior becomes so deviant that it can no longer be tolerated or construed as normal, people act to isolate the mentally ill person, both physically and conceptually."[15]

This led to a second sharp divergence between the campaign and the townspeople. It was part of the campaign to acknowledge that state mental institutions were not as good as they might be, but that the state was working very hard to improve them. Moreover, the idea was conveyed that mental hospitals are not always the best means of curing the mentally ill; that the hospitalized patient is maintained in an artificial situation isolated from the beneficial influence of normal social life. The people of Prairie Town, however, maintained the feeling that mental hospitals are the best possible places for the mentally ill. "Once a person is placed in a mental hospital, he is 'put away' both physically and from one's thoughts, and the picture of the mental hospital as a desirable place helps to assuage the guilt a person might feel at so isolating a friend or relative. Once a person is admitted to the hospital, he is virtually deserted by friends and relatives, as if contact were somehow contaminating and dangerous."[16]

"It is evident," concluded the Cummings, "that this whole complex of beliefs and attitudes is a product of the community's attempt to solve a perplexing problem. At the core of this solution is the need of the community to separate itself from deviant people. . . . The pattern of denial and isolation arises from the attempt on the part of the community to maintain its code of conduct and hence its own integrity by protecting itself from deviant behavior."[17] The pattern of beliefs and attitudes toward mental illness in Prairie Town, in other words, was not a patchwork of half-truths, fallacies, and inconsistencies, as it might at first appear. It was designed to preserve the community's existing values and patterns of behavior. When the community sensed that the educational program was, by its nature, an attempt to weaken and change this pattern of belief, the people of Prairie Town acted to protect itself by mobilizing against the project.[18]

Recalling the case of the Hutterites as compared with Prairie Town, one could not find more contrasting "definitions" of the same types of illness. Each of these culture groups has its own way of preserving a way of life. Illness is not an isolated phenomenon, to be defined in its own terms. It is deeply embedded in the social matrix, integrated within a culture-complex.

The Definition of Illness: II. Subcultural Differences

"I wish I really knew what you mean about being sick," a woman in a small New York community recently told an interviewer. "Sometimes," the woman added, "I've felt so bad I could curl up and die, but had to go on because the kids had to be taken care of, and besides, we didn't have the money to spend for the doctor—how could I be sick? . . . How do you know when you're sick, anyway? Some people can go to bed most anytime with anything, but most of us can't be sick—even when we need to be."[19]

As this woman asks: What does it mean to be sick in American society? We tend to regard disease largely as a natural event, beyond the individual's control. The prevailing values of American culture, it has been said, foster a mechanistic approach to the body and its functions. "The body is often viewed as a machine which has to be well taken care of, be periodically checked for dysfunctioning and eventually, when out of order, be taken to an expert who will 'fix' the defect."[20]

A mechanistic explanation, however, doesn't fit the poignant cry: "How could I be sick?" Such a statement asserts a great deal of voluntary control over illness. Moreover, if illness is divorced from motivation, how can "some people" be sick "anytime with anything," while "most of us can't be sick, even when we need to be?" The answer is implicit in the same interview. As this woman accurately explains, sickness is not only a matter of symptoms ("Sometimes I've felt so bad I could curl up and die. . . ."); it is also a pattern of behavior. She makes it clear that one isn't really sick unless one goes to bed. To keep on taking care of your "kids," or, in other words, continuing your normal life activities, means that you are *not* sick.

The distribution of sickness in any given society is complicated by the variation in the perception of symptoms. A distinction must be made, just as it was in the discussion of illness relative to different cultures, between the clinical definitions of illness and the social definition of the sick role. As further illustration, consider the case of Mrs. A.[21]

Mrs. A, in an interview concerning health in her community, talked very frankly and willingly about her own cold and about her husband's hernia, but "was confused about what illness really meant." At the time of the interview, her ankles were badly swollen, and she had a marked shortness of breath, even after so slight an effort as putting a stick of wood in the stove. She complained about her ankles, and showed the interviewer how they were pitted. But she did not indicate any concern about these conditions, and said quite directly that *there was no reason for seeing a doctor*. Her mother, she said, had swollen ankles and shortness of breath for some years before she died, and had not seen a doctor.

In other words, dyspnea and edema were not perceived by Mrs. A as signs of illness. A cold fitted her definition of illness, and she had been treated by a doctor for it. Her other symptoms, however, which proved to be far more significant than the cold, caused her little concern. Subsequently, Mrs. A was hospitalized for a cardiac condition.

Obviously, however, Mrs. A's behavior in this instance is not characteristic of "Americans." It is typical, however, of a certain type of American. We refer to Mrs. A's *social class*. Social class, we will argue, is one of the most important factors in the differentiation of subgroups within our society. Moreover, it vitally affects health and illness in general, and in particular, it is a source of differential perception and response to illness.

Any discussion of class differences is likely to encounter some resistance among Americans. It is not so much a matter of being unaware of classlike social distinctions; rather it is a denial of the influence of such differences, in spite of the continuously accumulating evidence to the contrary.[22]

The class concept is a method for describing how a society organizes social differences. There is no question that, in every community, social differences are real. Whether because of wealth, occupation, or personal qualities, a group of people are identified as superior to the others, just as there is always at the opposite end of the scale a group regarded as the most inferior. As Koos writes, in his excellent study of health in a community he calls Regionville:

> The "Cabots and the Lodges" exist, by whatever name, in most communities, and keep their distance from "the ordinary folk." These "common people," in turn, look with some condescension upon those with lesser abilities and accomplishments. Each of these groups constitutes, in effect, a stratum in the community; each recognizes (if only vaguely) that it is superior to and/or inferior to other groups. Each appears, even to the casual observer, to have its own beliefs and habits, its own special ways of behaving, its own symbols of accomplishment or defeat.[23]

Observers of American culture are not unanimously agreed, however, on the major criteria of social class distinction. Some believe that the primary determinant is prestige, a matter of subjective self-identification and evaluation by one's fellows. Others believe that power, economic and political, actual or potential, is the basic class factor.[24] In research on social stratification, it has been found that the most consistently valid index of social class is occupation. In practice, however, a multi-variable index is almost always preferred.[25]

Koos found that the people of Regionville thought of themselves in a way that matched closely their ranking of different occupations. Koos separated three main class divisions. In Class I were "the successful people in Regionville": the town banker, a successful businessman, the resident manager of a local manufacturing plant, a doctor, the minister. Rated at this level were those who had the security of a salary or income from their own business, having special educational qualifications, or wearing "the halo of a profession." It was Koos's finding that "these individuals were definitely set apart in their own minds and in the minds of others as important members of the community."[26]

There are, of course, variations within a recognized social class. Koos gives two illustrations of such variation in Class I. Mr. Jones, a minister, had an income of less than $4,000, while Mr. Smith, a banker, had an income of more than $10,000, yet "each saw himself as a member of the same social class." Banker Smith was a member of a social clique "that takes a drink and plays a little poker now and then," yet he admitted Mr. Jones to be a member of the same social class because "he is an educated man with a big responsibility in the community, and the town couldn't get along without his kind." Mr. Jones, in turn, disapproved the drinking and poker-playing habits of Mr. Smith, but saw him as a member of Class I "because of his activities in the community, not that I agree with his personal habits." Each had his own friendship group, even though Mr. Jones admitted that his friendships were more widespread than those of most people because of his role as minister, but each saw the other as a member of Class I for approximately the same reason—participation in community affairs.[27]

In Class II were "the major portion of Regionville's breadwinners. Some were highly skilled; others had a minimum of skill but had worked into jobs that required attention to detail for adequate performance. . . . Class II earned wages rather than salaries. With no educational qualifications that set them apart, no professional halo, and jobs that were sensitive to seasonal and cyclical fluctuations, Class II families had to be oriented more to the present than to the future. Incomes were significantly lower than those of Class I." This was a home-owning group, characterized by stable families.

In Class III were the families whose breadwinners held the least skilled jobs. As expected, work was therefore most sensitive to seasonal and other types of fluctuation. A majority rented their homes. Residence was clustered in one part of the village. There was more mobility of residence, and a higher proportion of working wives.

It will be recognized that these divisions are characteristic of a small, partly rural community. (Regionville is a town in upper New York State.) The class divisions would be different in larger, more industrial communities.

The influence of class position on the attitude of Regionville's people toward illness is perhaps best illustrated in the following table. Here are summarized the replies of respondents who were asked to indicate whether each of a selected list of readily recognized symptoms was significant and should be called to the attention of a doctor.[28]

PERCENTAGE OF RESPONDENTS IN EACH SOCIAL CLASS RECOGNIZING SPECIFIED SYMPTOMS AS NEEDING MEDICAL ATTENTION[a]

Symptom	Class I ($N = 51$)	Class II ($N = 335$)	Class III ($N = 128$)
Loss of appetite	57	50	20
Persistent backache	53	44	19
Continued coughing	77	78	23
Persistent joint and muscle pains	80	47	19
Blood in stool	98	89	60
Blood in urine	100	93	69
Excessive vaginal bleeding	92	83	54
Swelling of ankles	77	76	23
Loss of weight	80	51	21
Bleeding gums	79	51	20
Chronic fatigue	80	53	19
Shortness of breath	77	55	21
Persistent headaches	80	56	22
Fainting spells	80	51	33
Pain in chest	80	51	31
Lump in breast	94	71	44
Lump in abdomen	92	65	34

[a] Percentages rounded to nearest whole number. Koos, Earl Loman, *The Health of Regionville.* Columbia University Press, New York, p. 33. Reprinted with permission of the publisher.

In his interpretation of this table, Koos writes: "It was assumed from the beginning that there would be some differences in the attitudes of the social classes toward the several symptoms, but the significance of the differences was unexpected. Recognition of the importance of the symptoms was uniformly high among the Class I respondents. Only two symptoms—loss of appetite and backache—were checked as needing medical attention by fewer than 75 per cent of these respondents. Class II respondents, in general, showed less sensitivity. For only one symptom—continued coughing—did Class II respondents have the highest percentage of recognition; for two others—backache and joint or muscle pains—the percentage of recognition dropped below 50 per cent. In sharp contrast, Class III respondents showed a marked indifference to most symptoms, ten being checked by 25 per cent or less. Only three symptoms were checked by 50 per cent or more, and these were all associated with unexplained bleeding."[29]

Obviously, for the people of Regionville, illness is not a simple equation whereby symptom ⟶ (leads to) diagnosis and treatment. Becoming "ill" has a variable threshold, influenced by many different factors: fear, concerns about cost, the relative need for treatment as related to age and the role of the individual in the family. As one housewife said, "If something was wrong with my husband, we'd get it fixed right away. He earns the money, and we can't have him stop work. I can drag around with my housework, but he can't drag around and still earn a living."

An equally important reason for disregarding a symptom relates to group expectations. As a Class III housewife stated: ". . . I'd look silly, wouldn't I, going to see a doctor for a backache . . . if I went to the doctor for that, my friends would hoot me out of town. . . ."

Regionville is not an isolated case example of relationships between social class and illness. Fully forty years ago (1921 to 1923) a comprehensive illness survey was conducted in Hagerstown, Maryland, by Sydenstricker.[30] This study revealed an inverse relationship between illness and socioeconomic status. It should be noted that illness in the latter study is defined from the view of the medical profession. Thus in terms of the objective medical criteria, there is more illness as one goes down the social scale.

Subsequent studies, by and large, have supported the findings of the Hagerstown survey. It was discovered further that the lower socioeconomic classes, in spite of having the greatest proportion of sick persons (clinically defined), consulted physicians and were hospitalized least.[31] These findings are additional confirmation of the results of the Regionville study concerning how people perceive and respond to illness.

Chronic illness, which places the greatest burdens upon the individual and his family, also is found to increase as one descends the social ladder. This was true in the original Hagerstown survey, and remained true when the same sample was resurveyed twenty years later in 1943.[32] Other studies agree.[33]

However, even though relationships between social class and illness long have been documented, the interpretations of their relationships are less well supported by research. Common sense tells us that those who are best able to afford it will make the fullest use of medical care, just as they will of other goods and services. It is precisely this interpretation, stressing the economic factor, which has been most accepted to explain the relationships between class and illness.

The economic interpretation, however, is not sufficient to explain all the available facts. As only one example, Myers and Schaffer studied a clinic where ability-to-pay was eliminated as an important element in acceptance for long-range psychotherapy.[34] They found that even when the economic factor was held constant, acceptance for therapy and the character of subsequent clinical experience were related significantly to the patient's social class; "the higher an individual's class position, the more likely he was to be accepted for treatment, to be treated by highly trained personnel, and to be treated intensively over a long period."[35]

Myers and Schaffer did not have the necessary data to explain these findings. Their main accomplishment was to eliminate the economic argument as sufficient in itself for the now well-documented picture of the differences in mental illness according to social class.[36] Explanations were suggested, however.

"The psychiatrist's values concerning who should be treated appear to influence the acceptance of patients."[37] This is one suggested explanation. Yet where do such values come from, and how are they maintained?

The values of the physician derive from two major sources: from his professional group and from his own position in society. As discussed earlier, the profession places high priorities on a rational scientific ethic. Since class position in the United States is so strongly related to education, the physician's intellectual values will find their closest counterpart in middle- and upper-class patients. Moreover, physicians themselves are recruited in large proportion from the middle class; more specifically, the evidence is that they come largely from professional families.[38] Thus the communication process that is so vital to the therapeutic relationship may be expected to be more effective between a doctor and a patient from similar social backgrounds. The result, quite apart from ability to pay, would be detrimental to the lower social classes. The research of Myers and Schaffer, Hollingshead and Redlich, and of Rennie and his associates indicate that this is, indeed, what happens in the case of mental illness. Although there is less evidence available for other types of illness, a similar problem of communication is probable as a vital factor in all therapeutic relationships.

We have presented social class as one of the important ways in which a complex society organizes its structure. Material wealth, we have agreed, is a critical symbol of class differences in our society, but, we have added, the explanation of class is unsatisfactory if it stops there. Once organized, group structure of this type has its own sustaining force. As evident in Regionville, the implications for the perception of illness are important.

Next, we turn to the response of people following the perception of illness. The pattern of this response in behavior to illness has been described as "the sick role." What, more exactly, is meant by this descriptive term?

The Sick Role

Like all social roles, the sick role is a pattern of expected behavior with characteristic obligations and privileges. This may be illustrated by a hypothetical example.

In a business organization the office workers behave according to certain standard expectations. They arrive at a prescribed time. They dress in a rather standard manner, allowing for limited individual variation. They perform their specialized tasks, whether it be those of a typist, bookkeeper, filing clerk, or receptionist, at a pace that is standardized. These are the basic obligations of their occupational roles, and as long as they are met, appropriate privileges are expected. These privileges include material rewards in salary, pensions, promotions; they also include psychological rewards such as respect for one's work, trust, and so on.

Each member of this office force is expected to meet the obligations of his occupational role. To deviate by arriving late, or by failing to sustain expected standards of efficiency, invites penalties. The system of rewards and penalties is designed to preserve the norms of the office, or, in other words, to prevent deviation.

Certain kinds of deviation from the norms, however, are allowed. One is based on the sick role. If Mr. Jones, a bookkeeper, appears late one morning, and he is flushed and leaves his desk frequently, he may, without any penalties, go home early if he convinces his employers that he is "sick." If, on the other hand, Mr. Jones has a hangover from too much drinking the night before, he may feel sick, but it is not likely that he will be granted the special privileges of the sick role. Illness, in other words, is deviance; but it is a form of deviation society accepts as legitimate.

There are four well-established aspects of the expectation system we call the sick role.[39] First, there is exemption from the performance of normal social obligations; and secondly, there is the exemption from responsibility for one's own state. These are the major privileges. The obligations have been described as the requirement that the sick person must be motivated to get well as soon as possible and to seek technically competent help.

In the hypothetical illustration above, the bookkeeper, Mr. Jones, is exempted from his job responsibilities if he is sick. Moreover, he may expect to be freed from his normal obligations as husband and father. Of course, this is relative to the nature and severity of his illness. Moreover, generally, it is required that, in any illness of consequence, a physician must verify the fact of illness. The physician is a "legitimizing agent" in the process whereby a sick role becomes established.

Further variation in this exemption occurs according to sex, age, and situation. A woman in a job situation, for example, may expect to receive more readily the privileges of minor illness than a man who, because his is the "stronger sex," is expected to be tougher and to have more stamina. In the home, on the other hand, it is the wife who is more likely to avoid the sick role than the husband. This problem for the wife of a young family, whereby she feels unable to be sick, is inherent in the structure of the modern family, and will be discussed in detail later.

The second major privilege of the sick role, the exemption from responsibility for one's own state, assumes that the individual is incapacitated by forces beyond his voluntary control. Also it assumes that he is unable, under his own power, to regain his health. Again returning to the hypothetical example of Mr. Jones, the bookkeeper, one can see quickly how important this question is. The very same set of symptoms lead to very different consequences, depending on whether Mr. Jones is judged to be responsible for his own condition. Drowsiness, frequent urination, and feverish appearance are not enough in themselves to qualify one for legitimate illness. If these symptoms are believed to be a result of drinking, Mr. Jones will probably be judged responsible for his own state and therefore *not* qualified for the privileges granted to the sick. In general, this has been a complicating element in our society's attitudes toward alcoholism. Only recently has there been increasing acceptance of the idea that heavy drinking and alcohol addiction are the result of forces that are beyond the voluntary control of the individual, and therefore should be accepted as illness.[40]

A major condition for the granting of the privileges of illness is the obligation to be motivated to get well. Moreover, the sick individual usually has a time requirement placed on his behavior. He must want to get well as soon as possible.

A closely linked obligation is the obligation to seek help, usually from a physician. If an individual claims the privileges of the sick role without consulting a physician, he cannot for long expect others to accept his behavior. If he does not consult a physician, he invites doubt that his motivation to get well is genuine. If he does *not* want to get well, the question is raised that perhaps he *is* responsible for his own condition. Finally, his legitimate right to exemption from his normal life obligations comes under question. He risks loss of job, marital conflict, and the like.

In general, it may be claimed that all exemptions, all special allowances for deviation from the normal, take the form of special grants or gifts, and that implicitly, a certain amount of ambivalence accompanies the giving. "Give him a finger, and he takes a hand." "You'll spoil him." "Don't take advantage of the situation." These are common phrases and, in all of them, one finds a sense of qualified giving. In the special exemptions allowed to the patient, one finds the same sense of limits, of qualification to, of boundaries beyond which a legitimate privilege becomes a violation. When a patient steps across this boundary, he is no longer privileged, he is a "malingerer." He may be exempted from normal obligations to work just so long as he is defined as "really" sick. Most of us will be able to recall how, in the course of an illness, the loved one caring for us grew increasingly cold and unsympathetic as the illness lingered "too long."

Similarly, the exemption from responsibility for one's own state has implicit limits. "Now, pull yourself together. There is nothing wrong with you that work won't cure."

Just as the exemptions may be withdrawn if the sick individual is perceived as "taking advantage" of his sick role privileges, so also he is penalized if he avoids his sick role obligations. "You just don't want to get better—that's your trouble." "If you don't feel well, why don't you go to see a doctor?"

We have already mentioned variation in the sick role according to sex. Another variant is based on the type of illness. The mentally ill individual has been a special case for a long time. If he is clearly psychotic, he may be granted an additional privilege; that is, he is not expected to assume voluntary responsibility for being motivated to get well, or for seeking proper help himself. Thus it has been deemed appropriate to coerce psychotics to hospital commitment. For other forms of illness, it must be voluntary.

The neurotic, on the other hand, has frequently been harshly judged in moral or ethical terms. The insane are considered "not responsible for their acts." But neurotics are commonly *not* defined as ill. They are considered by their doctors, as often as not, to be "crocks," "malingerers," "uncooperative patients," or derogatively, "neurotics."

Age is another important factor determining the sick role. A child is granted special privileges, as far as the expected obligations of illness, but the child too is subject to the negative injunction "brat," "unreasonable," "spoiled" when he doesn't behave as he is expected to (or as an adult would).

Another source of significant variation in the sick role is its underlying social situation. Perhaps the most dramatic illustration of the influence of situation is found in the hospital. In sickness as a general problem, the field of forces acting upon the patient include:

(a) his attitude toward self;
(b) his attitude toward the significant members of his every day life, that is, family, work-partners, friends, and so on;
(c) his attitude toward his physician(s).

When the patient becomes hospitalized, he is placed in a new social situation that involves additional influences on his behavior and on his illness and treatment.

(a) The patient's relationship with his therapist is radically altered by the setting. For example, the patient no longer initiates, through appointment and visit, his contact with the physician. He is now subject to his personal physician's schedule of rounds in the hospital; in addition, he must deal with physician-strangers who are part of hospital routine, especially the interns and residents.
(b) The patient is a member, in a special status, of the overall social structure of the hospital.
(c) If he is on a ward, he is subject to the particular social demands characteristic of the ward.
(d) On the ward, and sometimes even as a private patient in a single room, he becomes subject to the influences that derive from relationships with fellow-patients.
(e) His relationships with nurses, attendants, and others on the hospital staff are also the source of potentially strong influences on the way he responds.

Each of these important relationships in the patient role will be discussed in detail later. The basic context of all for the sick role, however, is the family. No matter how illness is defined, the family is the primary institution, both for the socialization of its members concerning how to behave in the sick role and as the most immediate social context in which the special privileges and obligations of the sick role are dispensed. Therefore, in the next chapter, our discussion will be concerned with the family as the primary social context of illness.

NOTES TO CHAPTER 4

1. Sigerist, Henry E., "The Special Position of the Sick" in Roemer, Milton I., editor, *Henry E. Sigerist on the Sociology of Medicine.* MD Publications, New York, 1960, pp. 10–11.
2. *Ibid.*, p. 11.
3. Parsons, Talcott, *The Social System.* The Free Press, Glencoe, Ill., 1951, chap. 10.
4. Sigerist, Henry E., *op. cit.*, p. 12.
5. Stiles, Charles Wardwell, *The Rockefeller Sanitary Commission for the Eradication of Hookworm Disease.* Judd and Detweiler, Washington, 1911.
6. Redlich, F. C., "The Concept of Health in Psychiatry" in Leighton, Alexander H., John A. Clausen, and Robert N. Wilson, editors, *Explorations in Social Psychiatry.* Basic Books, Inc., New York, 1957, p. 142.
7. Kubie, Lawrence S., "Social Forces and the Neurotic Process" in Leighton, Clausen, and Wilson, *op. cit.*, p. 80.
8. Eaton, Joseph W., and Robert J. Weil, *Culture and Mental Disorders.* The Free Press, Glencoe, Ill., 1955.
9. Eaton, Joseph W., and Robert J. Weil, "The Mental Health of the Hutterites" in Rose, Arnold M., editor, *Mental Health and Mental Disorder.* W. W. Norton and Co., New York, 1955, pp. 235–236.
10. Cumming, John, and Elaine Cumming, *Closed Ranks:* An Experiment in Mental Health Education. Harvard University Press (for the Commonwealth Fund), Cambridge, Mass., 1957. See also, by the same authors, "Mental Health Education in a Canadian Community" in Paul, Benjamin D., editor, *Health, Culture, and Community,* Russell Sage Foundation, New York, 1955, pp. 43–69.
11. *Ibid.*, p. 44.
12. *Ibid.*, p. 60.
13. *Ibid.*, p. 61.
14. *Ibid.*, pp. 60–61.
15. *Ibid.*, p. 61.
16. *Ibid.*, p. 62.
17. *Ibid.*
18. *Ibid.*, pp. 63–64.
19. Koos, Earl Lomon, *The Health of Regionville.* Columbia University Press, New York, 1954, p. 30.
20. Zborowski, Mark, "Cultural Components in Responses to Pain" in Jaco, E. Gartly, editor, *Patients, Physicians and Illness.* The Free Press, Glencoe, Ill., 1958, p. 265.
21. This case description is taken from Koos, Earl Lomon, *op. cit.*, pp. 31–32.

22. See Gordon, Milton M., *Social Class in American Sociology*, Duke University Press, Durham, N. C., 1958, pp. 193–195; Hollingshead, A. B., *Elmtown's Youth*, John Wiley and Sons, New York, 1949; Centers, Richard, *The Psychology of Social Classes*, Princeton University Press, Princeton, N. J., 1949.
23. Koos, Earl Lomon, *op. cit.*, pp. 14–15.
24. As examples, the "prestige" school is represented by Lloyd W. Warner and Associates, *Social Class in America*, Science Research Associates, Inc., Chicago, 1949; the "power" school, by Robert S. Lynd and Helen M. Lynd, *Middletown in Transition*, Harcourt, Brace and Co., New York, 1937. See also Koos, Earl Lomon, *op. cit.*, p. 15n.
25. See discussion of socioeconomic status scales in Gordon, Milton M., *op. cit.*, pp. 212–222.
26. Koos, Earl Lomon, *op. cit.*, pp. 18–19.
27. *Ibid.*, pp. 19–20.
28. *Ibid.* (Table 3), p. 33.
29. *Ibid.*, pp. 32–33.
30. Sydenstricker, Edgar, "A Study of Illness in a General Population Group: The Method of Study and General Results," *Public Health Reports*, vol. 41, 1926, pp. 2069–2088.
31. An excellent review of these studies is included in Graham, Saxon, "Socio-Economic Status, Illness, and the Use of Medical Services," *The Milbank Memorial Fund Quarterly*, vol. 35, January, 1957, pp. 58–66; reprinted in Jaco, E. Gartly, *op. cit.*, 1958, pp. 129–134.
32. Ciocco, Antonio, "Chronic Sickness in Relation to Survivorship Twenty Years Later," *Human Biology*, vols. 18–19, 1946, pp. 33–48.
33. For a review and fine discussion of this problem, see Lawrence, P. S., "Chronic Illness and Socio-Economic Status," *Public Health Reports*, vol. 63, 1948, pp. 1507–1521; reprinted in Jaco, E. Gartly, *op. cit.*, pp. 37–49.
34. Myers, Jerome K., and Leslie Schaffer, "Social Stratification and Psychiatric Practice: A Study of an Out-Patient Clinic," *American Sociological Review*, vol. 19, June, 1954, pp. 307–310.
35. *Ibid.*, p. 309.
36. In addition to the studies already cited, see Hollingshead, August B., and F. C. Redlich, *Social Class and Mental Illness*, John Wiley and Sons, New York, 1958; Leacock, Eleanor, "Three Social Variables and the Occurrence of Mental Disorder" in Leighton, Clausen, and Wilson, *op. cit.*, pp. 308–341; Srole, Leo, and others, *Mental Health in the Metropolis:* The Midtown Manhattan Study, McGraw-Hill Book Co., New York, 1962, vol. 1.
37. Myers, Jerome K., and Leslie Schaffer, *op. cit.*, p. 310.
38. See Hall, Oswald, "The Stages of a Medical Career," *American Journal of Sociology*, vol. 53, March, 1948, pp. 327–336; see also Rogoff, Natalie, "Recent Trends in Urban Occupational Mobility" in Bendix, Reinhold, and S. M. Lipset, editors, *Class, Status, and Power*, The Free Press, Glencoe, Ill., 1953, p. 445.
39. The following analysis of the sick role is based largely on Talcott Parsons' *The Social System*, pp. 439–447. (See note 3 to this chapter.)
40. See Straus, Robert, "Alcoholism" in Rose, Arnold, editor, *op. cit.*, pp. 434–447. (See note 9 to this chapter.)

Chapter 5

THE FAMILY

> *... Before I treat a patient ...*
> *I need to know a good deal more about him,*
> *Than the patient himself can always tell me.*
> *Indeed, it is often the case that my patients*
> *Are only pieces of a total situation*
> *Which I have to explore. The single patient*
> *Who is ill by himself, is rather the exception.*
>
> Sir Henry Harcourt-Reilly,
The Psychiatrist, in
T. S. Eliot, The Cocktail Party[1]

IN THE VERY RECENT PAST the home was the main setting of medical care, and the physician's principal role was that of "family doctor." Today, by contrast, a physician visits the home of a patient rarely, except in extreme emergency. Particularly in large industrial centers, but also in many medium-sized cities, it has become the custom for doctors to limit their practice almost exclusively to the office and the hospital. The patient who is too ill to come to the office is brought to the hospital, with the decision made usually by a telephone call between the family and the physician.

The explanation for the elimination of the home from the practice of medical care is most commonly a technological one. That is, the technology of modern medicine, its diagnostic and treatment procedures, are said to be too complex for the traditional black bag of the family physician. Even the private office appears to be giving way to the "clinic," in which a group of doctors work in partnership under a common roof, or in a shared suite, in order better to provide the expensive mechanical equipment, technical assistance, and space required for the most advanced scientific medical practice. More and more, private offices have been built within the hospital itself, again on the premise that modern medicine requires close and quick access to technological methods that are impossible to provide within the old-style private office of the doctor-entrepreneur.

Undoubtedly, the evolution of medical technology has contributed significantly to the change away from the home as the center of medical care. However, the objective requirements of the new technology were not the only causes of the change. Perhaps of equal importance were changes which occurred in the family itself. The modern American family, it has been said, is a precariously balanced, emotionally highly charged system, lacking in ready shock-absorbers to handle, within itself, serious illness.[2] If this is true, the inability of the modern family to cope with illness has contributed to the trend toward hospital care, perhaps in equal measure with the expanded technological requirements of scientific medicine.

However, the attitude of the medical profession toward the family has begun to show signs of reversing itself. This change expresses itself in several ways. First, there is renewed interest in the family as a significant element in the process of illness, so that in the doctor's initial approach to the patient, the family assumes renewed importance as part of the history and context in which illness has occurred. One finds, for example, a variety of experimental teaching programs in medical education that attempt to restore the home visit for the student and the physician.[3] Underlying the thinking of these programs is the assumption that firsthand knowledge of the patient's family is a basic requirement of understanding his illness.

Secondly, there is a revival of belief that the home itself is a valuable setting for medical care.

Both trends, the earlier one discounting the family and the more recent one upgrading its role in medicine, raise questions about the family itself. What occurred in the history of the American family that contributed to its loss of functions in illness? What is there in the family more recently that has given it a place in medicine's attempts to advance its science and methods of treatment? These are the major questions to which this chapter will be addressed.

The Modern American Family: Its Form and Origins

The family, in its wide variety of forms, is actually a composite of several different types of groups. As the literature of research on the family designates them, the most basic unit is the *nuclear* family, subdivided into the *family of orientation* and the *family of procreation*.

The nuclear family, which is also sometimes called the conjugal family, describes a man and woman joined in a socially recognized union and their children. Birth, the basic life experience around which the family as a social institution is organized, is important to every human being in two ways: one is born into a family, and one is the parent of the newborn. The former is called the family of orientation, because it is in this group that the individual is socialized and linked through his parents with the rest of society; the latter has been called the family of procreation, because it is in this group that the individual has children of his own.

This distinction becomes useful for the study of both the history of the family as a changing social institution, and the relationships between family structure and other social institutions. For example, in western society of the nineteenth century, the typical pattern was one in which several generations were closely tied in a variety of ways. Children, as they became adults and married to form their own families, were likely to continue residence in the same community as their parents, and to continue to respect their parents' authority in important matters. In other words, the family of orientation dominated the family of procreation, and the nuclear family was, in itself, subordinate to an extended more inclusive kinship group, consisting of members who spanned several generations. This type of family contrasts sharply with the family group that is typical of today. The American family, in its prevailing form, has become concentratedly a conjugal unit. Ties between the generations have been loosened, so that the significance of the family of orientation has been reduced.

As cross-cultural studies have demonstrated, the patterns of family organization are almost infinitely variable.[4] In every culture, however, the relation of the family formed by marriage to the original families of the husband and wife is a critical factor. Whole societies, in anthropologic descriptions, have been categorized according to this factor into two polar types: the first has been called the familistic society, in which the family of orientation completely dominates the family of procreation, and the second is the nonfamilistic (or individualistic) society, in which the dominance of the family of orientation is completely superseded by the independence of the immediate conjugal unit.

The familistic type of family organization is perhaps best represented in the Bible. It is a type of social organization well adapted to the needs of pastoral and agricultural economies, and small community life. A certain logical pattern of relationships appears to follow from its basic structure:

> . . . Authority within the kinship system is not likely to be equalitarian, for there is clearly great power of the older generation over the younger and often great power of the husband over the wife. In addition, the age of marriage is likely to be quite young and marital choice to be determined by the parents rather than the young persons themselves. This means that romantic love is ruled out as a basis of marriage. . . . The newly married couple will tend to live with the parents rather than in a separate household. . . .[5]

Obviously, the freedom of the individual in this system is severely limited, including not only the selection of marriage partners but also a wide range of other types of behavior. Characteristically, the freedom of the woman is most closely proscribed. In times of crisis, however, the social system provides immediately available safeguards. The care of the child, for example, is normally distributed over many adults. When extraordinary conditions such as birth, death, and illness require that the mother must leave the child, either temporarily or permanently, another adult, well known to the child and trained to the task, is close at hand.

With the coming of modern industrialism in western society, the bonds of extended kinship have loosened. The nuclear family, smaller in size than before and with much more limited function, has become the primary kinship group. Freed of control from the extended kin group, the energies of the modern family are focused inward upon itself. No longer important as an agency of economic production, as it was when the large majority of the population lived on farms, nor a political unit, as in the clan, the modern family's social purpose has become mainly that of supplying the needs of its members for love and affection.

It is not unusual for Americans to look back nostalgically to the small town and the extended family which are so close in our heritage. Modern industrialism, however, with its huge urban complexes, has brought with it what appears to be an irreversible evolution in the family. The small family, occupying its own small living space and moving as a free unit, has become the dominant pattern. As one student of the family has written: "This small family system originated in Western industrial civilization and is now being diffused, along with other features of industrialism, to the rest of the world. It seems likely that eventually the whole of mankind will have a family organization roughly similar to that found in the United States today."[6]

To be sure, there are exceptions to the trend we have described. The Negro family and the farm family are but two examples. More than anything else, what we call the modern American family is the family of the urban middle class. Nevertheless, there is general agreement among sociologists that it is the urban middle-class pattern that prevails today and that sets the standard for the rest of America. For these reasons, the American middle-class family pattern has been taken as the point of departure for this discussion of the prototype of the modern family.

The Problem of Illness in the Modern Family

On the one hand, the American middle-class family appears to be well adapted to the special requirements of an urban industrial society. On the other hand, it is a type of social structure that is vulnerable to certain kinds of strain, among which one of the most grave is illness.

When faced with the problem of illness, the family of our contemporary society is heavily dependent upon the medical profession and the hospital. Both of these institutions, as we have stated, have increasingly drawn the patient away from the home as a center of medical care. In seeking to show how the structure of the family has contributed to this trend, in combination with technological advances in the medical profession, we turn at this point to an analysis of the major roles in the family: the wife-mother, husband-father, and child.[7]

With the jettisoning of its economic and political functions, the major significance of the family as a social institution has become the perpetuation of cultural patterns essential to the society, particularly its values. For the adult members, this leads to what has been called a "maintenance" or regulatory function. For the child, it is socialization.

It is the wife-mother who bears, within this structure, the major social and emotional responsibility. She is the mediator of the various family relationships, the arbiter of conflict, the perpetuator of solidarity, and the main emotional provider.

The husband, in spite of the increased number of working mothers, is the main representative of the family in the outside world. His occupation is the primary determinant of the family status. In the community, he bears the major responsibility for the family.

The child is obligated primarily to "grow up," to be a good boy so that he will be a good man. The emphasis is upon him (or her) as socializee, on training for adulthood. No longer is he expected to be an important part of maintaining the family as a unit of economic production.

This division of the labor in the family concentrates the strain of illness upon the wife-mother. The father and child are occupied for the most part outside the home. Characteristically, at the beginning of each day, the family disperses; the father goes to work, the children go to school, leaving only the mother and infant-children at home. When the family reconvenes, it is for the servicing of physical and emotional requirements that depend mainly upon the wife and mother.

Much has been said and written in recent years about the changes in the role of the father. It is popular to decry the "feminization" of the adult male role in the family, with the implication that an insidious conspiracy has been at work to undermine the traditional male prerogatives. If, indeed, the adult male is assuming increased responsibility in the household in areas where once the woman acted alone, it is more likely the consequence of the special strains implicit in the structure of modern family.

The American father, contrary to the fantasies of popular culture, was never typically a privileged monarch in his home, his easy chair a throne, and his family a group of subjects who waited upon his wants. Quite the contrary, he worked in the home, for there was a wide range of needs which, unlike the modern automated house or apartment, required the father's hands and responsibility. His work in the home and family dovetailed with that of his wife and children, in a reciprocal pattern of relationships. In the modern family the basic functions during those times of the day when the male is present are limited mainly to the preparation of meals and the care of children. If a husband, therefore, returning home to find his wife busy with young children and their mealtime and bedtime needs, allows himself to be drawn into the sharing of either cooking or child care, is this feminization? Or is it simply a quite logical response against the alternative of withdrawing altogether from an integrated role in the activities of a family?

What does this family structure provide for a crisis like serious illness? There are only two responsible adults.[8] Drawn together by attractions based on the cult of romantic love, the wife and husband see themselves as equal partners, held together mainly by emotional attraction. When a child enters the group, he is mainly dependent upon the mother for emotional love that, consequently, must be shared with the father. In illness either the father or the child will require a concentration of the mother's affectionate attention, thereby creating a strain on the family system. An illness to the mother herself is clearly the most disturbing of all. More than one busy young mother has been heard to cry: "I can't even be sick!"

Illness, on the other hand, is not only a source of strain upon the family. It also provides what Parsons and Fox have called, ". . . a tantalizingly attractive solution to . . . family based

... social pressures." It offers a way for withdrawing legitimately from responsibilities. Furthermore, "even in those instances where the etiology of the disorder is primarily physicochemical, the nature and severity of symptoms and the rate of recuperation are almost invariably influenced by the attitudes of the patient."

> It is easy to see, therefore, how the wife-mother . . . might "choose" the sick role as an institutionalized way out of her heavy "human relations management" responsibilities in the family; or how she might seize upon illness as a compulsively feministic way of reacting to her exclusion from the life open to a man. Similarly, the passive-dependent role of illness offers the husband-father . . . respite from the discipline and autonomy which his occupation demands of him.[9]

For the child, illness offers a method of escape from the progressively more exacting obligations to behave as a grownup. For the elderly person, "occupationless, and with no traditionally assured place in the families established by his sons and daughters, through illness [he] may once again become an integral member of a meaningful social group, cared for either by his grown children or by a medical community of some sort."[10]

The risk of overgeneralization is great in this type of brief overview of a highly complex problem. Nevertheless, the weakness of the American family when faced with serious illness seems undeniable. Under these conditions, the development of institutions to care for the sick outside the home may be said to have served a positive function in American society. When one considers all of the intensive emotional involvements so characteristic of the urban middle-class family's relationships, the argument is credible that treatment is more easily effected in a professional milieu like the hospital than within the family. Technological developments provided the opportunity to treat illness outside the family, while the strains inherent in the family structure predisposed people to take advantage of the extra-familial organization of medical services.

This is not to say that the hospital, the nursing home, and the doctor's office have made the home an obsolete setting for the treatment of serious illness. The medico-scientific world of the hospital can be formidable, indeed, for the patient, and, as a result, it can be something less than therapeutic for his illness. The latter problem will be discussed in detail in later chapters. At this point, attention is called only to the fact that the coldness, the routinization, and dehumanization of treatment in many hospitals have caused a reaction against the trend toward hospital treatment and, at the same time, a revival of interest in the therapeutic merits of home care.[11] The rapidly rising cost of care in medical institutions is another significant factor in this reaction. The black-and-white picture drawn by public journalistic campaigns, however, falsely creates a sense of competition where it does not rightfully belong. In the final analysis, the home and the hospital must become complementary agents of patient care, not competitors.

The main point, at this stage of the discussion, is that the modern American family contains structural weaknesses that contribute to the need for extra-familial institutions of medical care. Now we will turn our scrutiny to the social processes within the family structure. How does the family function, as a social system, when faced with illness?

The Family as the "Field" of the Patient Role

In our description of the field of forces underlying the doctor-patient relationship, the family was pictured as the major context of patient behavior. Analogous to it was the medical profession as the major context of the doctor's role. (See the diagram on page 63.) If anything, the family is the more sensitive social unit in this picture. The doctor can, to some extent, individualize his behavior, disconnecting himself from his profession. The patient, however, is often not an individual in the true sense; the patient *is* a family.

The full significance of this idea is perhaps best conveyed by example. For this purpose, a detailed account is presented below of the experiences of the Q-family. This consists of a paraphrase of and quotations from an actual case, as reported by Dr. Henry Barber Richardson in his book, *Patients Have Families*.*[12]

---

* Reprinted by permission of the publishers from Henry Barber Richardson, *Patients Have Families*. Cambridge, Mass.: Harvard University Press, Copyright, 1945, by The Commonwealth Fund, New York, pp. 5–47.

The Q- Family

Catherine Q-, a twelve-year-old girl, was the first member of her family to be brought to the outpatient department of a large metropolitan hospital. She complained of a sore throat.

With Catherine on her visit to this clinic was her mother, Mrs. Q-. Although this was her first visit to this institution, Mrs. Q- was not a stranger to hospitals. The oldest of her three daughters, Laura, who would be eighteen years old now, had died several years earlier from rheumatic heart disease. Laura had been treated in another hospital by an eminent heart specialist. Moreover, there had been other illnesses in the family that had been treated in several different hospital clinics.

Mrs. Q- and Catherine, her youngest daughter, were directed to the pediatric outpatient clinic. Looking at the experience from the patient's view, what do we see?

Mrs. Q- approaches this visit with heavy concern, thinking of her first daughter who died, comparing this hospital with the other in which the results were so tragic. Several months earlier, her second daughter, Agnes, had been sick. The doctor had said she had a heart murmur. He spoke of rheumatism. And now her youngest child. Recently, also because of a sore throat, Mrs. Q- had taken Catherine to another hospital, where the doctor said she had chorea which, he explained, was a rheumatic ailment. That had passed quickly; but what will the doctor at this new hospital say?

Mrs. Q- and Catherine open a door into a wail of protesting babies. What follows is described below.

> A mother with a baby is talking to a young doctor in a white suit. . . . "Next. What's the matter with the child; sore throat?" (Yes, she. . . .) "Let me see her throat. Now her chest. That's all. Go across the hall to the small window."
>
> The registrar now questions Mrs. Q-. "Yes, Madam. Name of child?" (Catherine Q-.) "Address? Ground floor?" (You see I'm a . . .) "Number of rooms?" (Four.) "Rent?" ($6.25 a week.) "Age?" (Twelve.) "Occupation?" (Public School.) "Father?" (Martin, mechanic, born in the city.) "Mother?" (Catherine Q-, housewife.) "Who referred her? The school doctor?". . . . "Adults in the family?" (Two.) "Children in the family?" (Two.) "Number

working?" (One.). . . . "Fifty cents, please. Go up one flight of stairs to your right."

(Upstairs, a nurse meets Mrs. Q- and Catherine.) "You can leave your daughter here while I weigh her. The doctor will be ready when he gets through with his patient. . . ." (The doctor isn't as young as I expected.) "Will you sit here, Mrs. Q-, and tell me about your daughter? Sore throat and fever for a week? Father and mother are well, are they? Daughter at home has heart trouble? First daughter died of heart trouble? At what age? . . . .No serious illnesses?"

The physical examination reveals nothing in the throat, but there is a loud heart murmur, without enlargement of the heart. The opinion is recorded: "Questionable heart disease of congenital origin." An x-ray of the chest for the heart is recommended, and a skin test for tuberculosis. Both the x-ray and the tuberculin test prove to be negative. After one more visit at the end of the week, the case is referred for cardiac appointment. However, a pencil notation on the record states that Dr. X (of the cardiac clinic) is not making any more appointments.

At this point Catherine's visits to the hospital stopped for two years. After the two-year period, she returned, this time to the adult medical clinic, because in the meantime she has passed the maximum age for treatment in the pediatrics clinic. The record reads: "Patient was sent from school for examination of the heart. One year ago [actually two] seen in the pediatrics clinic, where a diagnosis of possible congenital heart disease was made. Since then has been up and around, active and well. One year ago while trying to do two years of school work in one she grew irritable, 'nervous' and jumpy, and her doctor advised that she be kept out of school for six months."

On this visit, the heart was "rapid and regular," but the same murmur was found. The *Impression:* "Over-active heart in an adolescent girl. Question of rheumatic heart disease, mitral insufficiency." *Recommendations:* "Electrocardiogram; x-ray of chest; basal metabolism." None of these recommendations was carried out and the next visit was again two years later.

At the next visit, the presenting symptoms are totally unrelated to a cardiac condition. Nevertheless, the pattern is repeated. Action is again deferred, pending the outcome of laboratory work. Again, the mother does not carry out the recommendations.

In the meantime, Mrs. Q- has appeared at the medical clinic for treatment herself. Her symptoms involve dizziness, feelings of weakness, flushes, and indigestion. In giving her marital history, she states that her two living children have "heart disease." In her own personal history, she tells of having "high blood pressure" when she was between eighteen and twenty. On her record, the impression (provisional diagnosis) is: (1) moderate hypertension, (2) menopausal syndrome (that is, symptoms of menopause), (3) hypothyroidism, (4) indigestion, etiology? (indigestion of unknown causes). In the recommended laboratory work, all reports are normal. None of the subsequent blood pressure readings showed a high blood pressure. Nevertheless, from this point on, Mrs. Q- speaks of herself as having "high blood pressure."

The third member of the family, the elder daughter Agnes, was admitted to the medical outpatient department two years after her sister's first visit. Her symptoms are weakness and tremor of the legs for two weeks. Again, the history taken from the mother emphasizes the "heart disease" of the children and her own "high blood pressure." In the summary of Agnes' first visit, the following is recorded: "A sixteen year-old girl who has become increasingly lazy and sluggish and who complains of weakness and tremor of the legs on descending the stairs. Constipated, and inadequate diet intake because of finances. Physical examination reveals nothing abnormal, except that she is slightly undernourished. *Impression:* Malnutrition, slight. Inadequate intake due to poverty. *Treatment:* Encouragement that the child has no heart disease and is well. *Medication:* Cod-liver oil tablets." This record bears a medical student's signature, and the "OK" of a doctor.

This is the first mention of the possible connection between illness and economic stress. This is also the first time that a question was raised about the validity of the diagnosis of heart disease which has dominated the thinking both of the family and of the examining physicians in the outpatient department.

The fourth and last member of the family is Mr. Martin Q-. He came to the outpatient department three years after his wife's first visit. Like his wife, he was, at the time, in his mid-forties. Dr. Richardson's review of the record of Mr. Q-'s first visit is as follows:

> Mr. Martin Q- is a little man with a pinched expression and a furtive look, who sits quietly but with an air of restlessness, like a bird perched for flight. He has an ingratiating manner which betrays his desire for approval. The record of admission adds the fact that both his parents were of Irish stock, but were born in the United States. The occupation is reported as mechanic and the employer is given as WPA. Weekly income of the family, $25. Rent free for service as janitor. A note on the record, dated a few days later: "Patient insists he cannot pay x-ray fees." A year later the record was to show instead of WPA the statement, "unemployed for a year," coupled with the statement, "Home Relief $22.80 a week."
>
> Mr. Q- has been troubled with hemorrhoids for eighteen years, and at one time, as we find out later, he expressed the fear of cancer in connection with them. We can imagine his sensations when the admitting doctor in the outpatient clinic refers him to the surgical clinic. . . . For over ten years he has been having trouble with his stomach. (Let's see, ten years. Wonder what happened then. Oh, yes, the industrial depression.) Family history: mother died of tuberculosis, no date given. Father died of heart attack, no date. Review of parts of the body includes pyorrhea, toothache, slight spitting of blood six months previously, "nervous heart." "Has practiced withdrawal for fifteen years, marital relationship otherwise satisfactory." (Seems like a large qualification.) *Present illness:* Stomach trouble, fullness, belching, for approximately ten years, increasing in frequency and severity, not relieved by treatment. This is worse when he is lying down at night, and he vomits nearly all night, as many as twenty-five times, being repeatedly awakened. *Physical examination:* slightly undernourished. No evidence of recent weight loss. No positive physical findings, except slight pyorrhea, with many teeth missing and many bad cavities. *Impression:* Cancer of stomach. This is qualified by the highly important question mark. Recommendations for laboratory work include extensive x-rays of the gastrointestinal tract, but these are negative. . . . The patient was given belladonna to relieve spasms of the stomach.

Much like the rest of his family, Martin Q- received an intensive and highly skilled investigation of his medical condition. In spite of the multiplicity of organic symptoms, however, none of the findings was sufficient to explain his difficulties. Finally, a psychiatric examination was ordered, resulting in a diagnosis of "mixed psychoneurosis with anxiety and conversion symptoms"; the probability that his vomiting was connected with his emotional state was asserted.

When Dr. Richardson reconstructed the medical picture of the Q- family as a group, he found that a minimum amount of attention had been given to the integration of the findings for each of its separate members. The clues were all in the medical records, but they had not been used to gain full understanding of the illnesses and, consequently, treatment had not been effective. For example, (a) it took two years for the first suggestion to appear in the records that the financial status of the family might be connected with illness; (b) four years passed before emotional stress was considered to be a vital factor; (c) four years passed before social service facilities were consulted. The social worker then discovered that the family had been in contact with a number of organizations in the city. In connection with the social service report, a wealth of information became immediately available concerning the intra-familial relationships and tensions. These were highly relevant to the medical problems of the individual members of the family, and to the family as a unit.

The relationships within the family have a continuing focus upon two outstanding events: the death of the first child, Laura, and the economic depression. However, the evidence reveals that difficulties in the family, particularly between the husband and wife, were present before these catastrophes, so that one cannot speak of the latter as *the* "causes." For example, Martin Q- earned a good salary during the early period of the marriage; however, the family were not able to manage and went into debt. Thus they were particularly vulnerable immediately to the economic effects of the depression. Moreover, Mrs. Q- assumed a manipulative and dominant position in the family from the start. Her mismanagement of the family finances is only the beginning of a pattern whereby she acts to prevent her husband from taking a secure and independent position as the breadwinner of the family. Later, this is played out in a circular sequence of complaint and discouragement. She complains that he is not working, and that she must work to support the family. When he moves to correct the situation by getting work, she discourages him by warning that he "is not well enough" for the kind of work that is available.

The sexual relationship in the marriage is manipulated in a similar way by Mrs. Q-. She reported to the psychiatrist that she was aware very soon after it was started that withdrawal (coitus interruptus) as a method of contraception was not satisfactory to her husband, and that it seemed related to his increased tension and stomach trouble. However, she was not willing to act to change this aspect of her relationship with Martin Q-. The depression and the death of Laura were the coincident events that were used as the basis for beginning this sexual practice. However, more than ten years later, after discussing it with her doctors and apparently gaining insight into its ill effects upon her husband, she could not change. Quite obviously, Mrs. Q- used the sexual aspect of her relationship with her husband to fit a motivational pattern in which her own dominance over the other members of the family was the goal.

Mrs. Q- has manipulated her oldest living daughter, Agnes, in a manner quite similar to the pattern with her husband. Again, illness is used as a device to maintain the social organization which she unconsciously prefers. With Agnes, Mrs. Q- constantly invokes the image of her dead daughter, Laura, as a form of invidious comparison. Agnes is constantly reminded how beautiful and how intelligent Laura was, how perfect a daughter the now-dead girl was and would have been. By comparison, Agnes' dullness in school and her plain looks are never allowed to be forgotten. In the meantime, Mrs. Q- indulges the youngest sister, Catherine. She is particularly attentive to Catherine's "heart condition," while encouraging her to be smart in school and pretty (like her dead sister). Agnes is hemmed in between an idealized image of a dead older sibling and the indulgence of a younger one. She learns, thereby, that there are literally two ways to get the affection and security which she craves: by death and illness. It is not surprising, therefore, that Agnes starves herself because of what the psychiatrist judges to be "a fear of eating."

Again, one could easily conclude that the major circumstance of the food-deprivation that led to a serious anorexia nervosa in Agnes was caused by the family's financial situation. Undoubtedly, the financial difficulties were a contributory factor. However, it is just as indubitable that the financial hardship was not a sufficient cause. With the relief of financial difficulties, the pattern of Agnes' self-deprivation continues. Her behavior remains fearful, depressed, and dependent. She accepts the dependence assigned to her by her mother, and does not easily give it up. Eventually, Agnes was given psychotherapeutic treatment over an extended period of time. Her dependence on her mother, however, persisted stubbornly, to yield slightly only very late in her treatment.

Agnes is, it would appear, a key figure in the family's informal social organization. She is the butt of Mrs. Q-'s most vocal complaints, and the workhorse of the household. She is a scapegoat who becomes the object of her mother's neurotic conflicts and social frustrations. Her sister, Catherine, on the other hand, is not much better off. Even though it appears that she is indulged by the mother, and encouraged, she is pressed into an extreme anxiety that almost matches that of her sister.

Catherine, according to a psychologist's report, appears to be a girl of low average or dull-normal intelligence. Yet her mother dreams of her going to college, and, in effect, drives her to unrealistic ambitions. Catherine has responded with an extraordinary effort to meet her mother's wishes. The cost, however, is substantial. Her anxiety is found to focus on school examinations. Nervousness about her schoolwork caused her finally to break down and become ill. Sickness, indeed, is her most effective escape from the demands made upon her. She learns that sickness like that of her dead sister is a most ready means to elicit her mother's affectionate attention. Sickness also is a means of excusing her, at least temporarily, from the extraordinary effort required to meet the role of intelligent and beautiful daughter, which is her assignment within the family.

Summarizing the portrait of the Q- family's medical problems, the outstanding feature is the manner in which illness has been woven into the total fabric of family life.[13] Treatment of the organic symptoms that are present in each individual member's case can only be palliative unless it is calculated from a full perspective of the family's social organization.

Discussion

The drama of family life is perhaps nowhere given fuller expression than in illness. Illness, as we described it in the previous chapter, provides an individual with an acceptable exemption from his normal social obligations. It is, in this sense, a type of social deviance; and like all social deviation, poses an implicit threat to the community. The effects of illness radiate through the family to the community. The family is most vulnerable to its threat, and appropriately, is the first line of defense. As the most important social context in which illness occurs, the family is the agency that generally decides whether a member is sick or not; then it takes the first steps in the care of the sick. This is the most obvious function of the family in illness, and often the only one of which we are aware; but there are more.

In microcosm, the family represents the society; it is the first medium for introducing each new member to the norms that bind the complicated social life of the community into a stable structure. This function, which we call the socialization of the child, is always a variable, dependent upon the individual characteristics of family members. It is possible, however, to construct models of family behavior, against which the particular case may be compared. One perspective from which such a model may be constructed is that of the society at large.

To show the relevance of such models for the study of behavior in illness was the major purpose of this chapter. Most significant, it was contended, is the type of family that is characteristic of the American urban middle class. Its distinctive features are:

(a) its small size;
(b) the independence of its principal unit, the nuclear family, from other parts of the kinship system;
(c) its lack of diversified functions;
(d) its concentration, in social purpose, on supplying and managing the needs of its members for love and affection;
(e) its readiness for mobility, both geographic and sociologic.[14]

In the nuclear family the most pertinent roles are husband and wife, mother and father, son and daughter, brother and sister. In its organization as a role system, certain standard patterns of expectation may be described. For example, in the urban middle-class family, the wife tends to expect her husband to treat her as an equal. She expects her husband to be independent, to have initiative, and to plan for future success in his occupation. However, in his relations with her and with the children, the husband is expected to be cooperative, to share responsibility, and to have consideration for each individual. The husband, in turn, expects his wife to be a helper in his plans for economic and social success. He expects her to put his success goals above any personal career or occupational goals of her own and to develop the social and domestic skills suitable to his particular occupational status.[15]

There is, of course, considerable variation from this pattern, but the urban middle-class type, as described, is believed to be the "modal" pattern of American Society. By class and ethnic factors, patterned variation does occur, however. Thus working-class families place less emphasis on the equalitarianism of the husband and wife and are not so dominated by success goals. The husband is the "provider," but not the "status-bearer" of the family. Even more striking variations in pattern are found in the Negro family and among ethnic subcultures that retain strong orientations based on their cultural heritages.

Studies of American class structure have revealed that the division of labor between the father and the mother is much more specialized in the lower-class family than in the middle-class family. Typically, the lower-class man works outside the home, and does no work in the home. His wife cares for the house and children and performs all household tasks except those demanding physical strength beyond her capacity. Indeed, these are the two primary sources of male authority in the lower-class family: his physical strength and earning capacity.[16] If either of these is taken away from him, the lower-class husband-father is rendered particularly vulnerable to illness. Studies of class factors in mental illness offer increasing evidence to support this hypothesis.[17] Particularly because jobs for women, in service occupations for Negro women, and in factories for both white and

Negroes, are growing in number while automation and other factors are undercutting the earning opportunities for unskilled men, the American working-class family has been observed in the process of becoming a "matriarchate." At least in the transition, the adult male members of such households appear to be responding in growing numbers with pathological behavior of some kind, in alcoholism, mental illness, or physical illnesses of psychogenic origin.

Martin Q- presents a not *un*typical example. As long as he maintained his position as the family breadwinner, harmonious relationships were preserved in the family, even in the face of the severe illness of Laura. However, when Martin Q- lost his job, the resulting feeling of stress he began to feel appears to be a major factor in the gastrointestinal illness which, from that time, became his chronic problem.

The psychiatrist finds that Martin Q- is unable to conceive of his unemployment as being a consequence of forces external to himself. He adjusts to his violation of his self-image as the provider of his family by becoming sick. In the sick role he finds a legitimate way to be without work. Another method that Mr. Q- tries, abortively, is drinking. It is revealed that his father was an alcoholic under similar life circumstances. Martin Q-, however, does not continue heavy drinking; the reasons for his voluntary abstention are not clear.

Mrs. Q-, at least to some degree, perceives her husband's problem according to the values that prevail in her social class. "It's our situation that gets him (Mr. Q-) down," she says. "A man should not be around the house all the time. He has to be out, be with men."[18] Even the problem of sexual adjustment between Mr. and Mrs. Q- appears to have at least some association with his failure to meet the cultural expectation of the male head of the household. It was when Martin Q- lost his job that coitus interruptus was begun, ostensibly to avoid further pregnancies. Would Mrs. Q- have been able to initiate this practice which was so obviously unsatisfactory to her husband, if Martin Q- had retained his position as the "provider" and therefore as the head of the household? Also, one must ask, was Mrs. Q-'s tendency to discourage her husband's attempts to find regular employment again motivated in part by her sexual rejection of him? Did Mrs. Q- use her husband's failure to meet cultural expectations as a means to legitimize her personal feelings in the relationship, even though the result is so destructive to her husband and to the family? These questions introduce another level of analysis, involving the individual motives of members of the family and their effects upon the family as a small-scale social system.

It is worth pausing at this point to be certain that we have made clear what we have called two distinct levels of analysis. The first is the role system of the family with reference to the culture. It is this level that is involved in the statement by Mrs. Q-: "A man should not be around the house all the time. He has to be out, be with men." What this means, more abstractly, is that a working-class man like Martin Q- is expected to be a provider and thereby working outside his home most of the time. Moreover, his leisure-time life, also, is distinctly male and separate from his family. These are role expectations that refer to a social system external to the family; they are not specific to Martin Q-, the individual, but to Martin Q- as a "type" of person in a given class status in the American society.

However, even as we establish a framework for comparing the Q- family according to its general type, we must add that it has a unique existence as a particular family group. Within the Q- family, problems must arise that are particular to the management of its own group dynamics; they are internal dynamics.[19]

When the Q- family is analyzed according to the social relations within the group, two very striking features are the dominance of Mrs. Q- and the isolation of her husband. The arrangement of the family members may be charted as follows:

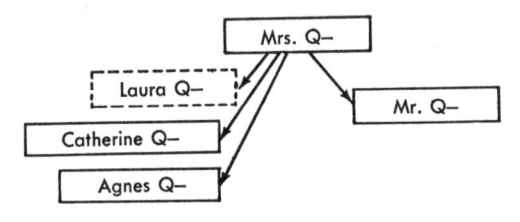

```
                    ┌─────────┐
                    │ Mrs. Q- │
                    └─────────┘
        ┌─────────┐    ╱│╲    ┌─────────┐
        │ Laura Q-│   ╱ │ ╲   │ Mr. Q-  │
        └─────────┘  ╱  │  ╲  └─────────┘
      ┌───────────┐ ╱   │
      │Catherine Q│     │
      └───────────┘     │
        ┌─────────┐     │
        │Agnes Q- │─────┘
        └─────────┘
```

The inner dynamics of this family appear to be largely implicit and unspoken. Explicitly, Mrs. Q- speaks of her husband and to her husband in terms of the norms of conduct that are appropriate to the adult male in his social class. She urges him to find work, to be "out of the house," to be the provider, and to have little or no responsibility in the home. Implicitly, however, whenever he attempts to fulfill these normal obligations, she discourages him. She assigns (implicitly) to him a passive, dependent role, telling him that he is not strong enough physically for the work that is available to him.

Martin Q- accepts the implicit role assignment of his wife, but at what appears to be a great cost. His illness, diagnosed as psychogenic in origin, is the means whereby he resolves the conflict between his conception of his normal role (provider, head-of-household) and the fact of his passive dependence upon his wife. Furthermore, there is no recourse for Martin Q- through his children. As far as we know, Mrs. Q- completely dominates her children as well as her husband, preventing their integration in emotionally meaningful ways by manipulating them into divergent life patterns.

Laura Q-, although deceased, is, next to her mother, the most significant figure in the family. Her image is invoked to inspire Catherine and to subjugate Agnes.

Agnes, though the oldest living child, is the lowest in the family's hierarchy of status. Agnes is assigned by her mother to a role of servility and self-abnegation. With Laura and Catherine designated as her superiors in beauty and intelligence, Agnes is assigned and accepts a servant's position in the family. Her frustrated wishes for love and affection are, like those of her father, expressed in illness. Here she uses the model of her dead sister: she develops heart symptoms, and reaches for death with a psychogenic illness which makes food intake impossible (anorexia nervosa).

Catherine also accepts on a manifest level the role assignment of her mother; but, through illness, implicitly rejects the assignment.[20]

Summary

Our sketch of the doctor-patient relationship has followed closely a model that included the following: (a) the doctor's role, drawn to show the importance of (b) the medical profession as the main institutional context of his behavior; and (c) the patient's role as it is based upon (d) the family as the primary source of behavior in illness.

If the picture were left as it is, one would still see a social system in which every patient deals essentially with his own doctor. This image is hardly realistic. It leaves out the most significant institution in modern medicine, the hospital.

Serious illness, as our study of the family has shown, cannot easily be cared for within the modern family. Modern medicine, with its complex technology and specialization of function, cannot be practiced with complete effectiveness out of a black bag, or even in an individual office. As a result, the hospital has developed as the major social institution of modern medicine. Therefore, before elaborating further the dynamics of the doctor-patient relationship, we must study carefully how the hospital intervenes in this relationship.

NOTES TO CHAPTER 5

1. Eliot, T. S., *The Cocktail Party:* A Comedy. Harcourt, Brace and World, Inc., New York, 1950, p. 114.
2. Parsons, Talcott, and Renée C. Fox, "Illness, Therapy and the Modern Urban American Family," *The Journal of Social Issues*, vol. 8, 1952, pp. 31–44; reprinted in Jaco, E. Gartly, editor, *Patients, Physicians and Illness*, The Free Press, Glencoe, Ill., 1958, pp. 234–245. The paper is also reprinted in Bell, Norman W., and Ezra F. Vogel, editors, *The Family*, The Free Press, Glencoe, Ill., 1960, pp. 347–360.
3. Several summary views of this educational movement may be consulted for details. For a general description, see "Report on Experiments in Medical Education," *Journal of Medical Education*, vol. 31, August, 1956, pp. 515–552. For description and interpretation, see Berry, George Packer, "Medical Education in Transition," *Journal of Medical Education*, vol. 28, March, 1953, pp. 17–42. One finds a very thorough discussion from historical and sociological points of view in Merton, Robert K., "Some Preliminaries to a Sociology of Medical Education" in Merton, Robert K., George G. Reader, and Patricia L. Kendall, editors, *The Student-Physician*, Harvard University Press (for the Commonwealth Fund), Cambridge, Mass., 1957, pp. 3–79.
4. For an excellent review, see Davis, Kingsley, *Human Society*, Macmillan Co., New York, 1949, pp. 414–416.
5. *Ibid.*, p. 417.
6. *Ibid.*, p. 418.

7. Parsons, Talcott, and Renée C. Fox, *op. cit.* This article is one of the very few examples of this particular type of analysis. Our subsequent discussion of the family and illness is based in large part on Parsons and Fox's presentation.

8. This is not without exception, of course. Young couples do sometimes go to live with the parents of the bride or of the groom. Glick reports that in ordinary times approximately one out of five couples in our society moves in with relatives or lives in rented rooms as lodgers (in a parental residence) for a while after marriage. The proportion of couples living in this manner sharply declines until middle age and reaches a low point of about 3 per cent for couples in their fifties. Glick, P. C., "The Family Cycle," *American Sociological Review,* vol. 12, 1947, pp. 164-174.

9. Parsons, Talcott, and Renée C. Fox, *op. cit.,* p. 35.

10. *Ibid.*

11. As only one sample of popular reaction to so called "dehumanization" in hospitals, see Berg, Roland H., "A Report on Hospitals," *Look,* vol. 23, February 23, 1959, pp. 16-19. For the medical point of view, see Reader, George G., "The Cornell Comprehensive Care and Teaching Program" in Merton, Reader, and Kendall, *op. cit.,* pp. 81-101.

12. Richardson, Henry Barber, *Patients Have Families.* Harvard University Press (for The Commonwealth Fund), New York, 1945, pp. 5-47.

13. See Henry, Jules, and Samuel Warson, "Family Structure and Psychic Development," *American Journal of Orthopsychiatry,* vol. 21, January, 1951, pp. 59-73.

14. See Parsons, Talcott, and Renée C. Fox, *op. cit.*

15. Spiegel, John P., "The Resolution of Role Conflict Within the Family" in Greenblatt, Milton, Daniel J. Levinson, and Richard H. Williams, editors, *The Patient and the Mental Hospital.* The Free Press, Glencoe, Ill., 1957, p. 547.

16. See Myers, Jerome K., and Bertram H. Roberts, *Family and Class Dynamics in Mental Illness,* John Wiley and Sons, New York, 1959.

17. *Ibid.,* p. 67.

18. Richardson, Henry Barber, *op. cit.,* p. 27.

19. For a more detailed theoretical discussion of external and internal social systems, see Homans, George C., *The Human Group,* Harcourt, Brace and World, Inc., New York, 1950.

20. This method of role analysis is described by John P. Spiegel in "The Social Role of Doctor and Patient in Psychoanalysis and Psychotherapy," *Psychiatry,* vol. 17, November, 1954, pp. 369-376.

PART THREE

THE HOSPITAL AS A SOCIAL INSTITUTION

Chapter 6

ORIGINS OF THE TEMPLE OF MEDICAL SCIENCE

Sickness is a matter of alarm, not of logic. Even when society acts with a logical end in view, it must be prepared to yield at many points to the nonlogical sentiments of the individual whose survival is threatened.

EDWARD D. CHURCHILL, M.D.,
"The Development of the Hospital."[1]

DURING THE PAST CENTURY the locus of medical practice has shifted from the home to the hospital. Much more was involved than a change in the setting of patient care. The implications both for the physician and for the patient have been revolutionary.

The hospital was not always, as it is now, a "temple of medical science."[2] Created as a refuge for the pauper and the friendless, the hospital belongs to the community, and its form has varied with the needs and goals of society. The doctor, on the other hand, has preserved a position as a free member of society. The medical profession was organized and consistently remained independent of the hospital. Strong bonds between the two developed; but, in contrast to the monastic orders, medicine escaped from the heavy burden that full responsibility for the building and maintenance of hospitals might have loaded on its shoulders. Today this historic fact may easily be lost sight of as we see a blending of the duties of the profession with the mission of the hospital.

That the doctor has been and continues to be essentially a guest in the hospital is not by chance. It is an expression of an inherent duality of purpose that has existed in the hospital since its origin.

The doctor's role is preeminently that of the healer, but healing is only one of the two major functions of the hospital. The other is to comfort. It has not been the doctor, but others, particularly the nurse, who have filled the role of comforter in the hospital. Moreover, the close historic association with organized religion, as well as with the care of the poor, has made the hospital a house for medicine but not medicine's house.

Still, one may ask, can healer be separated from comforter? The sick, by definition, are helpless to some extent and are made thereby dependent upon others for the elemental requirements of everyday living, as well as for specific help in combating the causes of illness. To serve the sick, therefore, is it not required both to comfort and to heal as an integrated combination of functions rather than a dualistic separation?

The answer to this disarmingly simple question is quite complicated. Logic suggests that the dualism is unnecessary. A study of the history of the hospital, however, reveals that nonlogical factors often have exerted the most important influence upon its development. As an eminent physician-historian has written: "To present in chronologic sequence the predecessors of the present-day hospitals and imply that there has been a steady transition from the primitive to the simple and from the simple to the complex, would create the illusion that the hospital has an autonomous destiny and a momentum of its own. Actually it is but an organ of the society that creates it."[3] Moreover, "the quest of individual man for survival and for relief of suffering is surrounded by his own nonlogical desires and actions as well as those of his friends and family. Society may respond to the situation by equally nonlogical sentiments that range from pity to complete indifference."[4] What might be called the "illusion of logic" is tempting but, as we shall try to show, it is only an illusion in the case of the hospital.

A second pitfall follows from the overwhelming significance of scientific technology in the hospital today. We have observed, for example, that the nurse has become more and more a skilled technician as the complexity of the technical demands of good medical care has increased. As the techniques of healing have fallen increasingly to the nurse, a shift has been observed in her role from comforter to healer. The concern for the patient's comfort, it has been argued, is inherently secondary in importance to healing, and the changing role of the nurse is used as a demonstration. The implication is that he who cannot help, comforts. The fallacy of such reasoning lies in its implicit assumption that the science of healing and the "art" of comforting are at opposite ends of a single continuum. They are, in fact, two separate functions that are not necessarily related. That the ascension of one sometimes leads to the neglect of the other does not change the fact of their separateness.

At this point in the discussion, we seem to be moving in a curious kind of circle. It is true, we have said, that the dualism of healing-comforting is a significant factor in the hospital, but it is not logical. Next, we asserted that it is logical that advances in the technology of medical care may occur together with advances in our ability to help comfort the sick; but, we add, it is not true—or, more accurately, it does not tend to happen that way. Let us see if we can straighten out the circle.

Our first step will be to present a brief historical view of the development of the hospital as a social institution. This, in turn, will become the point of departure for a discussion of some special aspects of the general hospital. Subsequent to that, we will discuss in detail the mental hospital. The latter is chosen as an example both of some problems that are generic to hospitals and of problems unique to the kind of illness that is its central concern.

The Hospital: Origins and Development[5]

It is common to assume that the hospital is motivated simply "to care for . . . [the] sick man and by so doing restore him to his occupation as a useful member of society." However, from its very beginning when religion was its primary propelling force, the hospital has been guided by a variety of motives, among which the logic and humaneness of healing were often secondary.

Without doubt the most powerful single stimulus to the development of the hospital can be found in what Edward Churchill calls "those attributes of man that seek to find expression in the Christian religion." Christianity for nineteen centuries "has cherished, nourished, and guided the hospital as a traditional and sometimes convenient means of obeying the commandment of mercy and compassion."

The teaching of St. Paul, "and now abideth faith, hope, and charity, these three; but the greatest of these is charity," set down for all time the principle that the inward mysticism of spiritual life must be joined by some outward expression of love toward one's fellow man.[6]

The Christian hospital actually came into being after Emperor Constantine recognized Christianity and established it as the state religion. At the Council of Nicaea in A.D. 325, the bishops were instructed to establish a hospital in every cathedral city. Curiously, the concept of charity, which is considered the originating motive for these hospitals, quickly degenerated into the practice of almsgiving as a means of salvation. St. Chrysostom (344 to 407) taught "if there were no poor, the greater part of your sins would not be removed; they are the healers of your wounds."

Thus, almsgiving that supported the early hospitals was neither motivated by the thought that social conditions might thereby be bettered, nor was it an expression of the original Christian concept of charity. The aid to the poor brought by these early hospitals was not a simple act of brotherly love but a complicated device directed toward securing grace and salvation for the almsgiver.[7]

In the early Christian hospitals, there appears to have been some systematic attempt to differentiate the medical and social functions. This was a differentiation that was lost sight of as "in the eyes of society the ills of poverty became blended with the ailments of disease."[8]

During the following centuries the hospital developed in pathways closely related to the major events and forces of the time. "As late Roman society took on the form of medieval feudalism many of the early Christian hospitals suffered by diversion of their funds, either into ecclesiastic channels on the one hand, or to the purposes of the Barons who were no less avaricious than the bishops." The Crusades (1096 to 1291), providing the consecration of war, offered an alternate, somewhat more grand, "pathway to heaven" compared to almsgiving. On the other hand, the Crusades led to the need for more hospitals for both the crusaders and their victims. Consequently, hospitals were established during this period. It was during the age of monasticism, however, when the largest number of hospitals were founded.

The medieval hospital was a house of shelter and care, rather than an institution for medical treatment. The ecclesiastics who staffed them were at one time skilled in the medical practices of the day, but gradually this skill withered under the influence of church doctrine.

> Belief of the clergy centered in the power of prayer, fasting, and the ability of the saints to work marvelous cures. A devout sufferer wandered from place to place with the hope that some miracle, stories of which were on the tongue of every fellow patient-pilgrim, might occur in his case. Itinerant friars and other holy men brought miracles to those too ill to travel.[9]

The Reformation brought in its wake drastic changes in the hospital, just as in all other aspects of life. In England the hospitals were changed most radically when the Reformation Parliament of Henry VIII dissolved the monasteries (1536 to 1539). This type of political action effectively negated the ecclesiasticism that had prevailed. However, although the hospital ceased functioning, in the minds of men, primarily for the salvation of the soul, it did not become transformed immediately to an institution based on a knowledge of disease and the application of science to the cure of the sick. This development did not crystallize until the great voluntary hospitals were formed in eighteenth-century England.

The dissolution of the monasteries by Henry VIII left England virtually without hospitals for two centuries. "This clean break with the ecclesiastic past gave free opportunity for a fresh start." Out of the "enlightenment," the spirit of this new beginning was found. "Humanitarian" is the name used to describe this spirit that found expression in voices like those of Locke, Newton, and Hume.

The new hospitals were based on individual gifts and initiative and on coordinated voluntary efforts and subscription. The emphasis was on *philanthropy* that was *socially constructive, not* merely almsgiving. The whole movement was still tied to Christian ethics but "other great forces were at play."

The Hospital and the Medical Profession

During the medieval and renaissance periods, when the medical profession organized itself into the structure required for its development as we now know it, medicine as a profession remained independent of the hospital. It is still independent, although recent trends link them more closely.

In practice, the hospital belongs to the social order, and is molded by society's needs and the means which society wishes to provide. "The doctor is a free member of society. He may attach himself to the hospital; it is part of his tradition voluntarily to contribute his skills to the care of the sick poor." He does *not*, however, traditionally take responsibility for organizing and maintaining the hospital.

In the eighteenth and nineteenth centuries, the physician came to be welded more closely to the charity hospital. Several motives moved him: "first, the ethical humanitarian response evoked by a vivid firsthand knowledge of the suffering that accompanies disease; second, the urge for increased knowledge and experience that might sharpen his skills; and third, the responsibilities of a teacher to impart the art to those qualified to consume it."[10]

Nevertheless, the full development of the modern hospital, and the doctor's role within it, could not take place until the acceptance of methods of antisepsis and asepsis by medicine and the hospital in the late nineteenth century. Prior to that, the hospital was truly a death house. As late as 1788, the death rate among patients at the Hotel Dieu in Paris was 25 per cent, and that of surgeons and attendants from 6 to 12 per cent a year.[11] "Hospitalism" was the term that came into use, describing the great danger of cross infection in the hospital.

"No event in history so altered the relation of the hospital to the social order as one single contribution coming from medical science in the last quarter of the nineteenth century," Churchill writes. "To understand this change it is necessary to set the clock back seventy-five years and learn the sinister implications of the term 'hospitalism,' a word that is now happily forgotten. In spite of the compassion of religion and the nobility of ethical motives, and notwithstanding an increased understanding of disease and a growing effectiveness of remedies, to enter a hospital as a patient at that time meant taking a calculated and by no means insignificant risk. It was no mere happenstance that the hospital was dedicated to the sick poor. The risks of entering a hospital had to be balanced against the hazards of a sickness in the hovel of the pauper, or the inability of the stricken traveler to find shelter and care in a strange community, or the necessity and urgency of some malady requiring the operative skill of a surgeon otherwise unavailable. In the absence of these or similar circumstances of dire necessity, no one in his right mind could consider a hospital a desirable or safe place in which to take up temporary residence."[12]

"Hospitalism" was finally banished by Lister, who applied the discoveries of Pasteur to wounds and devised the procedures of antisepsis and asepsis that were to minimize for all time the hazards of cross infection. And it was only with the end of hospitalism that the doors of the hospital opened to all classes of society.

> The almsgiver and the philanthropist now could seek the hospitality and care of the institution that they had created as a refuge for the pauper and the friendless. The sick of all classes began once more to make pilgrimages, this time to the hospital as a temple of medical science. They sought knowledge and skills rather than faith and miracles.[13]

The hospital awakened to a new era in its history. For both patients and physicians, the consequences were extremely significant.

Without any question, the revolutionary changes that began in the hospital eighty-five years ago were based in the scientific revolution occurring in medicine. "While Miss Nightingale and the followers of Pasteur were making it safe for people to go to hospitals," a recent study reports, "the development of modern medicine was making it more and more desirable for them to do so and at the same time increasing the value of the hospital to the doctor."

> Doctors needed more precise control of patient care than was possible with unskilled attendants in the home, if they were to give their patients the full benefit of scientific advances. Highly skilled nursing was vital. The reforms in nursing education which occurred at this time provided young women equipped with the needed skills. This training was given in the hospital. Gradually it was realized that the

skills developed there could be helpful to nurses who were employed to care for sick people in their homes. But their services could be directed and utilized more effectively in a specal institution.

Precise and elaborate rituals of aseptic surgery could be observed more easily in a special wing of a special building than in a hurriedly rearranged bedroom or domestic kitchen. When aseptic methods made it safe for the surgeon to open the abdomen, and other body cavities, there was a rapid increase in the number and complexity of operations which he dared perform. This resulted in such a great increase in the number and complexity of surgical instruments that transporting them became a problem. During the past fifty years clinical applications of research discoveries, such as x-ray, the measurement of basal metabolism, the electrocardiograph, and radioactive isotopes, necessitated the development of costly and bulky equipment. Laboratory examinations were becoming increasingly important in patient care and could be made available more promptly and efficiently when the patients were gathered under one roof than when they were scattered through residential areas.

As a result of these developments, the hospital became the place where the best, rather than the worst, care could be given — first to surgical patients and later to an increasing number suffering from medical illnesses. At length it was only in the hospital that the doctor could find resources for the care of many of his patients at a cost which was not prohibitive.*[14]

In association with these very logical and fortunate consequences of technological development, however, there were other quite different ones. The need for technical skills, for example, exceeded the ability of physicians to supply them. Nurses and new categories of technicians were mustered into the breach. In this situation the patient, although safer than ever, sometimes found himself less comfortable than ever. His needs outside of those specific to the technical aspects of the healing process continued to be important not only for a sense of well-being, but as a vital part of the healing process itself. The underlying dualism of purpose in the hospital, in other words, persisted, and in unanticipated ways made itself apparent in the modern hospital just as before.

* Reprinted by permission of the publisher from Temple Burling, Edith M. Lentz, and Robert N. Wilson, *The Give and Take in Hospitals:* A Study of Human Organization in Hospitals, G. P. Putnam's Sons, New York, 1956, p. 5.

For the doctor, the hospital became essential for the proper care of major illness. His interests have blended with the function of the hospital, leading to a sense of ownership and sense of responsibility that, historically, is new. Similarly, the function of the hospital in the education of new doctors has changed.

For centuries medical education was more or less a form of apprenticeship training. To a considerable extent, in this country as in England, medical apprenticeship was pursued in, and under the management of, voluntary hospitals. However, a radical revolution in medical education coincided in the United States with the modernization of hospitals. Basic to medical education, as to the hospital, was the problem of integrating methods of medical practice with related advances in the natural sciences.

The direction taken by American medical education, unlike that of England, was toward association with the university. It is now the very rare exception to find an American medical school that is not affiliated with a university. This relationship has been most stable for the first two years of professional school, the so-called preclinical or basic science years. The organizational patterns of relationships between the university and the hospital have been more varied.

One of the approaches to the clinical education of physicians has been to continue bedside training in voluntary and also governmental hospitals that have become "affiliated" with university medical schools. Under this system, clinical teachers are recruited from among successful practitioners who continue in private practice but agree to devote a portion of their time to teaching. The hospitals receive the benefit of service from students, interns, and residents recruited by the university. This seemed a logical enough arrangement; but in the experience with this approach, several unanticipated difficulties become manifest.

On the one hand, the traditions that developed out of the apprenticeship period were against it. The hospital was prone to view patient service as the primary goal and the education of physicians as "a harmless by-product of the care of the sick."[15] Only grudgingly did it admit that participation in medical education brought benefit to the hospital.

Secondly, the new skills and knowledge introduced into medicine as the by-products of scientific advances were not well adapted to the apprenticeship method which persisted at the bedside. As Churchill reports, ". . . a different type of guidance became necessary in the education of the doctor. The student of today must be encouraged to think for himself and acquire a faculty of critical judgment that will stand him in stead throughout his entire professional life. It is no longer feasible to limit training to the acquirement of skill in the use of existing tools and methods; the student must be educated so that he can learn to use new tools and change to more effective methods as these become available."[16] In other words, the frame of reference that is basic to scientific inquiry was adapted to the clinical practice of medicine as well as to the "preclinical" laboratory sciences; and, as a consequence, the needs of clinical teaching changed in a way that was difficult for existing hospitals to meet. If one asks why hospitals could not fulfill this important educational function, the answer is hardly self-evident. After all, the clinical professors had been recruited from among the famous and successful. Why were they not suitable teachers? Of course, some of them were; but, it must be added, many were not. Edward Churchill, an outstanding surgeon himself, gives the following explanation:

> It was found that "success" in practice might be acquired on the basis of other attributes than an open and inquiring mind. As is the case with musicians, the ability of the virtuoso to perform is by no means an index of his ability to teach. Again, preoccupation with a large private practice left too few hours to be spent with students, particularly since bedside instruction in small groups was displacing the didactic lecture given to the class as a whole. But a professional staff hierarchy had grown up in the hospital, whether the institution was under the management of a governmental unit or under the Board of Managers of a voluntary charity. The practitioners in control of the wards had achieved their positions by virtue of long and meritorious service that brought advancement by rigid rules of seniority. They had acquired vested interests that the university could not challenge.[17]

In answer to the problem, a new type of hospital began to appear, the university hospital, which was owned and organized specifically for the purpose of medical education.

A similar story can be told concerning the third major motive of the medical profession, the urge for new knowledge to add to medical skill. Just as the "ethical humanitarian response to the suffering of illness," and the responsibility to communicate the art to new doctors impelled the medical profession more and more toward the hospital, so did the drive for scientific research.

All of these recent developments seem to follow a logical enough course. However, even the compelling logic of science has been forced to wait on very nonlogical sentiments prevailing in society. Thus the name "temple of medical science" as it has been applied to the modern hospital raises questions that have a very old ring:

> It is possible that the profession is unconsciously drifting into a dangerous position not wholly unlike that in which the Church found itself before the Reformation. If one listens carefully, a faint ringing of bells can be heard when some miracle of medical science is recorded in solemn protocol; salvation in this world can be achieved only if you "consult your doctor," and the pain and anguish of the fires of hell will overtake the ignorant or wilful who fail to heed this admonition. The quest for individual survival in this world is fully as intense as the older hope for personal immortality in the next.[18]

The Temple of Medical Science: What God Does It Serve?

To speak of a "temple of science," as we have just done, is to speak of an anomaly. For a temple is by definition a fortress of tradition and ritual; it is stable and resistant to change. Science, on the other hand, is the opposite. As Weber has pointed out, the future obsolescence of today's "discovery" is part of the essence of scientific endeavor:

> In science, each of us knows that what he has accomplished will be antiquated in ten, twenty, fifty years. That is the fate to which science is subjected; it is the very *meaning* of scientific work, to which it is devoted in a quite specific sense, as compared with other spheres of culture. . . . Every scientific "fulfillment" raises new "questions"; it *asks* to be surpassed and outdated. Whoever wishes to serve science has to resign himself to this fact. . . . We cannot work without hoping that others will advance further than we have.[19]

Nevertheless, the metaphor is appropriate. The new scientific spirit of the hospital merged with a sense of faith that is very old. Like the religious temple, the hospital became a sacred place, a trusted source of help both to rich and poor. For the wealthy, instead of St. Paul's charity or almsgiving for salvation, the hospital became a favored object of huge gifts, and whole wards, wings or buildings were built as their personal monuments. Yet, even as buildings grew bigger, technical equipment more complex, and the range of services broader and broader, the awed, worshipful attitudes of the public began to change. Witness the recent charge of a popular weekly magazine that a "secret investigation of hospitals has confirmed what many Americans have long suspected: a hospital is not a fit place in which to be sick."[20]

The public attacks on the hospital that increasingly are being pressed, protest more than anything else the depersonalization of the patient. "A hospital resembles a factory, where patients are stored in neat white beds." "To the hospital staff, a patient has no name; he's the 'ulcer in 304.'" "Hospitals are run for the convenience of the doctors, nurses, and staff." "The patient's needs come last." These are but a few random selections from cartoon-captions, headlines, and newspaper column leads.

"The doctor-patient relationship is breaking down," it is charged. Who is at fault? "Too concerned with their own problems and dissatisfactions, the members of the staff lose sight of the patient's emotional needs. And even though his medical needs are ultimately satisfied, the patient regards the staff as hard, callous and uncaring."[21]

There is, of course, the possibility that these charges represent no more than the usual sensationalist muckraking that is fashionable in American journalism. In the publishing trade the dictum "Lincoln, dogs and doctors" is well known. During slow times, these three subjects seem to have a never failing fascination for the public. Moreover, attack and exposé, like crime and cowboys, are believed to have a "sales appeal" that beats the documentary and informative.

Unfortunately, however, there is evident substance to these charges. Overstated the case may be, but the underlying facts cannot be denied. Moreover, systematic efforts to study the roots of hospital problems have developed rapidly in the wake of World War II. These studies anticipated the journalistic campaigns, reflecting the deep concern of the medical profession and others concerning what they regard obviously as significant "real problems."

The Trend Toward Personalized Care

Like all social institutions, the hospital does not easily change customs and attitudes which are long established. Moreover, there is a rich record of accomplishment which the modern hospital rightfully claims in answer to the challenges of its reformers: many of the practices currently under attack were developed and have demonstrated their effectiveness in the fulfillment of complex medical and surgical goals. Nevertheless, trends toward significant change, this time in a direction determined by human or nontechnological factors, are unmistakable.

The outstanding change has been in the approach to the patient's response to his illness. The patient's feelings about himself, his physician, and the hospital have begun to assume, not secondary importance, but primary significance in his treatment. This is not to say that patient feelings were totally neglected before. However, whereas previously to make the patient "comfortable" was considered humanitarian, current changes in patient care assume that social-emotional components have a primary significance for the course of illness. This may seem a very slight change, but its consequences promise to be considerable. Instead of stripping the patient of all connections with his identity outside the hospital, and focusing on his principal complaint to the virtual exclusion of other considerations, "comprehensive care" is becoming the watchword.

Why, one may ask, is it at this particular time that the history of the hospital has taken this turn?

One answer is similar to that used earlier to explain new trends in medical education. (See pages 11–17.) Basically, the change began in medical practice itself. The very success of medical science during the past half-century has reduced fears of death associated with acute illness, and at the same time increased problems of health. "We are faced with the fact," an eminent physician recently declared, "that perhaps one-half of all patients or more have nothing wrong with them in terms of prospective death. But can we say that there is nothing wrong with them in terms of prospective life?"[22]

Patients, in other words, are more "healthy" in general than they were just two short decades ago. Advances in public health practice, in the prevention of specific illnesses, and in preventive medicine as a whole have eliminated some of what were medicine's worst problems a few short decades ago. In acute illnesses of the respiratory and digestive tracts, the threat to life has been drastically reduced. The improvements in therapy have been matched by advances in diagnostic method.

These advances and gains, however, have themselves created new problems and spotlighted old ones that were less visible in the shadow of the great medical threats of the past. With increased life expectancy, an older patient has emerged to demand new understanding of the problems of aging. And with the new skills available in physical diagnosis, the patient whose tests are "negative" but still feels ill has gained a higher status medically. The sick who have "nothing wrong" are no longer the focus of the psychiatrist alone but of all physicians.

Summary

This telescopic view of the history of the hospital has been designed to show that "the form of the hospital emerges as a resultant of many forces active in the social order of the times." The underlying process is *not* necessarily logical. The powerful logic of science, even in modern times, has been forced to wait on very nonlogical sentiments prevailing in the society. Christian ethics, science, war, economics have all been instrumental in the forming of the modern hospital. They continue to act as the influences from which the hospital of tomorrow will emerge.

History, however, provides only the background. Moreover, in so brief an account, the historical description lends itself to a misleading sense of logical progression. The modern hospital is actually not one type of institution: it is a complex of types. In general, the structure of the modern hospital may be differentiated from that of other historical periods, and it can be related to earlier forms. These statements are predicated on a longitudinal view. Looked at in cross-section, as in the next chapter, the modern hospital takes on a different appearance.

NOTES TO CHAPTER 6

1. Churchill, Edward D., "The Development of the Hospital" in Faxon, Nathaniel W., editor, *The Hospital in Contemporary Life*. Harvard University Press, Cambridge, Mass., 1949, p. 4.
2. *Ibid.*, p. 35.
3. *Ibid.*, p. 2.
4. *Ibid.*, p. 4.
5. The major source for this discussion is Edward D. Churchill, *op. cit.* Quotations, unless otherwise specified, are from that source.
6. *Ibid.*, p. 7.
7. *Ibid.*, pp. 7–8.
8. *Ibid.*, p. 8.
9. *Ibid.*, p. 12.
10. *Ibid.*, p. 30.
11. See Goldwater, S. S., "Concerning Hospital Origins" in Bachmeyer, Arthur C., and Gerhard Hartman, editors, *The Hospital in Modern Society*, Commonwealth Fund, New York, 1943, p. 9.
12. Churchill, Edward D., *op. cit.*, pp. 30–31.
13. *Ibid.*, p. 35.
14. Burling, Temple, Edith M. Lentz, and Robert N. Wilson, *The Give and Take in Hospitals:* A Study of Human Organization in Hospitals. G. P. Putnam's Sons, New York, 1956, p. 5.
15. Churchill, Edward D., *op. cit.*, p. 37.
16. *Ibid.*, pp. 37–38.
17. *Ibid.*, p. 38.
18. *Ibid.*, p. 36.
19. Weber, Max, "Science as a Vocation" in Gerth, H. H., and C. Wright Mills, editors, *From Max Weber:* Essays in Sociology. Oxford University Press, New York, 1946, pp. 129–158.
20. Berg, Roland H., "A Report on Hospitals," *Look*, vol. 23, February, 3, 1959, pp. 16–19.
21. *Ibid.*, p. 16.
22. Starr, Isaac, M.D., professor of therapeutics, University of Pennsylvania School of Medicine, in an unpublished address to first-year medical students, 1954. Taken from the materials of a continuing study of the sociology of medical education conducted by the Bureau of Applied Social Research of Columbia University under a grant from the Commonwealth Fund.

Chapter 7

THE GENERAL HOSPITAL AS A HUMAN ORGANIZATION

THERE ARE 7,000 HOSPITALS in the United States alone, employing 1,200,000 full-time workers, and spending an estimated $4,000,000,000 each year. Among the factors that have contributed to this development are several we have already discussed, including the need for hospitals created by technological advances in the science of medicine, the growth of the general population, and changes in the family. Even more notable perhaps has been the change in lay attitudes toward acceptance of the use of hospitals for a wide spectrum of medical problems. The result is a vast and complicated institution, comparable in many respects to other complex organizations characteristic of our age.

The hospital has become a bureaucracy, and this, without doubt, is the most significant experience it shares with contemporary political, industrial, and educational institutions. To understand hospital bureaucracy, one must study its problems of communication, lines of authority, status hierarchy, value systems, and power—all very familiar in the general sociological study of complex organizations. There are, on the other hand, problems that are unique to this particular institution, those derived from its history and special purposes. Analogy can take us just so far and then the path of hospital analysis takes its own turn.

Perhaps the most extraordinary feature of the hospital is that its two most important members, the doctor and the patient, are *in* but not *of* the hospital. "The physician," it was observed in a recent study of hospitals in the United States, "has enjoyed a highly autonomous role in the hospital organization. This autonomy has been laden with power to direct the course of the organization; explicit authority has been immense, and implicit authority perhaps even more potent. It is important to recognize that the doctor's ability to produce desired effects in organizational life has been joined to a flourishing negative capability—a freedom *from*—for escaping many of the ordinary demands of that life. In a curious sense, any doctor who is not a full-time department head in a teaching hospital has been a 'guest' of the organization, much as the other primary party to the curative transaction—the patient—has been a guest. But the medical man has been a guest with very special prerogatives, one who like 'the man who came to dinner' has insinuated himself into a dominant position in which he could regulate the temperature without paying the fuel bills."[1]

The doctor's role, however, is changing. The independent practitioner, accustomed to a purely private relationship with his patient and to absolute authority over auxiliary personnel when he came to the hospital, has joined a medical "team." Former aides have grown into full-fledged collaborators. His once unquestioned monopoly of professional status increasingly gives way to the claims of nurse, hospital administrator, social worker, dietitian, physical therapist, and others. The implications for all concerned are profound.

The role of the patient in the hospital is structured to a large extent by the nature of the illness.[2] In acute medical and surgical illnesses, the patient is more or less dependent upon others; he is a passive observer and not an active participant in the life of the hospital. As Wessen has noted, the patient under these conditions is, for hospital personnel, not so much a part of their social system as a *reference group* whom they serve and toward whom they orient many of their actions and attitudes.[3] A quite different situation is involved in long-term illness, where patients are a vital part of the hospital social system.[4]

Associated with each of these polar opposites of illness is a distinctive type of hospital. The first is the most familiar type, "the community hospital operated under the auspices of a voluntary organization for nonprofit purposes, where general medical, [obstetrical] and surgical care is offered and most patients are short-term guests."*[5] The second type, the specialized institution, for patients who need long-term care, is perhaps best characterized by the mental hospital.

To avoid confusion as we look at some of the organizational details of the hospital, each of its main types will be discussed separately. The general hospital is the subject of this chapter, to be followed by two chapters on the mental hospital.

The Hospital Troika: Three Sources of Authority

The troika, that fabled Russian sleigh, has become something of a household word in this country, thanks to a notable United Nations debate.[6] If, as is well known, it is something of a feat to keep a team of three horses, harnessed side by side, pulling together, how much more difficult would it be in the organization of men. Yet the hospital *is* such an organization. In its harness are three sources of authority: the Board of Trustees, the Office of Hospital Administration, and the Medical Staff.

In the hospital troika, the administrator is on one side, the medical chief of staff is on the opposite side, and the board is in the middle. The board holds the hospital in trust, representing the wishes of the donors and the community. The administrator and the medical chief of staff are the working heads of the hospital, in charge of the actual operation. The administrator is the custodian of property and equipment, the keeper of records, and the arbiter of the increasingly complex human relations that are part of a modern bureaucratic organization. The medical chief of staff retains his traditional responsibility, to provide the best possible medical care for the patients. More recently, research has been added as a new responsibility of the medical staff, a vital function that, only in modern times, has been attached to the hospital.

Such a group, if only because it is a triad, lends itself to problems of divisive conflict. In a three-person group, when a division of interest or opinion arises between two members, the third may be expected to become the target of a competitive struggle. Each

---

* Reprinted by permission of the publisher from Temple Burling, Edith M. Lentz, and Robert N. Wilson, *The Give and Take in Hospitals*. G. P. Putnam's Sons, New York, 1956, p. xv.

of the two differing parties seeks to persuade the third to his side and against the other. The triad, according to studies of small group interaction, is a basically unstable group in whom a working consensus is difficult to achieve.[7]

In the three-way grouping of hospital authority, the administrator and the medical chief of staff are, in many ways, natural antagonists. Each has special interests. The administrator is concerned with the financial stability of the hospital, and such problems as interdepartmental relations and the coordination of diverse working groups. "He has to think of all the possible internal effects of policy decisions and interest himself in many details of routine management."*[8] Doctors tend to be concerned not with these details, but primarily with technical, medical problems. These two points of view are bound to clash periodically. When, for example, a problem of patient care or of research calls for new equipment, the physician's characteristic tendency is to ask for immediate action without regard to budgetary considerations. The administrator is more likely to take a long view, to probe and question the importance of the request, and to think of its consequences in the various parts of his organization. The new purchase may require space, personnel, and so on. For the physician, there are other overriding considerations. To save lives, to advance knowledge, to effect cures or better diagnosis: these are the sacred prerogatives of medicine. For the physician, they take precedence over considerations of budget or administration.

In pursuing their often divergent interests, however, neither the medical chief nor the administrator has a clearly defined area of authority where he can function alone. Theoretically, the board, administrator, and medical staff have a common interest in adequate patient care, and changes can be effected only through the agreement and cooperation of all three. In actuality, one often finds a typical triadic struggle, in which the doctor and the administrator vie with each other for the support of the board.

In this contest the physician has become accustomed to certain clear advantages. For example, Harvey Smith, writing about

* Reprinted by permission of the publisher from Temple Burling, Edith M. Lentz, and Robert N. Wilson, *The Give and Take in Hospitals*. G. P. Putnam's Sons, New York, 1956, p. 37.

hospitals a decade ago observed: "There is almost no administrative routine established in hospitals which cannot be (and frequently is) abrogated or countermanded by a physician claiming medical emergency—or by anyone acting for the physician claiming medical emergency—or by anyone acting for the physician and similarly claiming medical necessity. Upon close observation," Smith added, "it is found that the actual authority of the medical man in the hospital is very great indeed. Although the conventional organization chart portrays the position of the medical staff as outside the line of authority, we observed physicians . . . exerting power throughout the hospital structure at all levels—upon nurses, ward personnel, upon patients, and even . . . directly upon administrators themselves."[9]

"What the physician had," another observer writes, "at the time when modern medicine had achieved many of its great advances in specific therapies and surgical virtuosity, but when hospitals were yet in a stage of relative organizational simplicity and traditionalism, was a workshop contrived for his convenience and a host of subservient auxiliary personnel. The high tide of the doctor-dominated hospital, perhaps extending from 1900–1950 (although its crest varied by region and type of institution), is preserved in the figure of the great doctor making his ward rounds to the bowing of nurses, the scraping of students, and the worshipful gaze of patients. But this picture of the brigadier inspecting a crack garrison is, like the stereotyped dramatic fiction of Hollywood and ladies' magazines—Dr. Kildare bracing his men (and women) in white—simply an exaggerated telling of the truth that the doctor was not only the central figure in the hospital but a towering one. He gave the orders to nurses, administrators, or whomever, and in his absence the organization ran in deference to precedents he had established or anticipations of those he would establish."[10]

The domination of the hospital by the physician was further increased by his social position in the community. Hospital trustees are selected to a large extent from the social leaders of the community. The leading doctors of the community move in much the same circles, allowing the development of an informal understanding between the two groups. The hospital administrator, on the other hand, as Burling and his associates point out, "rarely has either the income or the social prestige to enable him to share in these relationships. His relations with both board members and staff members are largely confined to hospital business where all are constrained by their particular roles. The fuller and more rounded mutual understanding which develops from more varied interactions doesn't have a chance to develop. The administrator can influence the decisions of the hospital triumvirate only through his formal relationships with the other two, whereas doctors and board members can influence one another and come to agreements about hospital policy during their informal contacts." *[11]

Professionalism is perhaps the most important element of any in this struggle. So long as the physician was the only professional person in the hospital, his authority, by and large, was supreme. His power originated mainly in his professional training and competence, rather than, like the administrator, by specific delegation from the hospital board. The doctor, in this way, had a position of unique independence in the hospital by being able to claim "professional rights" over and above any ruling of the hospital which he might oppose.

This monopoly of professional status in the hospital, however, is no longer clearly the possession of the doctor. Modern medical science, in its applications to practice, has made the doctor dependent upon a team, including an array of so-called "paramedical" personnel. The training and knowledge required for membership on this team has increased rapidly and, as would be expected, the aspirations of the different members of the team have kept pace with their increased responsibility. Nurse, social worker, and technicians have advanced their positions toward the full status of professionals. The administrator, too, moves toward the same goal.

"Today's hospital administrator," Robert Wilson wrote recently, in a study of the changing hospital role of the physician, "is coming to regard himself, and to be regarded, as a full professional. Just as corporate management is becoming profession-

---

* Reprinted by permission of the publisher from Temple Burling, Edith M. Lentz, and Robert N. Wilson, *The Give and Take in Hospitals*. G. P. Putnam's Sons, New York, 1956, p. 37.

alized with the advent of graduate business schools and varieties of executive training programs, so hospital management is now a field for graduate degrees and the appurtenances of a professional elite. Much more than his equivalent in commerce or industry, the hospital executive has felt the need to attain professional status in order to assert himself in an organization of highly schooled and status-assured specialists. His primary aim has been to match the doctor's prestige and formal array of intellectual and social credentials. Despite the formation of a 'college,' the writing of dissertations, and the existence of graduate schools, the administrator does not yet typically radiate the physician's professional splendor. He is gaining fast, however, and, as he does, he inevitably assumes a hospital role which reduces the doctor's charismatic potency. Administrator and M.D. are becoming colleagues in effect, rather than simply in the older titular relationship which masked a master-servant model of collaboration."[12]

This is but one aspect of a complex series of changes in the social organization of the hospital. If we look more closely at the concept of "authority" as it is used in organizational analysis, the full meaning of these changes may become clearer.

The relationship between the hospital administrator and the medical staff has been compared to the relationship in industrial corporations between "line" and "staff." The "line," in industry, is broadly defined as that part of the organization which is primarily concerned with production, or the basic work of making a product. The "staff" contains the operations of planning, designing, and research. In the former are the work crews of production. In the latter are the engineers and, increasingly, the research scientists.

This comparison to industry is fed by some apparent similarities between staff-line conflict and administrator-doctor conflict. On closer examination, however, the comparison is more apparent than real. The antecedents of the conflict within hospitals are quite distinctive from those in the factory. For example, the board of directors of a corporation exerts more authority than its counterpart in the hospital. Corporation directors have financial stake in their organization; members of a hospital board do not. The resulting difference is crucial. Secondly, the hospital administrator's opposite number in industry is the corporation president, chosen by the directors. The corporation president has much more discretionary power than the hospital administrator. A third and most crucial difference is found in the doctor's role. Because of the authority which the doctor derives from his profession, his position cannot be compared directly to any in the corporation. In spite of the changes caused by team medicine, the doctor retains prerogatives as a member of the oldest of the health professions. He was "in the saddle," as it were, for so long that certain rights of seniority continue.

Underlying the whole comparison is the fundamental difference of goals between the two institutions: the profit motive *vis-à-vis* service to the community.

What the hospital does share with the industrial corporation are elements of structure that appear to follow from the process of bureaucratization. Uniquely its own is the "troika" arrangement of authority and the resulting interdependence between the hospital's board, administrator, and medical staff.

Bureaucracy and the processes of social change that lead to its development have been of special interest to sociologists since the origins of modern sociology in the writings of Saint-Simon and Auguste Comte.[13] The next section of this chapter, therefore, will be devoted to bureaucracy as this concept is applied in general organizational analysis, and particularly in studies of the hospital.

Bureaucracy in the Hospital

Hospitals just prior to the modern period were much like small societies in which all the members are relatively visible to each other. Such societies have been described as "simple." This can be misleading. They seem simple because their behavior follows a natural-appearing rhythm, lacking in the specificity and formality that mark more modern urban societies. Actually, codes of behavior are often quite elaborate in preliterate societies as well as in their closest modern counterpart, the rural community. However, such standards characteristically are so implicit and informal that they are difficult for an outsider to comprehend. For the insider, however, they are deeply understood, learned from childhood, and controlled by the immediate disapproval of the community whenever transgression occurs. Anonymity is difficult to achieve in such a society, so that the spontaneous reactions of the community act as a most effective method of control.

Within such societies, the division of labor, insofar as it exists, is usually based upon sex. There is man's work and there is woman's work. Children are exempted only until what to us is usually a very early age, when they are initiated into the status and perform the roles expected of their sex. If the activities of the society require specialization, the skills required are likely to be passed from father to son, or on the basis of some magical or "personal" qualifications.

Hospitals were—and to some extent still are—intimate and traditionalistic societies. ". . . [They were] worlds within themselves," Burling writes. "Many employees lived, worked, ate their meals, and enjoyed fellowship within their walls. The chief division of labor was between men (doctors) and women (nurses). Turnover was slight and tradition was paramount. The individual soon learned what was expected of him, partly because it wasn't very different from what was expected of others, and partly because any attempt on his part to change the pattern was sure to bring forth the protest, 'but we *always* do it this way.'"

". . . With the changing technology and the increasing number of patients," Burling continues, "came a steady increase in the numbers of employees and in the division of labor among them. As people became 'specialists,' e.g., a telephone operator or a receptionist but not both at one time, the old feeling of solidarity was lost. A stage of transition was reached wherein people seemed to have few shared understandings. Communication became a problem."*[14]

Such changes, of course, are typical of a general type of organizational development in modern society, usually described summarily in the term "bureaucratization."

The conditions that produce bureaucracy, more precisely, are: (a) the significant increase of numbers of people, working or

---

* Reprinted by permission of the publisher from Temple Burling, Edith M. Lentz, and Robert N. Wilson, *The Give and Take in Hospitals*. G. P. Putnam's Sons, New York, 1956, p. 318.

living together for common purposes, (b) the growth of technology, (c) the elaboration of a division of labor, and (d) the intensification and expansion of types of specialization. Bureaucracy is specifically a "rational" response to such conditions; that is, it is a type of organization based on the principle that every part or structure and every action of its members are conceived logically for the most efficient achievement of given goals.

A bureaucracy typically includes a series of offices, arranged in a hierarchy of status. The privileges and obligations of each office are defined in detail by highly specific, usually written rules. Qualification for each office is closely defined according to the skills and knowledge required. As a result, offices are filled either through competitive examination, or through appointment based upon a careful review of experience and training.

The advantages of bureaucracy are easy to recognize. Its specific and, therefore, unambiguous requirements for behavior allow the individual to calculate quickly and accurately what to expect from others, as well as how to behave one's self. In effect, interaction is facilitated between offices so that personal animosities can be neutralized or at least subordinated to the effective maintenance of the organization. In this way also subordinates are protected from the arbitrary action of superiors, because the actions of both are prescribed by a set of rules that is mutually recognized.

Such advantages were probably most appealing when western man was closer to the feudal world. Saint-Simon, for example, writing immediately after the French Revolution, accurately anticipated modern bureaucratization and welcomed it as a liberating force. Against his own background, bureaucracy with its emphasis on rational order, and on achieved status, was distinctly a method in the service of freedom. "Saint-Simon argued that, in the society of the future, administrative methods would no longer entail coercion or force, and the administrator's authority would no longer be based upon birth or hereditary privilege. The authority of the modern administrator, he held, would rest upon his possession of scientific skills and 'positive' knowledge."[15]

As feudalism receded into the background, however, a new kind of threat to man's freedom appeared. The "rational" liberation from hereditary privilege was not without cost. Replacing the tyranny of a vested aristocracy, some began to fear, was the tyranny of impersonal mechanized organization, in which man is dehumanized.

Such dangers were observed quite early in the development of modern bureaucracy. Max Weber, in the late nineteenth century, wrote what is still a classic analysis of bureaucracy, foretelling both its advantages and disadvantages. He saw it not only as a rational-legal system, a method for the development of "a scientific society"; he believed that modern bureaucratic organizations would profoundly affect the character of society as a whole. Like other examples which he found in history, Weber perceived bureaucratic structure as a rationally conceived means which, in turn, would become an end in itself. While acknowledging its efficiency, he feared that bureaucracy spelled the destruction of individual personality and subjected it to a "dehumanizing regimentation."[16] Weber was, in other words, a prophet of the nonrational aspects of bureaucracy, anticipating in detail the fears about this organizational form which more recently have been expressed concerning the "organization man."[17]

Whether for good or for evil, however, bureaucracy is an established feature of modern society. To be sure, in the hospital its appearance was delayed, largely because the traditions surrounding the doctor's role were resistant to the formalism of bureaucracy. "When the independent practitioner came to the hospital," Wilson notes, "he essentially wished to preserve [the] . . . doctor-patient relationship undisturbed. If he could keep the relationship free from unsought incursions by the organization, while at the same time taking advantage of what the hospital could offer in the way of technical facilities and therapeutic environment, the physician would clearly enjoy the best of both worlds. To a fairly considerable extent, of course, this is precisely what occurred."[18]

The conditions from which bureaucracy develops would not be denied, however. As the numbers of patients increased and the technology of their care grew more complex, the labor of the hospital divided in elaborate hierarchical form. Wessen, for example, in his study of a New England general hospital (he called it "Yankee Hospital"), found twenty-three different occupational groups represented. These included, in the order of their status ranking:[19]

Physicians:
1. Visiting staff physicians (of various ranks)
2. Residents (and assistant residents)
3. Interns

Nurses:
4. Clinical supervisors and/or instructors
5. Head nurses
6. Staff nurses
7. Student nurses

Paramedical professionals and technicians:
8. Dietitians
9. Laboratory technicians
10. X-ray technicians
11. Social workers
12. Occupational therapists
13. Physical therapists

Semi-skilled workers:
14. Trained attendants (licensed practical nurses)
15. Medical technicians
16. Dietitian's aides
17. Ward receptionists and clerks

Unskilled workers:
18. Nurse's aides
19. Male aides
20. Ward helpers ("Pinkies")
21. Floor service maids
22. Cleaning maids
23. Janitors

Within this carefully arranged hierarchy, there is a dynamic process of specialization and role change going on. The nurse, for example, has expanded the range of her responsibilities to include much that was formerly the monopoly of the physician. The nurse was always responsible for most aspects of the patient's physical and social environment. Now she finds herself assisting the physician in more technically specialized tasks, but also continuing to supervise and perform the large area of functions that are uniquely nursing care, as well as coordinating and making arrangements for carrying out the total plan for patient care.

Of course, the nurse could not be expected to keep adding responsibilities to already demanding old ones. Her adjustment followed closely the bureaucratic model. More and more of the nurse's routine has been delegated to practical nurses, aides, orderlies, and others. Her technical tasks also are shared with technicians, social workers, physical therapists, occupational therapists, and so on. Like the physician, the nurse finds herself less occupied in direct personal care of the patient; instead, she must manage, coordinate, and cooperate in team endeavor.

In the process it is not surprising that the patient has sometimes felt lost. The integration in the hospital of the multitude of divided, subdivided, specialized operations—all designed, of course, to facilitate and improve patient care—became so demanding that orderly management in and of itself has often tended to dominate all else, including the purpose for which it originally was intended. This precisely is what Weber interpreted to be the great problem of bureaucracy, the enhancement of its rationally conceived method into an end in itself.

Two closely related developments stand out in the bureaucratization of the hospital: the first is the emergence of a "team" approach to medical care, and the second is the dynamic role change that is occurring for all the major participants. We have presented only a brief view of these developments, but hopefully enough to draw attention to the importance of current attempts to mobilize into efficient operation the complex technological and human relations problems of modern medicine without neglecting in the process the equally demanding emotional and social needs of the patient.

To bring these problems into clearer focus, two case examples are presented at this point.

The first case is an example of successful adaptation to change, in which we see the troika of authority pulling together.

Case 1. An Example of Functional Adaptation*[20]

This was a city hospital which had a close association with a medical school. Both hospital and school were venerable institutions with reputations for being among the best in their part of the continent. The board was composed of leading citizens who employed a superintendent to carry out their wishes. Board decisions were influenced to some extent by "top flight doctors," which is to say, men who were widely recognized in their community for professional skill, large practices, and good reputations. The concern of the board, medical staff, and administrator was to continue the excellent reputation of the hospital in that city. The local community, it might be said, was the standard against which they measured themselves and their achievements.

As times changed, the hospital prospered outwardly, growing in size and in the number of its patients and employees. The administrator added an assistant. However, in the meanwhile developments in medical education elsewhere were beginning to place this hospital at a disadvantage. The rise of heavily endowed metropolitan medical centers staffed by full-time faculty members with national reputations made it increasingly difficult to attract students and interns to a school and hospital where private practitioners with only local reputations continued to teach in their spare time.

When the hospital authorities became aware that even the sons of its most prominent doctors were going elsewhere for training, they faced a crisis. The hospital had to rise to meet the competition it was receiving from medical centers elsewhere, or else accept a permanent second-class position. Many other hospitals may have faced a similar situation with less in resources for meeting it. This one was not poor but like other hospitals it had many other financial drains upon it at this time. Nevertheless, it decided to accept the challenge. The decision was made to hire full-time staff men with international reputations based upon scientific publications and leadership. These men were given the task of reorganizing the teaching and research programs. To interest them and to hold their loyalty, the hospital had to offer them joint hospital-university appointments and to allow them full freedom to do research and teaching as they saw fit.

The presence of these men changed relationships in many parts of the hospital in very subtle but pervasive ways. There was no formal

* Reprinted by permission of the publisher from Temple Burling, Edith M. Lentz, and Robert N. Wilson, *The Give and Take in Hospitals*. G. P. Putnam's Sons, New York, 1956, pp. 67–68.

or legal change. The board and its administrator still had unquestioned authority to make and enforce policy decisions. But one does not tell a man internationally respected for research what he is to do. One discusses with him possible alternatives and welcomes his participation in making decisions. More day-to-day freedom was accorded these new department heads than had been given in the past, and more people had effective voice in decisions than before.

. . . In this hospital the distribution of power became modified. Authority became increasingly functional [that is, based upon the ability to do work, as opposed to "position authority," based upon place in a hierarchy], with considerable range for autonomy within their own fields being permitted for those of recognized competence.

The medical staff, some of whom had approved this series of innovations and some of whom had not, began to be caught up in the after-effects. There was a quickening of professional growth throughout the staff. The doctors were also aware that the medical field was advancing by strides and that to maintain status they would have to put forth effort to keep up and to achieve recognition for competence from their own professional associations. It might be said that the total environment was stimulating individuals to grow while, in turn, these individuals by growing helped to stimulate each other, thus increasing the tempo of total change. There was a period of almost universal striving on the part of individuals and groups.

The administrators were in the forefront of all these developments, smoothing the way for them and struggling to keep abreast of change too. . . . They relished the struggle and soon became leaders in their own professional organizations, encouraging the pooling of knowledge and techniques among administrators from all over the nation. In other words, just as the doctors were becoming specialists, so were they. They kept pace.

What would have happened to them if they hadn't continued to grow? Would they have been able to coordinate effectively their increasingly alert and ambitious staff? As it was, the board, the administration, and the medical staff were growing and changing all at the same time and in so doing, kept and renewed the respect they held for one another. No one group could afford to shrug off the opinions of another, for all were of recognized competence in their own area.

It should by no means be assumed that human relations in this hospital were entirely comfortable. Probably there were just as many problems as in any other institution, but to the outsider it appeared that a feeling of accomplishment underlay the ebb and flow of daily events. People were too busy to fret much about changes in personal advantage from one week to the next. Each was hard at work, growing with the institution. There was a common pride in their individual progress and in belonging to an organization that was recognized by all as increasing in esteem both locally and nationally.

Needless to say, relationships within the hospital "troika" do not always work out as well as they did in the hospital just described. There remains in many, if not most, hospitals a lack of clear definition of the major roles. Even though, as has been observed, the modern hospital has almost nothing in common with the medieval institution from which it has grown, many medieval customs persist. The doctor, for example, often does not seem fully aware of the implications of his change of interest and activity in the hospital. When he was a marginal figure, with little more than a charitable interest in the unfortunate poor who were the hospital's inmates, it was appropriate for him to be a privileged guest who did not concern himself with the administrative problems. Now that the hospital is the center of his activities, he cannot avoid new responsibilities that inevitably follow from being a full-time participant. To keep these new responsibilities in balance with the professional requirements of the physician's role has created a problem of profound adjustment for the doctor.

Similarly, the modern administrator resembles only broadly his predecessor, the hospital superintendent. In place of the direct control over housekeeping functions that he exerted in the past, he now must deal with an elaborate organization, in which he must coordinate more than directly control. "The administrator today," the Burling study concluded, "has responsibilities so complex that he must have expert knowledge in many fields in order to cope with them effectively. When he acquires such knowledge, he gains respect and stature in his relationship with his board and medical staff and frequently is given considerably more room to exert personal initiative than in the past. At the same time, the scope for initiative of his subordinates has also increased. They too have become expert in more complex tasks and require a greater degree of freedom in meeting their professional responsibilities. The administrator therefore has had to develop new skills as coordinator, a more subtle form of leadership in place of the direct authority he may have exerted in the past." *[21]

It is not surprising that, as each finds his role radically altered, the doctor and the hospital administrator often are in conflict. The second case illustration has been chosen specifically to show how some of the developments we have been discussing can produce an intense strain in the relationships between the physician and members of his hospital team.

CASE 2. AN EXAMPLE OF ROLE CONFLICT [22]

Aprilton, a small voluntary hospital in the southern part of the United States, has in recent years been the scene of dramatic change. This change involves a basic reorganization of the hospital and a drastic redefinition of the doctor's role. Aprilton is an especially revealing case for analysis because its traditional character has lain at the opposite pole from the large metropolitan teaching hospital; in a very real sense it has "furthest to go" in becoming a rational bureaucratic structure, and its medical staff is exposed to a more disturbing revision of roles than are the cosmopolitan physicians of large medical centers. The hospital is semi-rural, relatively small, and dedicated to healing as its only medical goal. It has been without the formal hierarchy of medical functions which accompanies a teaching program, and without the stimulating experimental atmosphere of research in progress. Aprilton is not, then, "typical" of American hospitals other than those classified as "small, rural, voluntary nonteaching"; yet, in the study of organizations, as in the study of individual personality, an abnormal case may illuminate patterns of maintenance and pathology more clearly than does an average institution.

Doctors have been the unchallenged masters of Aprilton throughout its history. The hospital administrator had, until the late 1940's, always been a nurse, frankly subordinate to the medical staff, accustomed to the role of handmaiden and faithful follower of orders. Only loose guidance had been exercised by the board of managers [the trustees], who are described as rarely visiting the hospital and primarily concerned that the books balanced. Aprilton, as a private institu-

* Reprinted with permission of the publisher from Temple Burling, Edith M. Lentz, and Robert N. Wilson, *The Give and Take in Hospitals*. G. P. Putnam's Sons, New York, 1956, p. 70.

tion, had not evolved any significant close relationships with its surrounding community and was quite free from public surveillance.

The summary picture is that of a hospital as private preserve of the medical staff, in which the doctor's role corresponded neatly to the classic model of independent entrepreneur, charismatically endowed. Something of the quality of hospital and doctor is seen in the nostalgic comment of an elderly lady who had been administrator in the good old days which for this institution were not long past:

"The doctors here have lost face and I can't see that. I don't think you can treat doctors the way they do [now, i.e., during the period of role-revision] and not have it hurt patient-doctor relationships. Now in the old days the doctor sat beside your bed and held your hand and that doctor-patient relationship meant something. Every family had its own doctor and next to the minister, he was the closest friend the family had. They believed in him absolutely and when you got sick and he came and held your hand as your friend, it meant something to you. Now that has gone. It has all gone. . . ."

What had happened to shatter this beneficent professional image? A genuine crisis in hospital affairs occurred when the board of managers faced twin situations of deterioration, in the quality of medical care and in the hospital's physical plant. The immediate threat was possible loss of malpractice insurance. To meet these hazards, the board secured Hill-Burton Act funds for physical reconstruction and appointed the first male professional administrator in Aprilton's history to reorganize hospital activities, primarily those of the medical staff. These moves resulted in the hospital's rising from a rating of 45 per cent adequacy in 1949 to 77 per cent in 1953, graded by American College of Surgeons' standards. In such a process of thoroughgoing and rapid change someone often gets hurt or at least feels hurt. Here, the principal injured "someone" was the doctors.

The newly appointed administrator, Mr. Madison, was a man in his middle thirties, experienced in hospital work, a registered nurse, and holder of a bachelor's degree in hospital administration. He considered himself a full professional, of stature equal to the doctors, and with a mandate to make Aprilton administratively sound according to current criteria of organization. Primary support for his moves came from the trustees, who had been forced by the crisis to interest themselves in modern administrative practice and to look beyond their local situation to national authorities [accrediting bodies] for counsel and example. He reported that his main opposition stemmed from the medical staff.

Mr. Hartnett, president of the board of managers, had assumed this position in 1949 and had been instrumental in hiring the new administrator. He recalled that, prior to this time, the board had conceived of its duties as simply those of checking with the administrator periodically to ensure that income matched outgo. But Mr. Hartnett immediately performed an act of rational trusteeship: he read, marked, learned, and inwardly digested a standard text on hospital management. His reading, coupled with the board's growing apprehension concerning malpractice insurance, led to Madison's appointment and to serious consultations with the head of an outstanding medical school, as well as with officials of the American College of Surgeons.

It is unnecessary to rehearse the junctures at which the board-supported administrator and the medical staff found themselves in conflict. These foci of difference ranged from the regulation of surgery and surgical privileges to the hiring and firing of nurses. What the trouble spots had in common was a progressive enlargement of the administrator's sphere of authority and a narrowing of the doctor's previous hospital role. Always in the background was the trustees' newly exercised power and their refusal to let the medical staff short-circuit the administrator by solving problems on a doctor-trustee basis. As Hartnett, the president, noted:

"Every once in awhile, a doctor will come and want to talk things over with me and I just won't hear of it. If it's something concerning the administrator, I think he should be in on it."

Dr. James, chief of the medical staff, commented on this situation:

"You take things up with the administrator and nothing happens, and when you go to the board, they tell you that you should go to the administrator not to them. You just go round and round."

It seems clear that patterns of communication are not entirely well arranged at Aprilton, and the physician can by no means be made the sole analytical scapegoat. Yet the statements strongly imply that one locus of strain inheres in the doctor's role change: the diffusion and formalization of authority tend to trap the free-wheeling professional in channels to which he is unaccustomed. One can see what it means to a traditionally high-status doctor to *have* to "go round and round." Important, too, is the doctor's habit of informal authority, which in days past could often be exerted directly on trustees in contexts outside the hospital; before the advent of the professional administrator, doctors and trustees might easily reach an accord in club or private home to be later presented to the much lower-status administrator as a *fait accompli.*

Dr. James goes on to describe a specific instance of "interference" with medical staff prerogatives:

"We think the technique in the nursery isn't what it should be. We think they should be careful with the use of sterile procedures, but when we say something about it, they tell us that it is none of our business. Now I think it stands to reason that doctors are in a better position to see what the nurse does or doesn't do than the administrator is, for the simple reason that we're working up on the floor and he's working down here. When we talk to him about it, he says that's interfering with the personnel."

In his older charismatic and functionally diffuse role, everything was legitimately the doctor's business. Now he is patently losing control over some features of his environment. The administrator, as a professional with a defined competence of his own, may appear both impertinent and ambiguous. Mr. Hartnett, when questioned about administrator-medical staff relations, said:

"Well, that's [the administrator's role] their main gripe to tell you the truth. You see they had always had things their own way. The former administrator gave the doctors just about anything they wanted. Not that it got her any place. They were on her neck night and day too. Now with Mr. Madison, he is a professionally trained person. That's what I keep hammering at them. He has had just as much professional training as they have had themselves but they can't understand that. They don't know how to take him."

And again:

"You know doctors are really funny. They are accustomed to interfering at every step of the way. They want to tell us how much we should charge the patients, how we should select our nurses, whom we should fire, and so on. Madison tells them that it's none of their damned business and it isn't."

A final aspect of the Aprilton case is of interest because it illustrates several themes in addition to those of bureaucratization and the rise of the administrator. The necessity for medical staff reorganization, especially in relation to surgical practice, brings out the way in which increasing medical specialization restricts the doctor's autonomy. Said Dr. James:

"I felt my privileges in the operating room should be changed to major instead of minor but nothing happens. . . . Some of the doctors don't get the privileges they feel they're entitled to. The privileges you get depend on when you first started to practice around here. You see, they have changed the rules."

The fine division of labor in modern medicine, and the introduction of rational criteria for gauging performance, mean that rules must change. Traditionally flexible medical roles become less secure. The medical staff, a group historically unregulated, must now impose on itself rather precise regulations.

Aprilton presents a picture of resistance by the physician to the role changes demanded by bureaucratization. Blocked in the use of familiar informal channels of authority, the Aprilton doctor responded with resistance to change and with frustration. The fact remains that a complex bureaucratic hospital has become the environment of much or most of the modern doctor's work. That he must accommodate to the new and often unfamiliar role demands of this environment, even though a radical revision of his self-image may be required, would seem to be an undeniable reality.

The picture we have drawn, because of its emphasis on change in terms of what the doctor must give up, may appear unintentionally bleak. The hospital, as Wilson comments in his interpretation of the Aprilton example, will continue to lean heavily on the doctor's special skills, "even while modifying his traditional role conception to accord with bureaucratic imperatives. If his role must change, it must also remain the same in certain important respects. In many situations, perhaps most notably surgery, his authority must be unquestioned. His relationship with the patient will retain a hard core of emotional interchange, of nonrational or even mystical elements, as an essential component of therapy. He will continue as a bridge between hospital, patient, and community, often softening the impact of the organization on the individual patient and interpreting one to the other. In the long run, the shaping of the doctor's hospital role may well afford a crucial limiting case, a test of the limits in the bureaucratization of the free professional. In microcosm, the relation of the medical expert to administrative and organizational *desiderata* rehearses what Zimmern remarked as the central problem of modern society: the right relation between knowledge and power."[23]

Summary[24]

The hospital has become one of the complex bureaucratic organizations of the modern western world. It has also taken a place at the focal center of modern medicine. In the wake of the former development have come a variety of problems that lend themselves to direct comparison with other typical organizations of our time, including the industrial corporation. As the "temple of medical science," however, the hospital has a uniqueness that defies comparison.

One of the special organizational features of the hospital is its tripartite source of authority, a troika composed of the hospital administrator, the board of trustees, and the medical chief of staff. Past advantages of the doctor as the final arbiter of authority have gradually diminished in the face of two outstanding developments in the bureaucratization process: (a) the emergence of the team approach to medical care, and (b) the resulting dynamic role changes for all of the hospital's major participants.

The physician's former monopoly of professionalism is gone. He grows increasingly dependent on a variety of skilled helpers who inevitably lay claim themselves to the professional rights and privileges that fit their rapidly developing skills and responsibilities.

In spite of the dynamic changes, however, the top billing in the hospital drama still goes to two actors: the doctor and the patient. In our discussion of the hospital up to this point, the emphasis has been on the physician and his medical team. This is appropriate for the general hospital where, by and large, the patient is cast in a passive role. We turn now to the mental hospital where the situation of the patient is reversed and he is an active, vital part of the social system.

NOTES TO CHAPTER 7

1. Wilson, Robert N., "The Physician's Changing Hospital Role," *Human Organization*, vol. 18, Winter, 1959–1960, p. 177.

2. The models of the doctor-patient relationship described in Chapter 1 (pp. 40–42) are based on a similar observation. See Szasz, T. S., and M. H. Hollender, "A Contribution to the Philosophy of Medicine: The Basic Models of the Doctor-Patient Relationship," *A.M.A. Archives of Internal Medicine*, vol. 97, May, 1956, p. 585.

3. Wessen, Albert F., "Hospital Ideology and Communication Between Ward Personnel" in Jaco, E. Gartly, editor, *Patients, Physicians, and Illness*. The Free Press, Glencoe, Ill., 1958, pp. 448–468.

4. Fox, Renée C., *Experiment Perilous*. The Free Press, Glencoe, Ill., 1959.

5. Burling, Temple, Edith M. Lentz, and Robert N. Wilson, *The Give and Take in Hospitals*. G. P. Putnam's Sons, New York, 1956, p. xv.

6. The incident in question began when the Russians introduced a proposal designed to change the office of the Secretary-General of the United Nations into a three-man secretariat. President Kennedy answered metaphorically. The Russians, said the President, were proposing a troika, with its picturesque team of three horses, harnessed side by side. It was a feat, the President added, to keep three horses pulling together; how much more difficult would it be in the organization of men.

7. See Simmel, George, "Quantitative Aspects of the Groups" in *The Sociology of George Simmel*, edited by Kurt Wolff, The Free Press, Glencoe, Ill., 1950, pp. 85–177; Mills, T. M., "Power Relations in Three-Person Groups" in Cartwright, D., and A. Zander, editors, *Group Dynamics*, Row, Peterson and Co., Evanston, Ill., 1953, pp. 428–442; Mills, T. M., "The Coalition Pattern in Three-Person Groups," *American Sociological Review*, vol. 19, 1954, pp. 657–667

8. Burling, Lentz, and Wilson, *op. cit.*, p. 37.

9. Smith, Harvey L., "Two Lines of Authority: The Hospital's Dilemma" in Jaco, E. Gartly, *op. cit.*, p. 469.

10. Wilson, Robert N., *op. cit.*, p. 178.

11. Burling, Lentz, and Wilson, *op. cit.*, p. 37.

12. Wilson, Robert N., *op. cit.*, p. 180.

13. See Gouldner, Alvin W., "Organizational Analysis" in Merton, Robert K., Leonard Broom, and Leonard S. Cottrell, Jr., editors, *Sociology Today: Problems and Prospects*, Basic Books, Inc., New York, 1959, pp. 400–428.

14. Burling, Lentz, and Wilson, *op. cit.*, p. 318.

15. Gouldner, Alvin M., *op. cit.*, p. 402.

16. *Ibid.*, p. 402.

17. See Whyte, William H., Jr., *The Organization Man*, Simon and Schuster, Inc., New York, 1956; Mills, C. Wright, *White Collar*, Oxford University Press, New York, 1951, and as a Galaxy Book (paperback) in 1956 and 1961.

18. Wilson, Robert N., *op. cit.*, p. 178.
19. Wessen, Albert F., *op. cit.*, p. 450.
20. Burling, Lentz, and Wilson, *op. cit.*, pp. 67–68. This entire case is quoted directly from the Burling, Lentz, and Wilson study. (See note 5.)
21. *Ibid.*, p. 70.
22. Wilson, Robert N., *op. cit.*, pp. 180–182. The case study is based upon field research conducted by Edith M. Lentz of the University of Minnesota.
23. *Ibid.*, p. 183. The remark by Zimmern is quoted from Sir Arthur Zimmern's *The Greek Commonwealth*, The Clarendon Press, Oxford, England, 1931.
24. As a general reference for this chapter, see Brown, Esther Lucile, *Newer Dimensions of Patient Care:* Part I, The Use of the Physical and Social Environment of the General Hospital for Therapeutic Purposes, 1961, and Part II, Improving Staff Motivation and Competence in the General Hospital, Russell Sage Foundation, New York, 1962.

Chapter 8

SOME EARLY CONTRIBUTIONS TO A SOCIOLOGY OF THE MENTAL HOSPITAL

IN THE HALF-CENTURY preceding World War II, "hospital care" came to be synonymous with "doctor's care," in both the general and specialized institutions. In effect, the hospital functioned as an expanded waiting and examining room, a special accommodation for the physician. Therapy was conceived of as the time spent with the doctor, or under the specific orders of the doctor. All else was secondary. Even the nurse was an instrument, more or less, primarily designed to carry out the doctor's orders. For the patient, the hospital was a place for two distinctly different experiences: there was the doctor's "therapy," and, lumped together, all the rest. For the hospital staff, the dichotomy was similar. There was the specifically therapeutic part of their job, and the rest was "custodial."

The attitudes associated with the therapy-custody dichotomy may have been appropriate for the acute and dramatic types of illness which dominated the general hospital until a short time ago. However, when medical science gained control over the most dangerous elements of acute infections, such attitudes became distinctly inappropriate. The reaction of the health professions since World War II has been to shift the view of the patient into a new perspective. The twenty-three or more "other" hours of the patient's day, the nondoctor hours so to speak, are being regarded as important in their own right. The patient's total experience in the hospital has come into the focus of therapeutic concern, replacing the preoccupation with the doctor's fraction alone. This observation applies to the hospital care of all types of illness; chronic illness, however, and particularly psychiatric illness were affected to a greater degree than others.

The period since World War II has witnessed a remarkable effort to understand the contributions to therapy that adhere to the hospital as a *total* social experience. In this chapter some of the background that contributed to this effort will be reviewed.

The Therapeutic Community: Some Early Examples

Although all of hospital care currently is taking a fresh look at "the other twenty-three hours," it was in the mental hospital that this shift in attitude started. Two papers by Harry Stack Sullivan in 1931[1,2] are generally used to date the beginning of what has since become a movement to create in the mental hospital a "therapeutic community."

Almost twenty-five years earlier, however, a remarkable book appeared that certainly must have helped to prepare the groundwork for Sullivan's new approach, just as it did for the whole mental health movement. This was Clifford Beers' autobiographical account of his own experiences as a patient, entitled *A Mind That Found Itself*.*[3]

At the time, Beers' primary purpose was to indict the brutality and neglect that prevailed fifty years ago in American mental hospitals. In this purpose, he succeeded brilliantly; the well-justified outrage that burst from the pages of his book served as a powerful catalyst to arouse public pressure for reform. Quite apart from his skill as a muckraker, however, there is another side to his story that has been much less noticed. His description of the hospital as a social environment is detailed and perceptive. Moreover, in his accounts of the importance of fellow patients for his own recovery, he anticipates the later theoretical conceptions of Sullivan and others.

---

* From *A Mind That Found Itself* by Clifford W. Beers. Copyright 1907, 1917, 1921, 1923, 1931, 1932, 1934, 1935, 1937, 1939, 1940, 1942, 1944, 1948, 1953, by the American Foundation for Mental Hygiene, Inc. Reprinted by permission of Doubleday and Company, Inc., New York.

Passages from this book are cited in "Notes to Chapter 8" on page 207.

"One of the greatest secret societies in the world," said Beers, "is the psychiatric hospital." As he entered this society, Beers first records the experience of a "rather agreeable routine," where, in spite of "the delusions which held me a prisoner of the police, and kept me a stranger to my old world," there was nevertheless a "new feeling of contentment." This new sense of well-being, he stated, had not been brought about by any marked improvement in health. Instead, he credited the environment which he called "more nearly in tune with my ill turned mind."[4]

In part, Beers explained this in negative terms; that is, the act of *leaving the scene* of his breakdown relieved his disturbance. "While surrounded by sane people," he writes, "my mental inferiority had been painfully apparent to me as well as to others." Reinforcing his sense of relief at leaving what had become a strange and threatening environment, was his discovery of fellow patients who were "in the same boat." The recognition of the fact that he was not alone in his state of illness became an important step toward the braking of its harmful effects.

Sullivan later was to make some closely parallel observations about the first stages of hospitalization. Psychosis itself he regarded as "disordered interpersonal relations nucleating . . . in a particular person."[5] He believed that the first step toward "social recovery," which he differentiated from "personal recovery," was to remove the patient from an environment in which the patient must feel great insecurity about his status to one in which he could feel a sympathy in the sameness of others. Just this, Sullivan believed, was achieved by admission to a custodial institution.[6]

Help came more directly to Beers during the next phase of his experience in the hospital in the form of a friendship with a fellow patient. Only through this friend was he able to place a limit on his delusional system.

Convinced in his illness that he was under constant surveillance by the law, Beers at first trusted no one. Even his brother was seen as an officer in disguise. As soon as he accepted the fact that he was among insane people, he was able to relate to his fellow patients because, as he put it, "[they] were really insane, and therefore [I believed] disqualified as competent witnesses in a court of law."

Therefore, following the inverted logic of his delusion, he could trust them. One of these fellow patients became a particularly close friend. Through this friend Beers was able to engage in a process of "testing reality" which was crucial for his recovery. No member of the staff could function in a similar way because, by the very nature of his delusion, the staff were perceived as spies for the legal authorities.

Because this is so vivid an example of the natural history of mental illness, and also because it is so instructive a case for the theses that will be developed later concerning the patient culture of the hospital, the initiation of Beers into the patient world and his subsequent utilization of it for therapeutic gain will be reproduced here in detail. Following is Beers' own description of his first steps "outside himself," toward a meaningful contact with another human being:

> A man who during his life had more than once been committed to an institution took a very evident interest in me and persisted in talking to me, often much against my will. . . . He finally gave me my confidence to such a degree that months before I finally began to talk to others I permitted myself to converse frequently with him—but only when we were so situated as to escape observation. I would talk to him on almost any subject, but would not speak about myself. At length, however, his admirable persistence overcame my reticence. During a conversation held in June, 1902, he abruptly said, "Why you are kept here I cannot understand. Apparently you are as sane as anyone. You have never made any but sensible remarks to me." Now for weeks I had been waiting for a chance to tell this man my very thoughts. I had come to believe him a true friend who would not betray me.
>
> "If I should tell you some things which you apparently don't know, you would understand why I am held here," I said.
>
> "Well, tell me," he urged.
>
> "Will you promise not to repeat my statements to anyone else?"
>
> "I promise not to say a word."
>
> "Well," I remarked, "You have seen certain persons who have come here, professing to be relatives of mine."
>
> "Yes, and they are your relatives, aren't they?"
>
> "They look like my relatives, but they're not," was my reply.

> My inquisitive friend burst into laughter and said, "Well, if you mean *that*, I shall have to take back what I just said. You are really the craziest person I have ever met, and I have met several."
> "You will think differently someday," I replied; for I believed that when my trial should occur, he would appreciate the significance of my remarks.[7]

These remarks of repudiation from a fellow patient, which, if they had come from a member of the hospital staff, would at best have only reinforced Beers' delusions, did not upset their relationship. Instead, Beers was encouraged to use his fellow patient as what he called his own private detective. Since the patient-friend had leave privileges to visit the nearby town, Beers decided to use him to check the circumstances of the "crime," which was the central event in his delusions. Although he rationalized that, in this way, he would convince his friend to become his ally against his persecutors, actually Beers appears to have been using his friend to test his own sense of reality against its contradictions by the hospital staff and visitors. There resulted the following incident, which proved to be a turning point in Beers' illness:[8]

> My friend had not stopped trying to convince me that my apparent relatives were not spurious; so one day I said to him: "If my relatives still live in New Haven, their addresses must be in the latest New Haven directory. Here is a list containing the names and former addresses of my father, brother, and uncle. These were their addresses in 1900. Tomorrow, when you go out, please see whether they appear in the New Haven directory for 1902. These persons who present themselves to me as relatives pretend to live at these addresses. If they speak the truth, the 1902 directory will corroborate them. I shall then have hope that a letter sent to any one of these addresses will reach relatives—and surely some attention will be paid to it."
> The next day, my own good detective went to a local publishing house where directories of important cities throughout the country could be consulted . . . [My fellow patient] returned and informed me that the latest New Haven directory contained the names and addresses I had given him. This information . . . did convince me that my real brother still lived where he did when I left New Haven, two years earlier. Now that my delusions were growing weaker, my

returning reason enabled me to construct the ingenious scheme which, I believe, saved my life; for, had I not largely regained my reason when I did, I am inclined to believe that my distraught mind would have destroyed itself and me, before it could have been restored by the slow process of returning health.

A few hours after my own private detective had given me the information I so much desired, I wrote the first letter I had written in twenty-six months. As letters go, it is in a class by itself. I dared not ask for ink, so I wrote with a lead pencil. Another fellow patient, in whom I had confidence, at my request addressed the envelope; but he was not in on the secret of its contents. This was an added precaution, for I thought the Secret Service men might have found out that I had a detective of my own and would confiscate any letters addressed by him or me. The next morning, my "detective" mailed the letter. That letter I still have, and I treasure it as any innocent man condemned to death would treasure a pardon. It should convince the reader that sometimes a mentally disordered person, even one suffering from many delusions, can think and write clearly. An exact copy of this—the most important letter I ever expect to be called upon to write—is here presented:

August 29, 1902

DEAR GEORGE:

On last Wednesday morning a person who claimed to be George M. Beers of New Haven, Connecticut, Clerk in the Director's Office of the Sheffield Scientific School and a brother of mine, called to see me.

Perhaps what he said was true, but after the events of the last two years I find myself inclined to doubt the truth of everything that is told me. He said that he would come and see me again sometime next week, and I am sending you this letter in order that you may bring it with you as a passport, provided you *are* the one who was here on Wednesday.

If you did not call as stated, please say nothing about this letter to anyone, and when your double arrives, I'll tell him what I think of him. Would send other messages, but while things seem as they do at present, it is impossible. Have had someone else address envelope for fear letter might be held up on the way.

Yours,
CLIFFORD W. B.

Within twenty-four hours, Beers was informed that his brother was coming to see him. Still skeptical, he waited till the afternoon. The meeting he describes as follows:

> I wandered about the lawn and cast frequent and expectant glances toward the gate, through which I believed my anticipated visitor would soon pass. In less than an hour he appeared. I first caught sight of him about three hundred feet away, and, impelled more by curiosity than hope, I advanced to meet him. "I wonder what the lie will be this time," was the gist of my thoughts.
>
> The person approaching me was indeed the counterpart of my brother as I remembered him. Yet he was no more my brother than he had been at any time during the preceding two years. He was still a detective. Such he was when I shook his hand. As soon as that ceremony was over, he drew forth a leather pocketbook. I instantly recognized it as one I had myself carried for several years prior to the time I was taken ill in 1900. It was from this that he took my recent letter.
>
> "Here is my passport," he said.
>
> "It's a good thing you brought it," I replied, as I glanced at it and again shook his hand—this time the hand of my own brother.

In retelling this story here, attention is directed to the significance of his patient-friend in Beers' steps toward recovery. Through a fellow patient, he was able to work out some of his problems in ways that were not possible with the hospital staff. Of course, it must be added that the kind of treatment Beers received from his physicians is not likely to be encountered anywhere today. Nevertheless, the fact remains that today, just as in Beers' experience, the mental patient can expect contact with physicians and other trained professionals only during a relatively brief part of his day. During the "other twenty-three hours," as recent studies document, a subculture or "patient's world" evolves with its own ways of initiating, socializing, and controlling the behavior of its members.

The question that has been raised is what, more exactly, is contributed to the therapeutic process from the patient's total social experience, including his participation in a "patient world." During the past decade, a series of descriptive studies of patient social life have been conducted, aimed at the answer of this question. Much of the groundwork for such study, however, was provided by the autobiographical accounts of Beers and others.[9,10,11,12]

These autobiographical accounts agree on the general pattern of the hospital experience. They describe an early stage of dependence by the new patient upon fellow patients. He is taught, first of all, *how to behave* in his new role as a hospital patient. Like Beers, an important set of psychological responses seem companion to this phase. It is a time for "finding one's self." "Who am I?" The patient seems to be asking, like a child. "What was I?" and, "What will I become?"

For the patient who, by definition, is in a disturbed relationship to the realities of his customary existence, this is a critical stage. As Beers put it so dramatically, "had I not regained my reason [by which he meant a restoration of contact with reality in the form of his brother and his 'own private detective'] when I did, I am inclined to believe that my distraught mind would have destroyed itself and me before it could have been restored by the slow process of returning health." Yet unless the fact and function of such experience is understood by hospital authorities, there are dangers for the patient even in the successful accomplishment of the first step in recovery which, in the passage above, is described by Beers. For, having tested and conquered his main delusions, Beers' general behavior took a radical turn. From a passive dependent, withdrawn state, he became assertive and independent. A new kind of testing seemed to engross him, not of the *fact* of reality, but of the *limits* of reality.

What Beers describes as therapeutic progress, however, was not so interpreted by the staff of the several hospitals in which he was a patient. Rather, his change from a stuporous but quiet patient into an articulate, energetic, and assertive one was interpreted as an increase of disturbance. Similar experiences are described by virtually all the published autobiographical patient writings.

Part of the expression of this change, for Beers, was a new type of relationship with fellow patients. From the one who needed help, Beers became the helper. In this phase of his illness, like his own "private detective" had done earlier, he "took a stranger," as he put it, under a protecting and commodious wing:

Mr. Blank [as I shall call him] was completely unnerved . . . I did all I could to cheer him up, and tried to secure for him that consideration which to me seemed indispensable to his well-being. Patients in his condition had never been forced, when taking their exercise, to walk about the grounds with other patients. At no time during the preceding fourteen months had I seen a newly committed patient forced to exercise against his will. One who objected was invariably left in the ward, or his refusal was reported to the doctor before further action was taken. No sane person need stretch his imagination in order to realize how humiliating it would be for this man to walk with a crowd which greatly resembled "a chain gang." Two-by-two, under guard, these hostages of misfortune get the only long walks their restricted liberty allows them. After the one or two occasions when this man did walk with the gang, I was impressed with the not wholly unreasonable thought that the physical exercise in no way compensated for the mental distress which the mental humiliation and disgrace caused him to suffer. It was delightfully easy for me to interfere in his behalf; and when he came to my room, wrought up over the prospect of another such humiliation, and weeping bitterly, I assured him that he should take his exercise that day when I did. My first move to accomplish the desired result was to approach, in a friendly way, the attendant in charge, and ask him to permit my new friend to walk about the grounds with me when next I went. He said he would do nothing of the kind—that he intended to take this man when he took the others. I said, "For over a year I have been in this ward and so have you, and I have never yet seen a man in Mr. Blank's condition forced to go out of doors."

"It makes no difference whether you have or not," said the attendant, "he's going."

"Will you ask the doctor whether Mr. Blank can or cannot walk about the grounds with my special attendant when I go?"

"No, I won't. Furthermore, it's none of your business."

"If you resort to physical force and attempt to take Mr. Blank with the other patients, you'll wish you hadn't," I said, as I walked away.[13]

It is not necessary to describe further this incident here, except to say that Beers carried out his threat and was, as a result, subjected to extreme restraint and isolation. His resort to physical means to help his patient-friend was interpreted by the hospital staff as a symptom of his illness.

In the context of this discussion, there are two important facts about this incident. First, there is the understanding and protection which is given to Mr. Blank by Beers, his fellow patient. Just as had been true for Beers earlier, there were important therapeutic functions in this type of relationship which were difficult or impossible to replicate in a relationship with either attendant or staff physician. Second, there is the hospital staff's convenient and even reasonable diagnosis of Beers' violent behavior as symptomatic of his manic phase of illness, while actually his resort to violence against the unyielding coercion of an attendant would seem quite "normal" under other circumstances. A further question may be raised concerning the roots of the attendant's behavior. As we shall see in later discussion of the studies of Stanton and Schwartz[14] and Caudill,[15] behavior by the staff that is rooted in frustration and conflict in the "staff world" may act indirectly to cause eruptions of disturbance among patients. Although the ways in which patients express their disturbance may be characteristic of their individual illnesses, they may still be responding in a collective way to influences that come from the adjacent staff world.

These two important steps in Beers' mental illness, one involving emergence from an extremely withdrawn, isolated psychological state toward trust and communication with another human being, and the other his assertion of independence and belief in himself by helping another patient, both were accomplished *in spite of* rather than *with* the help of his physicians and the hospital staff. The reasons were part of the conception of mental illness which prevailed at the time. The mentally ill, or "insane," were perceived as incurable, and illness was believed to be caused by irreversible lesions in the brain. The result was the practice of custody for the insane rather than treatment in the medical sense. Policies were designed to restrain the patient from violent and harmful behavior as protection of the community and, to some extent, as protection of the patient from himself. The acceptance of the stereotype of the insane as violent and dangerous to society undoubtedly contributed to the practice of establishing hospitals in isolated rural areas. This geographic location of the mental hospital, plus the general sense of hopelessness associated with care of the insane and the high cost of long term care, made the recruiting and retaining of professional staff difficult. The brutal and inhumane consequences in both private and public institutions were vividly described by Beers.

Yet, almost a century earlier, there had flourished in the United States an enlightened and effective management of mental diseases that was called "moral treatment." The methods of "moral treatment" are very similar to those that are increasingly being reinstated in mental hospitals today. Moreover, the results, measured in terms of cure, were remarkably good. How then, one must ask, could the changes in conception of mental hospital treatment have occurred that led to the low state Beers describes and that, to a significant extent, persist even to this time? A discussion of this question appeared recently in writings by Greenblatt and Bockoven.[16,17] Our own discussion, which follows immediately, is based for the most part on their papers.

"Moral Treatment": Its Decline and Revival

Moral treatment was based to a large extent on the teachings of the great French physician, Philippe Pinel. It was also rooted in the liberal philosophical and political movements of the nineteenth century. As Greenblatt and Bockoven point out, it fitted well into American life in New England at mid-nineteenth century, when communities were, for the most part, small and well-knit with members who were mutually interdependent and united by religious ties. The individual was held in high esteem in the village life of that time.

With Pinel, the leaders associated with the moral treatment movement believed that "insanity was not the result of an irreversible lesion of the brain, but that it was in very many instances curable if adequate attention were paid to psychological, experiential, or emotional factors."[18]

Moral treatment is described as being "no specific procedure aimed at a disorder specifically conceived." Rather, it was a way of life offered to the sick, in which the hallmark was a philosophy of mental illness on the part of the physicians that placed a high value on the individual patient and strong belief in his powers to recuperate. "It was an effort to create a favorable environment in which recovery could take place. Recovery or discharge represented to a large extent the natural course of the illness when it was not artificially obstructed. Moral treatment was the art of eliminating obstacles and providing aids to the recovery; these aids being whatever action seemed indicated to supply a psychological need."[19]

A fine description of one of these institutions appears in Charles Dickens' *American Notes:*

> . . . The State Hospital for the Insane [is] admirably conducted on those enlightened principles of conciliation and kindness, which twenty years ago would have been worse than heretical. . . .
>
> Each ward in this institution is shaped like a long gallery or hall, with the dormitories of the patients opening from it on either end. Here they work, read, play at skittles, and other games; and when the weather does not admit of their taking exercises out of doors, pass the day together. . . .
>
> Every patient in this asylum sits down to dinner every day with a knife and fork; and in the midst of them sits the gentleman [the superintendent]. . . . At every meal, moral influence alone restrains the more violent among them from cutting the throats of the rest; but the effect of that influence is reduced to an absolute certainty, and is found even as a means of restraint, to say nothing of it as a means of cure, a hundred times more efficacious than all the strait-waistcoats, fetters, and hand-cuffs that ignorance, prejudice, and cruelty have manufactured since the creation of the world.
>
> In the labour department, every patient is as freely trusted with the tools of his trade as if he were a sane man. In the garden, and on the farm, they work with spades, rakes, and hoes. For amusement, they walk, run, fish, paint, read, and ride out to take the air in carriages provided for the purpose. They have among themselves a sewing society to make clothes for the poor, which holds meetings, passes resolutions, never comes to fisty cuffs or bowie-knives as sane assemblies have been known to do elsewhere; and conducts all its proceedings with the greatest decorum. The irritability, which would otherwise be expended on their own flesh, clothes, and furniture, is dissipated in these pursuits. They are cheerful, tranquil, and healthy.
>
> Once a week they have a ball, in which the doctor and his family, with all the nurses and attendants, take an active part. Dances and marches are performed alternately, to the enlivening strains of a piano; and now and then some gentleman or lady (whose proficiency

has been previously ascertained) obliges the company with a song; nor does it ever degenerate, at a tender crisis, into a screech or a howl; wherein, I must confess, I should have thought the danger lay. At an early hour they all meet together for these festive purposes; at eight o'clock refreshments are served; and at nine they separate.

Immense politeness and good-breeding are observed throughout. They all take their tone from the Doctor; and he moves a very Chesterfield among the company. Like other assemblies, these entertainments afford a fruitful topic of conversation among the ladies for some days; and the gentlemen are so anxious to shine on these occasions, that they have been sometimes found "practising their steps in private," to cut a more distinguished figure in the dance.

It is obvious that one great feature of this system is the inculcation and encouragement, even among such unhappy persons, of a decent self-respect.[20]

These methods fit remarkably modern concepts of hospital treatment for the mentally ill. "Forbearance on the part of the hospital staff," it is explained, "allowed expression of antagonisms, while opportunity to work furnished release to creative urges and satisfaction as recognition. Games of chance and skill provided a setting for competitive drives, writing and acting of the drama gave rein to exhibitionistic tendencies, and plastic arts offered sublimation of childish impulses. Liberty to handle sharp instruments served to allay fears of impotence and mutilation and to reassure patients of their normality in these respects."[21] Yet Beers' description of an institution from the same part of the country, fully fifty years later, could hardly be more contrasting. All the coercive instruments of restraint and brutality which Dickens was surprised to find absent in moral treatment had been reinstated. How can one explain this strange turning forward and backward in the history of treatment of the mentally ill?

Several reasons for the "decline and fall of moral treatment" are given by Greenblatt and Bockoven. First was the increase in size of state hospitals after 1850. This action by legislators was against the recommendations of the leaders of the moral treatment movement who argued for small hospitals to preserve close human contact. Questions of economy and imitation of industrial methods, however, prevailed. The beginning of a situation that later was to be called the cause of poor mental hospital practice can be traced to this point in history:

While the cost of patient care in the general hospital rose with the per capita income, the cost in the mental hospital went down sharply. A proportional decrease in the number of physicians, with increase in that of attendants, removed the physician from his charges and left them largely in the hands of untrained staff. The doctor became administrator rather than personal therapist. In the meantime, the relative fall in the wages paid attendants increased the economic distance between physicians and them, and lowered the value of their job. Increasingly, the physician became an extremely busy man, too busy to indulge in simple human intercourse with either attendants or patients. In 1894 it was calculated that if each state hospital physician in Massachusetts worked ten hours a day and could move from patient to patient with the speed of light, he could perhaps give ten minutes daily to each patient.[22]

Another contributing factor in the shift away from moral treatment to the attendant-dominated, custodial institution was the great influx of immigrants into the United States at this time. The compassion and close contact required for moral treatment proved difficult to maintain with patients from "alien cultural backgrounds." Again, one finds in this historical example an "origin" of a modern problem, for as recent studies have documented,[23] distinctions of social class continue today to influence treatment of the mentally ill. The following passages from the annual reports of the Worcester State Hospital, 1854 to 1858 demonstrate these attitudes as they developed one hundred years ago:

> This large class of people stand in false relations to nearly everything about them . . . to which they cannot adapt themselves, influenced by motives often extravagant and wild. . . . They receive in prosperous times high wages, and are able at the cheapest rates to gratify vicious indulgences. They seek for labor in the most menial capacity, huddled together in the most objectionable places, neglect all rules of health, and prefer the excitement or solace of rum or tobacco to the quiet, intelligent influences of well-ordered homes.
> . . . The hospital at Worcester . . . is fast becoming a hospital for foreigners, and its doors are becoming practically closed against that class of person who for many years enjoyed its advantages. . . . The intelligent yeomanry of Massachusetts, who can afford to pay the cost of their board, and will not ask for charity . . . would have

shrunk most sensitively from living next door even to a wretched hovel, and from intimate association with those who are accustomed to, and satisfied with, filthy habitations and filthier habits.

. . . It would be no wonder, if the insanity of a highly educated, intelligent and refined person should be increased rather than cured, if the person is brought into close contact with those who are always coarse in their habits and tastes, rough in disposition, and filthy in their dress.[24]

Small wonder that, in the face of such attitudes, moral treatment was weakened and recovery rates began to fall. "In the highly reputed Worcester State Hospital [recovery rates] declined from about 50 per cent in the 1830's to 5 per cent in 1880."[25] Paradoxically, the result was to change the treatment practices for insanity so completely that, even in a costly private institution such as that at which Beers was first treated, the patient was treated more like a criminal than a sick person. Instead of being forced to associate with fellow patients who were "coarse in their habits and tastes, rough in their disposition, and filthy in their dress," as the board of the hospital worried earlier, the major problem of the patient came to be with a brutalized, ignorant group of attendants. These untrained workers, recruited largely from individuals who were unemployable in other occupations, came to dominate the mental hospital, encouraged by supervising physicians who were convinced that insanity was an incurable illness.

Another important, contributing factor to the "incurable illness hypothesis" and the associated decline of moral treatment was the growth at this time of the disease-entity approach in medicine. Advances in pathology and bacteriology provided diagnostic tools which were revolutionizing medical science in practice. Mental illness began to be considered, like other illness, to be outside the control, etiologically and therapeutically, of social and emotional factors. The reasoning behind this view is described as follows:

. . . Psychiatrists of reputation, like Pliny Earle, began to argue that mental illness was becoming essentially an incurable malady. . . . It was an inexorable march, they believed, toward malignancy. To prove their contention further, these clinicians began to point to the early reports emanating from the pathological laboratories where new techniques purported to show microscopic lesions in the central nervous systems of patients who had been mentally ill. These observations profoundly impressed many physicians, particularly those who leaned toward the biological interpretation of the etiology of disease. Psychotic behavior could no longer be looked on as representing an accumulation of bad conditioning that had resulted from unhappy stresses, social and emotional deprivations, and the like, but could be viewed entirely as the consequence of mechanical defects in parts of the brain. Psychiatry shifted from an attitude of accepting the challenge of mental illness as a problem to be attacked with every means at hand, to one which dared not try anything without clearance from the pathologic laboratory. If mental disorder was "organic" in etiology, the simplest and cheapest custody of the largest number of persons was the only answer to the social burden imposed by it.

The success of the pathological method in uncovering the etiology of general paresis (brain syphilis), describing its course, and relating the patient's symptoms to advance of the disease, contributed further to the dependence of the physician upon laboratory investigations. This inclination increased through advances in other physical sciences—physiology, pathology, and bacteriology. The more the laboratories grew in size and importance, the weaker the philosophical premises of the "moral" psychiatrists. Being men of faith who worked largely by intuition, they possessed no systematic theory of mental illness, such as was elaborated later by Freud; they carried on no organized research and instituted no training program for younger men who might follow in their footsteps. Thus, without any strong group of believers to stand against the force of "scientific" medicine from within or socioeconomic pressures from without, the spirit and content of moral treatment faded away, though residues of its externals survived here and there; residues that in some quarters passed as moral treatment itself, but in reality did much to discredit it. The peculiar custom of taking patients for walks, like exercising a dog, was such a residue; another was *persuasion* of patients to work (more to maintain hospital industries than to provide wholesome and instructive occupational activity); and another was the formalized dance performed by emotionally starved persons at the insistence of administrative authorities.[26]

The unfortunate fate of moral treatment thus became another example in the annals of the history of science, of the step backward which seems to be a necessary (if illogical) accompaniment of advances forward. In the recent history of medical science, such incidents have tended to represent short-lived and temporary halts in giant strides forward. For hospital treatment of the insane the reverse was true. Moral treatment was an all-too-brief beacon of promise and when it died, the giant step was backward.

What was needed was a systematic theory of mental illness strong enough to provide guidelines for diagnosis, treatment, and research in psychiatry—guidelines firm enough to resist fad and fashion and to yield only to arguments based on logic and evidence. Undoubtedly, it was psychoanalysis which emerged to serve just this purpose.

The effects of Freudian ideas upon hospital practice were to be of tremendous significance. In the first instance, however, it was not the hospital that felt the impact of psychoanalytic concepts; their most immediate and enthusiastic application was in the psychiatrist's office and clinic. In the hospital, the implications of psychoanalysis were more slow to be applied; moreover, when they were, their first consequence was to focus attention even more intensively upon the doctor-patient relationship. Unintentionally, the significance of the hospital environment as an intrinsic part of the therapeutic process was downgraded during the first phases of the psychoanalytic movement.

One very important early benefit of psychoanalysis was the humanizing of social attitudes in general toward the mentally ill. The consequences for mental hospitals were quick to be felt, both in the reduction of brutal and depersonalizing practices, and, more positively, in the added hope that was injected into the atmosphere of psychiatric therapy. Freud was not the only source of such influences, of course. The work of Adolph Meyer in this country and of Emil Kraepelin in Europe, among others, served similar humanizing purposes in the care of serious mental illness a half century ago.

Nevertheless, it remained a fact during the century following Pinel and the moral treatment movement that the hospital environment was left out in conceptions of therapy. Therapy was equated with intervention, either by somatic or psychological methods, and the physician was its exclusive purveyor.[27] Interestingly enough, the patient's adjustment to the social environment was the major yardstick of the success or failure of therapy, as indeed admission to the hospital was usually based upon a patient's inability to form and maintain satisfactory relationships with others. However, in spite of these evident facts, social processes generally were not included in the explanation either of the origin or treatment of psychiatric illness.

The Therapeutic Community: Concept and Program

Sullivan's reports of his experiments on a ward for schizophrenic patients is a historic signpost for the beginning of psychiatry's systematic concern with the hospital as a "therapeutic community." Arguing that psychiatry is the study of interpersonal relations and, therefore, that the psychiatrist should be concerned with what goes on between people rather than primarily with the intrapsychic, his work proved to be very influential in directing attention to the social aspects of mental illness.

"According to Sullivan," Arieti has written, ". . . nothing is intrapersonal or intrapsychic; everything evolves from the individual's relations with other people, especially people with whom he has lived in his childhood, his parents or parent substitutes . . . 'the significant adults' in the individual's life. Everything is interpersonal; all our thoughts and phantasies deal with people, either real or imaginary. . . . One might say that every type of dynamic psychiatry is interpersonal. Isn't Freud, for instance, studying what goes on between parents and children, when he describes and interprets the oedipal situation? . . . [but] Freud focused his attention not on the interpersonal relations but on the fight of the individual against his instincts. The parents are seen by Freud, mostly as a source of sexual strivings which the child has to inhibit. In his early writings, Sullivan, too, . . . gives considerable attention to these sexual strivings and stresses sexual maladjustment as the precipitating factor of neuroses and psychoses. Later, however, he comes to recognize the importance of the parent-child relationship in its totality. Sexual difficulties may enter, under exceptional circumstances, as the cause of the abnormal interpersonal relations. Generally they are the effect, not the cause of a poor parent-child relationship."[28]

This is not the place for a full review of the theoretical implications of Sullivan's position. The only point which is appropriate here is that Sullivan, in his rebellion against the intrapsychic emphasis which he found in all the different schools of psychiatry in the 1920's, helped to turn a spotlight on the social context of mental illness. More specifically, by his efforts to control the therapeutic environment in an experimental ward for schizophrenics, he was a stimulus to the application of social science to the study of the mental hospital.

The full effects of these ideas, however, were not to be felt until World War II. Perhaps their most intensive and interesting expression occurred in England, in the experiments in hospital psychiatry which Maxwell Jones conducted during and immediately following the war. It was Jones who popularized the term "therapeutic community."[29]

Jones describes the first steps in the conception of his program as a fortunate accident. While in charge of a ward of soldiers suffering from effort syndrome, a psychosomatic cardiac complaint, he decided that it seemed reasonable to explain to the patients some of the details of the psychological and physiological mechanisms involved in their symptoms. However, to do this individually with one hundred patients it would have taken many hundreds of hours and been monotonously repetitive. Moreover, wartime staff shortages made an individual approach impossible. As a result, a start was made in discussing at a didactic level the meaning of symptoms with the whole group of one hundred patients.

The lecture method was soon replaced by discussion groups, organized as seminars. The hypothesis basic to this program was that a greater understanding of the illness would help to relieve the symptoms. This idea was in itself consistent with prevailing "dynamic" psychiatric theory. However, the method for achieving sufficient emotional understanding for the relief of neurotic symptoms had generally been thought to require an individual and intense relationship with a physician. To work toward this therapeutic goal in a group and with such direct classroom type of method was the novel turn.

Educational techniques continued to play an important part in Jones' program. "It soon became evident, however," he reported, "that the discussion group was more than an educational meeting, it was affecting the whole social structure of the ward." As a result, his interest widened and he began to question the meaning of the sociological phenomena that occurred.

Immediately following the war, Jones continued his experimentation, but now with various kinds of mental patients, including sociopaths and chronic unemployables. He adopted the premise "healthy group life will make healthy individuals."

The attempt was made to reduce or eliminate the boundaries of time, space, and status that existed in more traditional psychiatric therapeutics. The patient's experience in the present, in the hospital, should be more continuous, Jones thought, with the realities of his past and his future. There were three main approaches toward these goals: (a) links with the community were forged to allow patients to work, when possible, in a normal setting while still living in the hospital; (b) in the hospital, programs were developed that closely simulated the conditions of the outside community, so that patients could engage in productive work aimed at quick return to society; (c) the hospital society was reorganized toward the breakdown of the original hospital hierarchy and freer communication between doctors, nurses, and patients.

The last approach was perhaps the most specific innovation which Jones introduced in his hospitals. Included was the attempt to change expectations on the part of patients for direct one-to-one relationships with a doctor, and to substitute a group life in which the staff, including the doctor and nurse, were to be an organic part.

Another distinctive feature was the use of democratic techniques, such as patient government and ward meetings in which the freedom of the patients to criticize the staff was encouraged.

As would be expected, a considerable amount of role change occurred in Maxwell Jones' hospitals. The absolute authority of the doctor was reduced and the importance of nurses, social workers, and other personnel was upgraded. Unlike the role change we have described in the general hospital, however, this was not a result of bureaucratization, predicated upon the increasing expertise and professionalism of the various members of a medical team; rather, it was the consequence of a changed orientation toward mental illness. The patient, it was hypothesized, was affected in all of his social relationships in ways that are significant in his illness. Therefore, all the social relationships of the hospital milieu should be treated as important. One step in such a process was to communicate to all of the personnel of the hospital their importance directly in the therapeutic process, and this was attempted by upgrading their status and by democratizing the hospital society.

The development of the therapeutic community program was an important stimulus to the demand for more systematic information about the hospital as a social environment. The emphasis of psychiatric hospitals on the custodial aspects of their programs was jolted sharply by the success of such wartime experiments. The inherent pessimism of the custodial approach could not but yield to the successes of wartime psychiatry. Of the estimated one million admissions to the military neuropsychiatric services, many were returned to duty. In striking contrast to the experience of World War I, most of these men were able to return to normal lives when World War II ended.[30]

The experience of the wartime hospitals set the stage for a large-scale effort by social scientists to study the hospital as a social environment. Mention should be made, however, of one outstanding example of this type of research that preceded the war. Howard Rowland made a study of two mental hospitals in New York State the findings of which appeared in 1938 and 1939.[31,32] Using a method of direct observation and participation in the activities and events of a mental hospital, Rowland's objective was "a systematic description of the more commonplace aspects of hospital life in order to permit some degree of generalization as a guide to further study."[33] This purpose was to be significantly fulfilled. As sociologists turned increasingly to the descriptive study of the hospital, Rowland's study was used as a guide and model.

In brief summary, Rowland's picture of the typical patient experience includes the following steps:

(a) First, the mental patient "loses caste" in the world outside the hospital. "He loses civil rights, social class position, economic power, and neighborhood and community esteem. Socially and politically, the individual is disenfranchised. He is lifted out of a complex society and is placed in a new social order which is vastly different."[34]

(b) He enters a new society, but is always conscious of the old "real" society. He is on the *inside* looking *out*.

(c) He learns that in this new society, the *social field* is *split* into *staff* and *inmate* worlds, living together in the closest proximity but separated sharply by a high sociological wall.

The patient, uprooted from his family and community, subordinate to the authority of a professional staff that is distinctly separate from him and therefore inaccessible in significant ways, is forced to be dependent on his peers—the patient world—for the fulfillment of a variety of emotional and social needs.

How does he fare in this world?

In this radical new direction in which illness has channeled his life, how useful are the values and rules of conduct that governed his experience in the past (in the "outside world")? In his feelings about himself, in his choices and judgments of companions, in his relationships with the "staff world," what are the dominant forces that will guide him?

To these questions, our attention will be directed in the next chapter as we review in detail the achievements of the sociological studies of mental hospitals that have been published since World War II.

Summary

The general hospital, as we have seen, has evolved from almshouse to "temple of science." Within close memory, it was a death house, a feared place of last resort. Its rescue from this state may be traced directly to the development of antisepsis. The latter, however, could not emerge until the science of pathology in its modern form was established. As medicine, in general, became more firmly associated with science, the modern hospital became its instrument.

The mental hospital, however, did not follow a parallel course. Indeed, as Beers dramatized, the movement forward in the hospital's medical services was accompanied by a retrogression to medieval psychiatric practices. Even with the great push forward supplied by the work of Kraepelin and Bleuler in descriptive clinical psychiatry and by Freud in dynamic psychiatry, the effects on the mental hospital were slow to be felt.

Even when brutality and neglect began to be corrected, and the psychiatric hospital was made a more pleasant place to live in, the care of its patients remained mainly custodial. This was not a matter of economics, although it is quite true that proper staffing and financing was a problem not easy to solve. It was rather the result of the conviction, no doubt influenced by the successes in other branches of medicine, that mental illness was somatic in origin. Thus the main purpose of the hospital became to provide patient material for the scientific study of mental illness. This approach was not without success. During the nineteenth century important advances in neurology were made. Also bacteriologists, using neurological data, were able to demonstrate that mental symptoms resulted from several infectious diseases. There was, for example, the important discovery that paresis was a late-stage syphilitic infection of the brain. However, while the superintendents of American asylums during the last years of the nineteenth century "toiled earnestly at autopsies seeking the local lesions which they rarely ever found . . . ,"[35] there was little effort expended in therapeutic care. The methods of restraint gradually went out of style, but in their place remained a "keeper" philosophy.

The growth of the influence of Freudian ideas helped to humanize the hospital, but again the emphasis remained on a severely limited part of the total life experience of the patient, his contact with the doctor. It remained for Sullivan, synthesizing the ideas of Freud, Adolph Meyer, and William Alanson White,[36] to design an approach that set out to treat the psychotic comprehensively in a hospital setting.

World War II witnessed the first relatively large-scale adoption of an orientation in modern hospital psychiatry that conceived of the full range of the patient's interpersonal experience as part of "therapy." Out of Maxwell Jones' experiments with the hospital as a "therapeutic community," a program emerged that had a widespread influence in postwar American mental hospitals.

These innovations were not accepted unskeptically, however. Instead, they were joined by efforts to describe systematically the hospital social environment. This spirit of experiment and self-scrutiny encouraged hope that fashions of hospital treatment would yield to a science of psychiatric therapeutics.

NOTES TO CHAPTER 8

1. Sullivan, Harry Stack, "Socio-Psychiatric Research: Its Implications for the Schizophrenia Problem and for Mental Hygiene," *American Journal of Psychiatry*, vol. 10, May, 1931, pp. 977–991.
2. Sullivan, Harry Stack, "The Modified Psychoanalytic Treatment of Schizophrenia," *American Journal of Psychiatry*, vol. 11, November, 1931, pp. 519–540.
3. Beers, Clifford W., *A Mind That Found Itself*. Doubleday and Co., Garden City, New York, 1956. Copyright, 1953, by American Foundation for Mental Hygiene.
4. *Ibid.*, p. 69.
5. Sullivan, Harry Stack, "Socio-Psychiatric Research . . . ," p. 978.
6. Sullivan, Harry Stack, *Conceptions of Modern Psychiatry*. William Alanson White Psychiatric Foundation, Washington, 1947, pp. 111–115.
7. Beers, Clifford W., *op. cit.*, pp. 73–75.
8. *Ibid.*, pp. 80–84.
9. Packard, Mrs. E. P. W., *Modern Persecution, or Insane Asylums Unveiled*. Published privately, Chicago, 1873.
10. Seabrook, William, *Asylum*. Harcourt, Brace and Co., New York, 1935.
11. Ward, Mary Jane, *The Snake Pit*. Signet Books, New York, 1955. Although this is a fictionalized account, it is based on the writer's experience as a patient. A more recent fictional account is Janet Frame's *Faces in the Water*, George Braziller, Inc., New York, 1961. It is a remarkable book both in substance and artistically.
12. Kerkhoff, J. D., *How Thin the Veil:* A Newspaperman's Story of His Own Mental Crackup and Recovery. Chilton Books, New York, 1952.
13. Beers, Clifford W., *op. cit.*, pp. 108–110.
14. Stanton, Alfred H., and Morris S. Schwartz. *The Mental Hospital*. Basic Books, Inc., New York, 1954.
15. Caudill, William, F. C. Redlich, H. R. Gilmore, E. B. Brody, "Social Structure and Interaction Processes on a Psychiatric Ward," *American Journal of Orthopsychiatry*, vol. 22, April, 1952, pp. 314–334.
16. Greenblatt, Milton, Richard H. York, Esther Lucile Brown, *From Custodial to Therapeutic Patient Care in Mental Hospitals*. Russell Sage Foundation, New York, 1955, pp. 407–416.
17. Bockoven, J. Sanbourne, "Some Relationships Between Cultural Attitudes Toward Individuality and Care of the Mentally Ill: An Historical Study" in Greenblatt, Milton, Daniel J. Levinson, and Richard H. Williams, *The Patient and the Mental Hospital*. The Free Press, Glencoe, Ill., 1957, pp. 517–526.
18. Greenblatt, York, and Brown, *op. cit.*, p. 408.
19. *Ibid.*, p. 411.

20. Dickens, Charles, *American Notes for General Circulation*. 3d ed. Chapman and Hall, London, 1842, vol. 1, pp. 105–111.
21. Greenblatt, York, and Brown, *op. cit.*, p. 411.
22. *Ibid.*, p. 412.
23. Hollingshead, August B., and Frederick C. Redlich, *Social Class and Mental Illness*. John Wiley and Sons, New York, 1958.
24. Quoted in Greenblatt, York, and Brown, *op. cit.*, p. 413.
25. *Ibid.*, p. 413.
26. *Ibid.*, pp. 414–415.
27. This conclusion was expressed recently in the introduction to a study of hospital therapy as follows: "During the past two or three decades, while marked progress has been made in the variety and use of psychiatric therapy, the profession of psychiatry has devoted itself primarily to attempting to understand the nature of psychopathology and how it could be altered through some process of somatic or psychological treatment. Thus, laboratory research tended to be concerned with physiological problems, while psychoanalytical studies focused upon reduction of intrapsychic conflict. Therapy was generally viewed either as intervention in the form of insulin or electric shock, and more recently of new drugs, or as psychological intervention by the psychiatrist who sought to establish a supporting interpersonal relationship with his patient. So fixedly was attention riveted upon these forms of treatment and so conditioned were psychiatrists to view the medical profession as the exclusive purveyors of "therapy" that as a group they failed to comprehend the extent of the potential usefulness to the healing process of other categories of personnel (and even of patients), as well as of the physical environment of the hospital in which patients lived. Equally they failed to comprehend or obtain preparation for another role that they might assume, namely, that of leader of a therapeutic team." See Greenblatt, York, and Brown, *op. cit.*, p. 5.
28. Arieti, Sylvano, *Interpretation of Schizophrenia*. Robert Brunner, New York, 1955, pp. 33–34.
29. See Jones, Maxwell, *The Therapeutic Community*, Basic Books, Inc., New York, 1953. This book was first published a few years earlier in England under the title *Social Psychiatry*.
30. For a detailed report of the experiences of military psychiatry in World War II, see Ginzberg, Eli, J. B. Miner, J. K. Anderson, Sol. W. Ginsburg, John L. Herma, *The Ineffective Soldier:* Breakdown and Recovery, Columbia University Press, New York, 1959.
31. Rowland, Howard, "Interaction Processes in a State Mental Hospital," *Psychiatry*, vol. 1, August, 1938, pp. 323–337.
32. Rowland, Howard, "Friendship Patterns in a State Mental Hospital," *Psychiatry*, vol. 2, August, 1939, pp. 363–373.
33. Rowland, Howard, "Interaction Processes in a State Mental Hospital," 1938, p. 323.
34. *Ibid.*, p. 325.
35. Shryock, Richard H., *The Development of Modern Medicine*. Rev. ed. Alfred A. Knopf, Inc., New York, 1947, p. 361.
36. Dunham, H. Warren, "The Field of Psychiatry" in Rose, Arnold M., editor, *Mental Health and Mental Disorder*. W. W. Norton and Co., New York, 1955, pp. 61–86.

Chapter 9

FINDINGS AND CONSEQUENCES OF SOCIAL RESEARCH

IT HAS BEEN OBSERVED that periodically conditions in the public institutions for mental illness are exposed in press campaigns full of indignant revulsion; the public reacts in support of reforms; and commissions are appointed to make investigations. In the end, the institutions are quietly forgotten and allowed to slip back into their former mold.[1]

Generally, it has been the conclusion of public officials during their moments of conscience that the defects and failures of state mental hospitals were a result of understaffing, insufficient budgets, lack of a research atmosphere, and inadequate professional manpower. However, in a state institution where each of these conditions was corrected, Barrabee found problems that resembled closely those of less fortunate sister institutions.[2]

It is further a common assumption that ownership by the state is, of itself, a factor that causes problems appearing to be endemic to mental hospitals. This, too, is refuted by data from a variety of sources. We have seen how Beers, a half-century ago, received equally poor treatment in both private and state hospitals. More recently, in a study of a well-reputed private mental hospital, Stanton and Schwartz concluded that "beyond much doubt, . . . even in a private mental hospital, closely connected to one of the most advanced psychiatric training institutions in the country, and restricting its clientele generally to those patients able to pay an average of $850 per month for treatment, many of the serious problems of the state mental hospital were still present."[3]

It has been suggested, therefore, that the way a hospital functions is dependent upon principles of social organization that are more basic than such variables as type of ownership, size, staff-to-patient ratio, and professional status of staff. Toward the uncovering of these principles, a series of detailed descriptive studies of hospitals, particularly mental hospitals, have appeared in recent years. In this chapter an attempt will be made to review and synthesize the achievements of these studies.

Communication, Duplicity, and Remotivation

The sociological study of hospitals, with only a few notable exceptions,[4] has been an active field of study only since World War II. Prior to that time, however, there had already developed a theoretical literature and a considerable amount of empirical study of other types of social organization, particularly the industrial, from which valuable analogies may be drawn to hospitals.

A recent review of the literature on organizations classified the early studies of industrial relations into two major categories.[5] First, there was the "human relations" approach, represented to a large extent by Kurt Lewin and his students. The second may be called "power structure" analysis. These two approaches have been antagonists; that is, they have argued critically each with the other about where the proper emphasis should be in the study of social structure. The human relations school underscores the importance of two-way communication among individuals. Conflicts, it is asserted, may be resolved by the clarification of views, and the freeing of access by one point of view to the other. The second approach places more importance on group loyalties and differences. Between workers and managers, for example, it is argued that there are real differences which cannot be solved just by opening up channels of communication. These differences are basic to the distinctive character of each group and can be solved only by bargaining and compromise. Moreover, the concentration of authority in one group tends to drive the other underground and thus to a life of duplicity.

Recent studies of mental hospitals fall heir to these theoretic approaches. Stanton and Schwartz[6] and Caudill[7,8], authors of two of the best-known hospital studies, have concluded from their observations that communication is the key process. Belknap[9] and Goffman[10,11,12], on the other hand, have emphasized the differences among various groups in the mental hospital according to the power-structure argument.

A third theoretical approach appears in the works of Greenblatt, York, and Brown[13] and of von Mering and King.[14] The emphasis of this approach is on the value system that dominates the activities of a hospital. They describe situations in which the attitudes toward patients may become dominated by the "Legend of Chronicity," with inevitable consequences toward custodialism in treatment, no matter what the structure of the hospital may be. They recommend the attitude of "social remotivation" for the increase of achievement toward therapeutic goals.

Our purpose here is to review in further detail these three theoretical approaches to the study of social organization, and to propose a set of hypotheses for future inquiry concerning social behavior on a psychiatric ward.

The Human Relations Approach

There are two observations that all sociological observers of mental hospitals have noted, irrespective of theoretical orientations. The first is the change of objective status in society that is concomitant with admission to a mental hospital. The patient loses civil rights, social class position, economic power, and neighborhood and community esteem.[15] On the other hand, the *meaning* to the patient of the loss of these rights and privileges may not be one of loss. Rowland, for example, concluded that it is therapeutic for many patients to be drastically removed from society. This point of view agrees with the statement by Beers[16] that the first step toward recapturing a sense of reality for a disordered individual is to be removed radically from one's "real world," freed of all the customary requirements of ordinary living. Goffman, on the other hand, believes that the patient suffers psychological loss together with the objective status loss. As will be said in more detail later, Goffman interprets these losses as the cause of a stripping of self-esteem that drives the patient into a double life in the hospital.[17]

The second observation that, virtually without exception, sociological observers have noted in mental hospitals is the boundary line between staff and patient. "The patients and employees live in two entirely separate worlds," Rowland observed, "yet these two groups live in the closest proximity."[18] Almost word for word, the same observation appears in the works of Stanton and Schwartz, Belknap, and Caudill. Again, however, the significance of this fact is interpreted very differently, according to the theoretical orientation.

For a detailed recapitulation of the human relations approach, we will discuss first the work of Caudill and associates.[19]

Caudill was a participant-observer in a hospital that was small, dedicated to principles of psychoanalytic treatment, and staffed with an adequate number of devoted, well-trained people. On the conscious level there was little, if any, of the bitterness and hostility between staff and patient that other writers have described. The separateness, however, was the same, with important consequences for the patients. Patients and staff, Caudill wrote, "lived 'in two entirely separate social worlds, yet . . . in the closest proximity.' While the staff exercised control over the patients, they did not give recognition to the patient world as a social group, but rather, they interpreted the behavior of the patients almost solely in individual dynamic-historical terms."[20]

". . . The staff," Caudill concluded, "both doctors and nurses, seemed unacquainted with many aspects of life in the patient group, and dealt with each individual as a separate entity in administrative details, as well as in therapeutic matters. In part, this was due to the fact that there was no channel provided by which the patients, as a group, could voice their desires to the staff. If a group of patients wished to make a request, this could be done only by each patient's taking the matter up, as an individual, with his therapist."[21]

The consequence of these implicit, but nonetheless highly significant, boundaries between staff and patient worlds was a situation that Caudill describes as follows:

> The lack of a channel of communication, and insufficient separation between administration and therapy, increased the mutual isola-

tion of patients and staff. Both patients and staff structured their actions in accordance with a set of values and beliefs, but because the values and beliefs of each group were only incompletely known or understood by the other, the two groups viewed one another in terms of stereotypes which impeded an accurate evaluation of social reality. Such a situation, when coupled with alternating periods of permissive and restrictive administrative control, probably helps to account for the mood swings in the patient group. One week a general air of depression would prevail, at other times the ward had the atmosphere of a hotel, while again a feeling of rebellion would come over the entire group.[22]

The patient group, Caudill observed, protected itself (since it lacked an adequate channel of communication to the staff) by "turning inward, and developing a social structure which was insulated as much as possible from friction with the hospital routine. Nevertheless, such friction did occur, and the subsequent frustration led to behavior on the part of patients which, although it overtly resembled neurotic behavior arising from personal emotional conflicts, was, in fact, to a considerable extent due to factors in the immediate situation."[23]

A very similar kind of phenomenon was observed by Stanton and Schwartz.[24] They, like Caudill, studied a relatively small hospital that had high standards of care, a psychoanalytic approach, and self-conscious devotion to the goal of creating a "therapeutic milieu." Nevertheless, the *staff-inmate split* emerged as one of their most important observations.

Although the staff and patient worlds are functionally divided, they are part of what Stanton and Schwartz call the same "social field." They described an incident that illustrates the significance of this divided but common universe of experience.[25] At the center of this incident was a junior physician named Dr. Landon. Dr. Landon was treating a patient under the supervision of a senior staff psychiatrist, Dr. Ulman. However, the general management of this same patient was the responsibility of another senior staff psychiatrist, Dr. Enright. A conflict developed in this three-way relationship which was followed by an eruption of disturbance among their patients. It is instructive to sketch briefly the details of the incident.

The junior physician, Dr. Landon, recommended that the patient in question be moved to another ward. Dr. Ulman, the physician in charge of the ward and therefore responsible for the patient, disagreed and, of course, his judgment prevailed.

When the junior physician next met with his training supervisor, Dr. Enright, he spoke of the case, and Dr. Enright agreed mildly with his student's judgment. As might be expected, Dr. Landon placed more emphasis on this judgment than his supervisor had intended and when he next saw Dr. Ulman, he again expressed his opinion about moving the patient, but now much more forcefully, borrowing new reasons from his discussion with Dr. Enright. And also as might be expected, Dr. Ulman guessed the origin of the junior physician's renewed opposition, with the result that he was annoyed and became all the more emphatic in his own position.

"By this time," Stanton and Schwartz wrote, "Dr. Landon had come to function as a selecting valve, transmitting and unwittingly emphasizing the aspects about which Drs. Ulman and Enright [the senior physicians] were in disagreement. In such a setting the authorities are prone to add distortions by making more extreme statements than they ordinarily believe. As this continued, Drs. Ulman and Enright tended to move to diametrically opposite positions, and the subject matter of discussion was restricted to this controversy. Dr. Landon, originally somewhat insecure, became more and more discouraged and uncertain, and tried even harder to get the problem straightened out. *Dr. Landon was under no obligation to quote accurately and was often unconscious of the fact that he was quoting at all.* In similar situations such activity has often been interpreted as an attempt of the junior physician to drive a wedge between the seniors, but in our experience it has never been possible to confirm this interpretation. Actually, Dr. Landon's real need—guidance in the management of the patient—had been largely forgotten."[26]

Such misunderstandings within the staff were thought to be effectively hidden from the patients. Quite the contrary, it was the finding of Stanton and Schwartz that patients were extraordinarily sensitive to conflict among the staff members, no matter how carefully guarded such incidents might be. Sensing the disturbance of their doctors, the patients themselves became upset. The problem was that, by the nature of their illness, patients were expected to become periodically disturbed. When such patients became upset, even though a whole group became disturbed at the same time, the staff did not perceive it as a group phenomenon. Instead, each patient was treated separately, and his disturbance usually was diagnosed as intrapsychic in origin, and treated as such.

In explaining these types of problems and their resulting disturbances, both Caudill in his study and Stanton and Schwartz in theirs emphasize *communication*. Lack of communication causes the patients to "turn inward," they say, and "to develop social structures of their own." Thus the split between patient and staff worlds may be deepened. When on the other hand, communication channels are opened up, when the blocks in these channels are eliminated, these two worlds join hands in common purpose. The conclusion of the incident between Dr. Landon and his senior colleagues is an example:

> The growth of misunderstanding was terminated by a conference between Dr. Ulman and Dr. Enright. *Each was surprised at what he found to be the real opinion of the other.* The surprise was a result of the fact that each had built up for himself a set of fantasies about the other upon the basis of Dr. Landon's reports alone; from the nature of the situation these reports were more extreme and uncompromising than their sources. Each one had a tendency to assume that the other was engaged in something somewhat unfair and not quite above board. This assumption made the direct discussion of differences even more unlikely. These suspicions also immediately disappeared with the conference. The development of the whole process of misunderstanding could not have happened if Dr. Ulman and Dr. Enright had remained in contact and discussed their differences between themselves rather than through Dr. Landon.[27]

One basis for the conclusion (by Stanton and Schwartz) that disturbances of the social field are so significant in the course of psychiatric illness was the dramatic improvement when disturbed patients were moved into a different social situation. The authors draw an interesting analogy to shock therapy:

While shock therapy is not used at the hospital under study, our findings suggest that favorable responses to shock therapy in the case of excited patients may possibly occur for reasons similar to those described here. Profound and dramatic changes such as are observed in shock therapy, which the senior author has seen in other hospitals, are no more profound and no more rapid than the changes produced, in the group reported here, by bringing about a particular change in the patient's social field.[28]

Caudill agrees in almost all basic ways with the interpretations of Stanton and Schwartz. He found patients and staff living close but separate, and sensitively responsive to the "climate" of their separate worlds. He was particularly interested in the patterns of value and behavior in these adjacent subcultures, and the methods of socialization particularly for patients.[29]

In the small teaching hospital which he observed, Caudill described a set of pressures which patients exert toward the socialization of new patients. These are classified as attitudes in four areas of life. He tells how new patients are instructed in the "appropriate" attitudes.

The areas of life are as follows:

(a) attitudes toward the self;
(b) attitudes toward other patients;
(c) attitudes toward therapy and therapists;
(d) attitudes toward nurses and other hospital personnel.

For example, the following story is told as an example of how patients "teach" a new patient how to think about himself:

On the second day, following a conference with his therapist, the observer expressed resentment over not having going-out privileges to visit the library and work on his book—his compulsive concern over his inability to finish this task being one of the factors leading to his hospitalization. Immediately two patients, Mr. Hill and Mrs. Lewis who were later to become his closest friends, told him he was being "defensive"; since his doctor did not wish him to do such work, it was probably better to "lay off it." Mr. Hill went on to say that one of his troubles when he first came to the hospital was thinking of things that he had to do or thought he had to do. He said that now he did not bother about anything. Mrs. Lewis said that at first she had treated the hospital as a sort of hotel and had spent her therapeutic hours "charming" her doctor, but it had been pointed out to her by others that this was a mental hospital and that she should actively work with her doctor if she expected to get well.

The observer later saw such pressure applied time and again to other patients, and he came to realize that the group attempted to push its members toward a middle ground where they would not, as in his case and that of Mrs. Lewis, attempt to deny the reality of the hospital.[30]

Concerning attitudes toward other patients, Caudill found that the main pressure was "toward suspension of judgment and *the muting of outerworld distinctions.*" During his first few days, the observer was frequently told: "You cannot really refuse anything people ask of you around here."

This phenomenon has been observed by each of the first-hand studies reported in this discussion. In addition, we have observed the same process, ourselves, in a Veterans Administration Hospital on the edge of the deep South. Although just outside the walls of this VA hospital the rules of Jim Crow are unquestioned, and virtually all the white patients are southern in their cultural background, the psychiatric ward is *not* segregated racially. Negro patients mingle freely among whites, and in the memory of ward staff, no serious incidents have occurred because of racial tension.

At a recent ward meeting in this southern hospital, the presiding officer of the patient self-government asked the group to discuss methods of punishment for individuals who did not fulfill their assigned responsibilities. The ward president was white. He described an incident in which patient X, a Negro, had failed to carry out a work assignment, despite a reminder which he, the president, had personally given to X. X spoke up in anger, saying, "The way you spoke to me, any self-respecting man would do just as I did—tell you to go to the devil."

There followed discussion in which the president of the ward self-government disclaimed any intention of rudeness and apologized. X was mollified and agreed to reassume his assigned responsibilities. Although X remained surly, no open criticism of him was voiced by the remainder of the ward, which was predominantly southern-white. Certainly, in any other setting in the southern city where this hospital is located, such an incident could not occur because of the strong racial attitudes which prevail. But, in the psychiatric ward, "the muting of outerworld distinctions" was complete.

Toward therapy and therapists, Caudill found that the patient world exerted pressure on new patients (a) to believe that the doctor was competent, (b) to cooperate with the doctor, and (c) *not* to question the doctor's authority. At the same time, since the patients all shared in some frustrations with therapy and doubts about the therapy and therapists, they were tolerant about occasional outbursts. They also showed some very astute, intuitive grasp of the doctor's own emotional or social problems.

The fourth pressure described by Caudill was toward cooperation with the nurses and other hospital personnel. There was a joking, sometimes biting relationship with nurses, who, in this sense, were regarded as "fair game." But, on the whole, the pressure was to keep fellow patients thoughtful and pleasant to nurses, and abiding by the rules as far as possible.

Caudill has emphasized the significance of patient influence upon peers to conform to the basic requirements set down by the staff. An underlying consensus of purpose is implied which joins the staff and patient worlds in a common cooperative effort. Differences that arise are mainly the result of breakdowns in communication between these separate but congenial groups. These breakdowns are crises that become more or less serious, depending upon the insight the staff are able to gain concerning the sources of disturbance. Caudill in his study and Stanton and Schwartz in theirs have argued that more often than not the source of such breakdowns is conflict that occurs within one of these worlds and the resulting tension that is transmitted to the other. They have been interested particularly in conflicts among the staff that, in spite of efforts to the contrary, are unconsciously transmitted to patients. In other words, their conclusion is that as long as emotions are managed without friction in the staff world, a favorable balance is maintained between the staff and patient groups. Furthermore, the pressures within both staff and patient worlds are designed to maximize this intergroup harmony and, when conflicts occur, to restore a "homeostatic" equilibrium.

These two studies, by Caudill and by Stanton and Schwartz, stand out as examples of the human relations approach.

The Power-Structure Argument

As we have said, the basic facts of observation, particularly the first experiences of hospitalization, are described in similar terms by all the writers whom we review here, regardless of theoretical point of view. Their interpretations of these observations, however, differ significantly. We turn to the work of Goffman as a first example of the power-structure argument.

Goffman perceives the "staff-inmate split" as a fundamental conflict.[31] The two worlds, he believes, are *not* united in purpose. The harmonious balance they strive for is *not* homeostatic; on the contrary, it is more in the nature of a truce between superordinate (staff) and subordinate (patient) groups. It is an arrangement whereby the subordinate group "plays the game" in order to preserve harmony and, more importantly, to prevent punishment or the withdrawal of privileges.

Goffman argues further that the implicit function of staff attitudes and actions, notwithstanding the sincerity of their therapeutic purpose, is an "assault upon the self" of the patient. In its most simple terms, the argument states that (a) the staff communicate to the patient that he has "done wrong" and (b) that the hospital will try to help him "correct his past mistakes." It does not matter that the staff will explain that they do not *judge* the patient to be responsible for his behavior. Socially, that is, according to the normative standards of the society in which this behavior occurs, it is deviant and morally "bad."

Goffman continues by noting that psychiatric therapy, particularly for the hospitalized patient, operates on the assumption that, before the patient can be cured, he must accept the fact of his illness. This seems reasonable enough, except that, again, a basically moral meaning has been injected into the process. Thus, for the patient, this means that he must admit his wrongdoing (sin?) before he can again "do right." The hospital, in its initiation procedures, exerts pressure on the new patient to "confess his wrongdoing."

The response of the patient, Goffman believes, is a study in duplicity. He strives to do what the staff want him to do, but this is a defensive and opportunistic maneuver. He is "playing it cool" to avoid punishment and to gain privileges, but secretly he denies the validity of what he perceives as an assault upon his inner self. In the patient world, on the other hand, he finds a separate system of values and an organized pattern of relationships that allow him to preserve his self-respect. Thus, like a Marano,[32] he adapts to two separate but adjacent worlds, presenting to his master the face he wants to see, but secretly maintaining a forbidden loyalty and identity. Particularly when the authority system of an institution, knowingly or unknowingly, becomes coercive, patients may be driven into a *sub rosa* life which they protect by "playing it cool."

An extreme example of coercive authority in a mental hospital has been described by Belknap.[33] He found that attendants were able to manipulate patient behavior with extreme effectiveness. In a typical ward in the state hospital which Belknap studied, there were three distinct levels of patient status, organized and tightly controlled by the attendants. These statuses were hierarchically arranged on the basis of ability (and willingness) to perform the daily work requirements of the ward. "This status system," Belknap concluded, "had two main functions: (a) to accomplish the daily housekeeping, cleaning and physical care of patients on the ward; (b) to organize patient behavior in routines which hold the ward to a secure level of orderly . . . conduct." The emphasis on custodial rather than therapeutic goals is unmistakable.

Belknap's description of a ward status system is a case that is best understood in terms of the organization of authority in the hospital. For example, any member of the staff in Belknap's "Ward 30" had the right to discipline any member of the inmate or patient class. Secondly, these disciplinary rights concerned many items of conduct, such as dress, deportment, manners, and the like. Third, misbehaviors in one sphere of life were held against the patient's standing in others. An individual who might fail to participate with proper enthusiasm in sports, for example, would be treated accordingly in work assignment. In combination, these three aspects of authority add up to a type of control that, in terms of its effect on the patient's self-image, raises serious questions whether a therapeutic goal is being served.

The authority system described by Belknap is backed by a system of privileges and punishments, which operate together in the following ways:

> The authority of the attendant is backed by both positive and negative power. This power is an essential element in his control of the ward. He can give the patient privileges, and he can punish the patient. The privileges consist of having the best job, better rooms and beds, minor luxuries like coffee on the ward, a little more privacy than the average patient, going outside the ward without supervision, having more access than the average patient to the attendant's companionship or to professional personnel like the physicians, and enjoying such intangible but vital things as being treated with personal kindness and respect.
>
> The punishments which can be applied by the ward attendant are suspension of all privileges, psychological mistreatment, locking up the patient in an isolated room, denial or distortion of access to the professional personnel, threatening to put or putting the patient on the list for electro-shock therapy, transfer of the patient to an undesirable ward, and regular assignment of the patient to unpleasant tasks such as cleaning up after the soilers.[34]

Quite obviously, the details of Belknap's description are not matched in the wards that were studied by Caudill or by Stanton and Schwartz. Some of the custodialism, and the paternalistic authority upon which Belknap dwells, can be reproduced only on the closed ward with very disturbed psychotics and with the senile and retarded patient. The kind of authority system he describes, with the strong role of the attendant, is characteristic only of the large state institution, understaffed and overcrowded. The same may be said of Goffman's description which, like those of Belknap, were drawn from a large state institution. However, there is evidence to suggest that the "duplicity hypothesis" is not necessarily limited to the large hospital or to the extreme of mental disturbance.

In our own study of a southern hospital, we observed a ward where patients are predominantly neurotic with a minimum of overt disturbance in behavior, and where conditions are deliberately permissive and attempt to be noncoercive. These conditions notwithstanding, there are signs of a "double life."

Our observers quickly were able to identify cliques of "playboys," who, during the evening and weekend hours, made it a kind of game to see how far they could flout institutional rules without getting caught. On the surface, their behavior was often exemplary. From their ranks came officers of patient government and leaders. However, in the privacy of the "unofficial" hours, they rebelled. Moreover, they seemed to establish connections with former patients outside the hospital in a manner that reminds one of the findings of a recent group of prison studies by Cloward, Ohlin, and others.[35]

The latter group of studies found that in progressive penal institutions, notable for their enlightened approach to the rehabilitation of offenders, prisoners created a staff-inmate split which, in effect, was just as significant as in old-fashioned prisons where a coercive authority system was frankly and rigorously enforced. The explanation is very similar to that used by Goffman in his study of the psychiatric hospital. First, the admission procedures of the prison worked to break down self-esteem, to deface the prisoner. The practices in themselves were humane and considerate, but they carried the age-old assumption that the prisoners had been "bad" and must become "new kinds of people" before they could again be "good" people. Only from fellow prisoners was one "valued for himself." As Ohlin and Cloward point out, it is a long and vigorous psychological task to change one's self fundamentally. Moreover, prisoners often have legitimate cultural explanations for their participation in crime. They are, not infrequently, brought up by subcultural groups to accept and value certain kinds of behavior that are "criminal" in the society at large. Out of such origins, the fact that they have "done wrong" cannot easily be accepted. They know that they have been caught, but, beyond that, self-recrimination cannot be expected on a self-evident basis. Yet staff attitudes tend to assume that prisoners have committed their crimes knowingly and should know that crime does not pay.

In one modern prison that was studied most intensively, the staff were humane, sincere, and hard working in their efforts to help inmates. The inmates, in turn, appreciated the efforts of the staff and cooperated with them. However, as pleasant and free of troubles as this relationship was on the surface, underneath there was the conviction on the part of the prisoners that what the staff were doing was not important in their own long-range life plans. They knew, for example, what it was like, realistically, to reenter society as an ex-convict. They had well-established informal sources of information about what the adjustment was like after getting out of prison. They also knew that, as sincere as the help was which the staff gave them during their stay in the prison, they would not get such help after leaving the institution. They would then be on their own in a hostile world where the status of ex-prisoner automatically disqualified them for most of the kinds of work and life patterns for which their "rehabilitation" had trained them.

In the *sub rosa* world of the prisoner, however, inmates found that they were respected as individuals: moreover participation in this world qualified them for realistic help when they got outside. In one segment of the outside world, they learned that they could expect to be welcomed with friendship and material help. Unfortunately, this was the segment they had come from originally and that was engaged in the kind of crime for which they had been sent to prison.

But what has this to do with mental illness, one is likely to ask? The answer is that the status "mental patient" has its corollaries in the status "criminal." Society places upon both a comparable stigma. Thus the staff of the mental hospital must run the same gamut of doubt and suspicion on the part of many patients that is found in prisons. When an institution is frankly autocratic and coercive, the patient world needs no rationalization for creating its own hidden life. When the hospital is humane and enlightened, there is still the danger that the efforts of the staff, no matter how well intentioned, will seem to be "nice but unrealistic" to the patients.

In the ward studied by the writer, many patients are admitted after being on medical and surgical wards. They come bewildered and resentful. They do not know what "we are here for." Others are alcoholics. The largest proportion have not been diagnosed as psychotic. Therefore, patient adjustment to this ward is a special problem. As humane and therapeutically progressive as its practices obviously are, the ward is subject to the unique resistances that, in other settings, cause the development of a double life in the patient world.

If the patient's role in the hospital and its consequences for therapy are to be fully understood, a compelling need is evident for further study of the duplicity hypothesis.

Social Remotivation

A third hypothesis concerning the hospital treatment of emotional disturbances has recently been given the name "social remotivation." Social remotivation is explicitly a program of action. It is directed at the attitudes that prevail toward patient care because the value system of an institution, it is argued, is the primary determinant of the effectiveness of hospital care. The entire network of relationships in the mental hospital, it is asserted, reflect the beliefs of the staff toward mental illness. The remotivation approach is more than a value theory, however. It assigns weight to elements of social organization that have contributed to the origin and persistence of the therapeutic pessimism found particularly in large public hospitals.

In their book-length explanation of social remotivation, von Mering and King make several points clear: (a) social remotivation is a program based upon the study of large state-supported institutions; (b) these institutions have been the dumping grounds for thousands of patients diagnosed as "chronic cases," and it has become a firmly entrenched conviction in most such hospitals that chronic patients cannot be helped, but only cared for in a custodial sense; (c) what therapy is given to such patients is usually predicated on an assumption that "bad" must be "rehabilitated" into "good." This implied value is harmful and, in social remotivation, is avoided. The term "remotivation" itself implies the loss of abilities and attitudes, and its program is designed to reestablish in patients a desire for the elements of a healthy emotional life.[36]

It is a well-known fact that American state mental hospitals have been, characteristically, "unmanageably large; . . . economically depressed, running on a fraction of the cost of general hospitals, schools, or jails; . . . chronically understaffed; and . . . usually cut off from the mainstream of professional life."[37] Recent figures show that in the United States there are 226 state, 47 county, and 324 private hospitals for mental disease as well as 39 V.A. neuropsychiatric hospitals. The median average daily resident patient population in 1954 for state hospitals was 2,043, for the county 267, for the Veterans Administration 1,343, and for the private 30.[38] In the large mental hospital there is seldom more than one doctor for every two hundred patients. Under such circumstances, limitations of time and energy alone would restrict the extent of therapy the doctor is able to give to his patients. However, certain attitudes by the physician have served to limit the scope of his efforts even more drastically. Particularly, it is the psychiatrist's persistence in the view that the only significant therapy for patients occurs in a direct physician-patient relationship.

Kennard, in his study of a large Veterans Administration hospital, found that, in spite of the fact that classical long-term psychotherapeutic techniques were used rarely or not at all in handling hospital patients, nevertheless it was this form of therapy that was "the most emphasized and prestigeful topic in lectures presented to resident doctors by the teaching staff, in the review of articles appearing in psychiatric journals, and in most informal conversations among the medical staff. . . . The hospital is not organized to administer this type of therapy, nor would it be possible with its present organization and patient load even if there were indisputable evidence as to its efficacy in treating psychotic patients. Nevertheless, there is an assumption that this is the preferred form of therapy to be utilized in the field of psychiatry. One physician who had charge of a building with 164 patients explained that he was able to take care of only six or eight patients at a time, implying that taking care of these patients meant carrying them in some form of individual therapy."[39] Kennard adds: "It is apparently assumed by exclusion that the patients' relationships and interactions with other patients and with staff members are not therapeutic. In many instances, they very well may not be. Yet it may be questioned whether the conversations that take place two hours a week are of therapeutic significance and all others of no significance."[40]

Under these conditions, including both the reality that state hospitals lack adequate professional staff and the fact that attitudes by the physicians themselves have limited their approach to the dilemmas of the hospital, one finds that the actual responsibility for patients is generally in the hands of nonmedical staff members. It was this situation that was the subject of the inquiry by von Mering and King in a survey of 20 state-operated hospitals throughout the United States. In addition, visits were made to 3 Veterans Administration hospitals, 4 joint university and state receiving and teaching institutions, and 3 private sanitariums.[41]

Von Mering and King found that, on the one hand, there were persistent examples of hospitals with autocratic administration, inflexible departmentalism, and reliance upon considerations of status, salary, and power. On the other hand, they found many "promising developments," in which changes in methods of care were being tried with great vitality and already evident success. In their analysis of these two opposing tendencies, it was concluded that the philosophy of patient care that prevails in an institution is the primary determining variable. Where a philosophy of pessimism is dominant, the patients tend to be assigned to a status that is considered untreatable. Their explanation is as follows:

> As a rule, when a mental patient is designated as having an acute illness he is regarded as belonging to a still treatable classification, irrespective of the specific diagnosis, and is therefore a worthwhile prospect for an individualized treatment plan. When the mental patient is designated as having a chronic illness, he is regarded by and large as belonging to an untreatable classification, irrespective

of the specific diagnosis and is therefore not a good candidate for the individual therapeutic approach. The designation "chronic" usually does not carry such consequences for therapeutic action in physical illness. For example, even in the case of incurable cancer, one therapeutic measure after another is tried, often to heroic proportions, in the hope that some benefit might accrue and the patient's life be prolonged. The individualized, clinical approach is more likely to be continued with the chronic patient who is physically ill, while with the chronic patient in a mental hospital it is easier to give up this approach because of the feeling that *a priori* it is a hopeless proposition.

In large mental hospitals the shift from a judgment of acute to a judgment of chronic is accompanied by a subtle and covert change in the expectations of staff relative to the patient's future. The change in expectation is largely unspoken, for it means admission of failure, an admission which is difficult to accept for anyone connected with medicine. However, implicit acceptance of a change in expectations can be noted in the statements of staff about individual patients when they express the hopelessness of any active treatment, for they know the patient will not get well.[42]

This philosophy of pessimism is rooted, according to the authors, as we have indicated earlier, in what they call "The Legend of Chronicity." The antidote they recommend is social remotivation, which they describe as follows:

> Its primary feature lies in a set of attitudes, toward the patient and toward the treatment process. In terms of the patient, social remotivation requires the acceptance of the patient as a worthwhile individual, capable of improvement, regardless of the degree of observable deterioration. Furthermore, its aim is to have the patient come to accept himself, as well as help him to be acceptable to others.[43]

The other side of the picture in the von Mering and King report was the encouraging evidence that the public mental hospital has been in an active state of change in recent years, keeping in close step and, at times, moving ahead of the dynamic changes occurring in psychiatry as a whole. Undoubtedly, two historical events have been most influential in starting the trend that has been decidedly away from a custodial and toward a therapeutic approach. The first was the vitality with which hospital psychiatry responded to the urgent conditions of World War II, and, of course, to the encouraging success of wartime experiments. In the process, many traditional practices were challenged and superseded in a way that is difficult to accomplish except under urgent circumstances. The second was the advent of new chemotherapy by the tranquilizing drugs.

The new drugs, however, set off in some quarters the premature belief that mental illness would succumb, in the dramatic manner of some infectious disease, to a relatively simple and direct method of pharmacotherapy. Substantial gains have been made with the use of tranquilizers. However, these drugs have been most successful as a first step in psychiatric treatment; they make patients, under various conditions, more amenable to help by psychotherapy and to social rehabilitation. A recent report has this to say: "The large reservoir of chronic patients in the State and VA hospitals has been reduced somewhat [by drug therapy] but not, however, to the extent originally hoped for. While appreciable improvement in their social adjustment and amelioration of distressing symptoms is frequently achieved, full remissions are still uncommon."[44]

These are the setting and the conditions for which the social remotivation program was conceived. Very likely, social remotivation itself has become possible only because it appears in a period when hospitals have been willing to try new departures from their institutional traditions. In this period of transition, the concepts of social remotivation have guided hospitals toward what it believes to be the most important factor in the therapeutic process, that is, the attitude of the therapy staff toward their patients.

In his history of the Boston Psychopathic Hospital, now called Massachusetts Mental Health Center, Milton Greenblatt has described the many different ways in which the social environment of the hospital has been used for therapeutic purposes.[45] This is an excellent example of the remotivation ideal in application. Included have been the radical revision of the roles of members of the hospital, as well as new methods of inservice training for all the staff. "However, of even greater importance . . . ," Esther Lucile Brown has said, commenting on the experience at the Boston Psychopathic, "is the effort, through informal but continuous means, to help attendants—as well as all other categories of staff—to develop latent attitudes. Such an effort," she adds, "is usually a concomitant of a broad attempt to remake the hospital as a social institution: to replace autocratic administration, inflexible departmentalism, and reliance upon considerations of status, salary, and power by more democratic procedures, greater general permissiveness and delegation of responsibility, reduction of departmental and status barriers, greater encouragement of initiative, and utilization of the concept of the therapeutic *team*."[46] These are some of the means by which social remotivation undertakes to provide meaning and method to the therapeutic task.

Summary

We have extracted from the literature three hypothetical explanations of the effect of the mental hospital's social environment upon its patients. The first two, which we called (a) the human relations approach, and (b) the power-structure argument, place their emphasis upon elements of the social structure as the major determinants of the patterns of behavior which emerge. Thus the human relations hypothesis focuses upon what might be called the circulatory system of the hospital. The major arteries of circulation are channels of communication, particularly those between the patient group and staff. If the flow of these channels is kept free of obstruction, this hypothesis contends that the total organism will remain healthy, and even be able to withstand the inevitable strains caused by conflict within one of the two substructures.

The power-structure argument, on the other hand, presents what we have called the "duplicity hypothesis." The focus here, as in the first hypothesis, is upon the patient and staff subgroups, and the communication between them. However, in the second theory, the interests and goals of each subgroup are asserted to be different, whereas the human relations theory assumes that they are held in common. If there are such fundamental differences of interest between staff and patient, they cannot expect to be resolved except by hard bargaining and compromise. If they are held in common, on the other hand, the vital requirement is that they communicate clearly to each other momentary problems and needs in order to maintain a long-range common purpose. According to some authors of the power-structure school, these basic interests of patients are so different from those of the staff that, given the autocratic authority structure that is common in large hospitals, patients are forced into a "double life" in order to find an outlet for this self-interest. It might be expected that a hidden patient culture and attitudes of duplicity by patients would work against the goals of the staff. On the other hand, if the staff methods are wittingly or unwittingly unsuited to the real requirements of patients, the duplicity attitude may function as a defense for the patient that is therapeutic.

The third approach, "social remotivation," underscores the importance of the value system that prevails in an institution. Although certain kinds of social structure appear to fit together with certain attitudes, this argument states, the primary determining variable is the attitude or value system. Thus attitudes of pessimism by the staff breed the same pessimism in the patients. "The Legend of Chronicity" becomes rooted and blocks recovery. On the other hand, belief in the possibility of recovery, no matter how deteriorated a patient appears, will increase the probabilities of recovery. Social remotivation recently has presented in able and vigorous statement both its theoretical foundations and a therapeutic program of action designed to help patients recover.

NOTES TO CHAPTER 9

1. Belknap, Ivan, *Human Problems of a State Mental Hospital*. McGraw-Hill Book Co., New York, 1956.
2. Barrabee, Paul S., "A Study of a Mental Hospital: The Effect of Its Social Structure on Its Functions." Unpublished Ph.D. dissertation, Harvard University, 1951.
3. Stanton, Alfred H., and Morris S. Schwartz, *The Mental Hospital*. Basic Books, Inc., New York, 1954.
4. In addition to the studies by Rowland and Sullivan described in the previous chapter, see Devereux, George, "The Social Structure of a Schizophrenic Ward and Its Therapeutic Fitness," *Journal of Clinical Psychopathology and Psychotherapy*, vol. 6, October, 1944, pp. 231–265.

5. Etzioni, Amitai, "Interpersonal and Structural Factors in the Study of Mental Hospitals," *Psychiatry*, vol. 23, February, 1960, pp. 13-22.
6. Stanton, Alfred H., and Morris S. Schwartz, *op. cit.*
7. Caudill, William, *The Psychiatric Hospital as a Small Society*. Harvard University Press (for the Commonwealth Fund), Cambridge, Mass., 1958.
8. Caudill, William, F. C. Redlich, H. R. Gilmore, and E. B. Brody, "Social Structure and Interaction Processes on a Psychiatric Ward," *American Journal of Orthopsychiatry*, vol. 22, April, 1952, pp. 314-334.
9. Belknap, Ivan, *op. cit.*
10. Goffman, Erving, "Characteristics of Total Institutions" in *Symposium on Preventive and Social Psychiatry*. Walter Reed Army Institute of Research, Walter Reed Army Medical Center, Washington, 1957, pp. 43-84.
11. Goffman, Erving, "The Moral Career of Mental Patients," *Psychiatry*, vol. 22, May, 1959, pp. 123-142.
12. Goffman, Erving, *Asylums*. Doubleday Anchor Books, Garden City, New York, 1961.
13. Greenblatt, Milton, Richard H. York, and Esther Lucile Brown, *From Custodial to Therapeutic Patient Care in Mental Hospitals*. Russell Sage Foundation, New York, 1955.
14. von Mering, Otto, and Stanley H. King, *Remotivating the Mental Patient*. Russell Sage Foundation, New York, 1957.
15. Rowland, Howard, "Interaction Processes in a State Mental Hospital," *Psychiatry*, vol. 1, August, 1938, p. 325.
16. Beers, Clifford W., *A Mind That Found Itself*. Doubleday and Co., Garden City, New York, 1956. Copyright, 1953, by American Foundation for Mental Hygiene.
17. Goffman, Erving, *op. cit.* This idea is included in all three of Goffman's writings which we have cited.
18. Rowland, Howard, "Friendship Patterns in a State Mental Hospital," *Psychiatry*, vol. 2, 1939, pp. 363-373.
19. Caudill, Redlich, Gilmore, and Brody, "Social Structure and Interaction Processes on a Psychiatric Ward," 1952, *op. cit.*
20. *Ibid.*, p. 330. See also note 18.
21. *Ibid.*, p. 328.
22. *Ibid.*, p. 329.
23. *Ibid.*, p. 330.
24. Stanton, Alfred H., and Morris S. Schwartz, *op. cit.*
25. *Ibid.*, pp. 360-361.
26. *Ibid.*
27. *Ibid.*, p. 361.
28. *Ibid.*, p. 364.
29. Caudill, Redlich, Gilmore, and Brody, *op. cit.*, 1952. All subsequent references to Caudill use this source.
30. The "observer" is Caudill himself, who posed as a patient for the purposes of this study. Neither the patients nor the staff (with the single exception of the hospital director) knew at the time that he was in the hospital specifically as a social scientist in order to observe patient life, and *not* as a regular patient. It may

be added that Caudill himself recommends against such hidden identity for future studies, and opinion within the sociological profession has come to favor the immediate open identification of participant-observers in the settings they study.

31. Goffman, Erving, *op. cit.* We base this discussion particularly on the article "Characteristics of Total Institutions," 1957. (See note 10.) This article, in expanded form, appears in Goffman's *Asylums*, pp. 1–124. (See note 12.)
32. The Maranos were a group of so-called Crypto-Jews who, following the massacres in Spain, in the year 1391, publicly accepted conversion to Christianity, but privately continued their practice of their ancestral faith. See Margolis, Max L., and Alexander Marx, *History of the Jewish People*, Meridian Books, Inc., and the Jewish Publication Society, New York, 1958, pp. 448, 458–469.
33. Belknap, Ivan, *op. cit.*, pp. 171–196.
34. *Ibid.*, p. 164.
35. See *Theoretical Studies in Social Organization of the Prison*. Social Science Research Council, March, 1960. In this volume attention is directed especially to Cloward, Richard A., "Social Control in the Prison," pp. 20–48, and Sykes, Gresham M., and Sheldon Messinger, "The Inmate Social System," pp. 5–19. See also Empey, LaMar T., and Jerome Rabor, "The Provo Experiment in Delinquency Rehabilitation," *American Sociological Review*, vol. 26, October, 1961, pp. 679–696; and Ohlin, Lloyd E., *Sociology and the Field of Corrections*, Russell Sage Foundation, New York, 1956.
36. von Mering, Otto, and Stanley H. King, *op. cit.*, chaps. 1 and 9.
37. Cumming, John, and Elaine Cumming, "Social Equilibrium and Social Change in the Large Mental Hospital" in Greenblatt, Milton, Daniel J. Levinson, and Richard H. Williams, *The Patient and the Mental Hospital*, The Free Press, Glencoe, Ill., 1957, p. 49.
38. Kramer, Morton, "Problems of Research on the Population Dynamics and Therapeutic Effectiveness of Mental Hospitals" in Greenblatt, Levinson, and Williams, *op. cit.*, p. 146.
39. Kennard, Edward A., "Psychiatry, Administrative Psychiatry, Administration: A Study of a Veterans Hospital" in Greenblatt, Levinson, and Williams, *op. cit.*, p. 38.
40. *Ibid.*
41. von Mering, Otto, and Stanley H. King, p. 21.
42. *Ibid.*, pp. 32–33.
43. *Ibid.*, p. 51.
44. Klerman, Gerald L., "PSC-NIMH Collaborative Study of Phenothiazine Treatment of Acute Schizophrenic Psychoses," Research Design (Draft III), Bethesda, Maryland, June, 1960, p. 28, mimeographed. Cited for support of this conclusion are the following: Brill, H., and R. E. Patton, "Analysis of Population Reduction in New York State Mental Hospitals During the First Four Years of Large-Scale Therapy with Psychotropic Drugs," *American Journal of Psychiatry*, vol. 116, 1959, pp. 495–509; Brooks, G. W., "Experiences with the Use of Chlorpromazine and Reserpine in Psychiatry: With Especial Reference to the Significance and Management of Extrapyramidal Dysfunction," *New England Journal of Medicine*, vol. 254, June, 1956, pp. 1119–1123.
45. Greenblatt, Milton, "Toward a Therapeutic Community" in Greenblatt, York, and Brown, *op. cit.*, 1955, pp. 37–248.
46. Brown, Esther Lucile, "Introduction" to Greenblatt, York, and Brown, *op. cit.*, p. 17.

PART FOUR

THE FRAME OF REFERENCE AT WORK

Chapter 10

THE DOCTOR-PATIENT RELATIONSHIP AS A SOCIAL SYSTEM

IN THE CASE of Mrs. Tomasetti, as presented in Chapter 1, a number of questions were raised but not fully answered. We saw one physician frustrated and angry, unable to help his patient, and a second physician who, though younger and less experienced, was successful with the same patient. There were obvious differences in their approaches; yet neither understood exactly what was happening, the successful doctor no more than his predecessor. Since they both began with the identical diagnosis and prescribed the same medical treatment, we assumed that the major variables to explain the change in the course of Mrs. Tomasetti's illness could be found in the socioemotional aspects of her relationships with these two physicians.[1] This has been the goal of all the discussion intervening since we first described this case: to uncover those elements of the doctor-patient relationship which, if adequately understood, would have enabled Mrs. Tomasetti's first physician to maintain a good relationship with his patient. For the second physician, it would seem equally important to understand "what he was doing right," in order to gain the control needed to enable him consistently to benefit other patients.

In this final chapter we will resume the perspective of the physician as we attempt to understand the social dynamics of the doctor-patient relationship. If our discussion has provided a fuller awareness of the field of forces acting upon the relationship with his patient, how can the physician put this awareness to work? In answering this question, we will seek both to integrate material that has already been presented and to amplify it, particularly with regard to the concepts of culture and social role.

Culture and Interaction Process

In the two medical relationships in which we observed Mrs. Tomasetti, one constant element was her cultural orientation. Like other small groups, each of these relationships may be described as a separate social unit with its own characteristic internal environment; both, however, share approximately the same external environment, of which Mrs. Tomasetti's cultural orientation is one factor.

Culture has been compared to a blueprint. It provides patterns of behavior that guide both expectations of self and other. It seems clear that the first physician expected from Mrs. Tomasetti behavior that either was not communicated to her clearly or in some way was so contradictory to her conception of herself that she could not respond positively. Can the culture concept be used for a better understanding of this particular problem-situation? We will try to answer this question first by scrutinizing more precisely what the expectations were in the relationships between Mrs. Tomasetti and her doctors.

Mrs. Tomasetti's first doctor treated her very much as an independent rational individual. He was aware of the possibility that the diet he prescribed might be difficult to follow because of the customs which prevailed in Mrs. Tomasetti's family. But he reasoned: "It is your own health that is involved. Your family, under these circumstances, will understand if you adopt eating practices that are unfamiliar to them. You are doing this because you must, not because you wish to violate the customs you have been taught, and, of course, they will understand."

From the frame of reference of American middle-class culture, this kind of reasoning, with its emphasis upon *individualism*, is quite fitting. Does it, however, fit the point of view of Mrs. Tomasetti? Do we know enough about the southern Italian culture to predict whether the individualism which the staff-doctor requires from his patient is, indeed, appropriate for Mrs. Tomasetti?

Fortunately, the values of Italian-Americans have been studied intensively by Florence Kluckhohn.[2] In her studies of the families of psychiatric patients, conducted with the collaboration of John Spiegel,[3] the evidence indicates that the individualism so typical of American culture is not appropriate for Italian culture. Out of her own cultural background, one should expect that Mrs. Tomasetti would value her family even more than self. She cannot easily relinquish her role as part of her family, neighborhood, and cultural group. The requirements of her illness are, indeed, threatening, but whereas her doctor sees it as a threat to her survival as an individual, most likely Mrs. Tomasetti will see it as a threat to the harmony of the social pattern she knows and values most. Preservation of the family network is, according to her orientation, "more important than the fate or goals of an individual. . . . [Moreover] individualism is not well understood, and is often feared as showing selfishness, disloyalty, or outright hostility to the family."[4]

A second assumption the staff-physician made in his treatment of Mrs. Tomasetti was that she would be willing to give up something that was important in the present for the sake of a future reward (better health). Attitudes toward time, however, are cultural variables. Here again, according to Kluckhohn's description of cultural value-orientations, the evidence indicates that the doctor is making an invalid assumption. From her particular cultural background, Mrs. Tomasetti may be expected to live fully in the present, and accept fatalistically what the future may bring.

A third value-orientation is expressed by the doctor's belief that man is dominant over the forces of nature including, of course, illness. But the traditional Italian view is that man is helpless before nature. Contrasting with the doctor's basic optimism about man's relation to nature is Mrs. Tomasetti's tragic fatalism. Her cultural background provides her with "little understanding of or confidence in the use of technical devices or scientific procedures. . . ."[5] Even her willingness to follow faithfully the insulin therapy is probably explained by a magical conception of its efficacy rather than faith in its scientific effectiveness.

A fourth value-orientation is expressed in the staff physician's emphasis on "doing." In harmony with American culture, the doctor is a doer. To take some action, to achieve, is his primary reaction to challenge. It is clear from the conference we described that the staff physician expected the same from Mrs. Tomasetti and, no doubt, from all of his patients. He would supply the medical advice, but his patients must *want to get well;* they are expected to take responsibility for following the doctor's orders and to try to get well. In Mrs. Tomasetti's cultural experience, however, spontaneous emotional expression takes precedence over doing.

By pointing up areas of "no fit" between Mrs. Tomasetti and her first physician, attention is called to *what not to do.* Can the value-orientation scheme also be used to help the physician decide what he can do that is more likely to help a patient of this type? With this question in mind, let us review the approach of Florence Kluckhohn.

Values are standards of *desirability*, "couched in terms of good or bad, beautiful or ugly, pleasant or unpleasant, appropriate or inappropriate."[6] The concept overlaps with *norms* that are rules of conduct, specifying what should and should not be done by various kinds of people in various kinds of situations. Culture organizes its norms with reference to values; or, in other words, values provide the criteria of desirability by which concrete goals of action emerge, and which, in turn, guide the patterns of conduct.[7] We do not mean to present a deceptively simple explanation of a complex concept that has many subtle shadings to its meaning.[8] For our present purpose, we will be content to define values as conceptions of the desirable—of the desirable qualities of objects, behavior, or social structures, and systems.[9]

Value-orientation is a concept that has been used to refer to clusters of values that arrange themselves around important themes in society. Gunnar Myrdal, for example, in his classic study of American attitudes toward its Negro minority, spoke of a configuration of value-orientations that make up the "American Creed."[10]

Florence Kluckhohn prefers to classify the major types of value-orientation according to life-problems that are crucial and common to all human groups. Value-orientation, she states, is an extension of the value concept that refers to "highly organized conceptions of vital aspects of human behavior."[11] The five problems which Kluckhohn regards as basic to all human groups, together with the names she gives the value-orientation associated with them are as follows, stated in the form of questions:

1. What is the character of innate human nature? (*Human-Nature* Orientation)
2. What is the relation of man to nature (supernature)? (*Man-Nature* Orientation)
3. What is the temporal focus of human life? (*Time* Orientation)
4. What is the modality of human activity? (*Activity* Orientation)
5. What is the modality of man's relationship to other men? (*Relational* Orientation)[12]

In addition to facing these same problems, Kluckhohn asserts, all cultures choose their solutions from certain logical alternatives. (For example, each culture chooses between the conception of man's inner nature as being basically evil, basically good, or a mixture of good and evil.) Therefore, in the comparative study of cultures, one finds much variation, but the variation of value-orientations is neither limitless nor random: ". . . it is both as definite and as essential as the demonstrated systematic variation in physical and biological phenomena."[13]

In the relationship between Mrs. Tomasetti and her first doctor, it is not difficult to see how the patterns of cultural value-orientations arrange themselves into two quite opposite patterns. In the physician, one finds individualism, future-orientation, belief in man's dominance over nature, and an emphasis on doing —all interdependent and mutually reinforcing. They are value-orientations that serve the needs of modern American industrial society very well in many respects—but in this instance, they are so deeply embedded in the frame of reference of the physician as an individual that he takes them for granted in himself and expects them to guide the behavior of his patients. In Mrs. Tomasetti, on the other hand, a cultural pattern directly opposite from that of her doctor is equally served by a set of integrated value-orientations: the preeminence of collateral family-type relations over individualism, a time-orientation to the present, a sense of powerlessness before the forces of nature, and a spontaneous emotional type of responsiveness.

The influence of the cultural factor is not uniform in this example; it varies with the stages of the illness and their associated interpersonal requirements. When Mrs. Tomasetti is comatose, her first physician is able to treat her medical needs. In the first steps out of this extreme condition in her illness, he is again able to help her. As soon as she leaves the controlled environment of the hospital, however, the relationship is lost, almost before it has an opportunity to get started. What is important in life for the physician is so different from that for his patient that they never achieve a really meaningful social contact. Each action that is taken in this relationship is like the behavior produced by the effect of one billiard ball upon another, where no systematic relations are maintained once the force is expended.[14]

As demonstrated by the student-physician in Mrs. Tomasetti's case, there are more hopeful alternatives. Although he was not fully aware of it himself, his behavior fitted into a social pattern which was close enough to that of his patient to allow her at least to establish a comfortable and meaningful relationship with him. To an extent, this was a fortunate accident, since he admitted that he would have approached the patient in much the same manner as his predecessor except for the latter's obvious failure. However, it need not have been an accident. Given an understanding of the cultural components, much of what actually happened in this case, for both physicians, was predictable.

For example, when Mrs. Tomasetti first saw the student-physician in the hospital, he encouraged her to talk freely. He was acting from what he thought were logical considerations; namely, the direct methods tried before had not worked, so perhaps if the patient were encouraged to talk about herself and her life patterns, she would reveal hitherto unknown factors that would help in the management of her dietary needs. From the viewpoint of Mrs. Tomasetti, on the other hand, this appeared to be an interest by the doctor in her and her life as she herself valued it. In contrast to the first physician's explanations, warnings, and threats, all in terms of values that were quite alien to her, this was the kind of behavior she was accustomed to from family and friends. In the terms used by Florence Kluckhohn, this patient was first approached with a demand "to do" something, when her customary approach to life was less that of "doing" and more of "being." By allowing her to express the spontaneous emotionality that was deeply embedded in her cultural orientation, the student-physician opened the way for the establishment of a more meaningful relationship. Put in still another way, a social system was created that, by achieving a quick harmonious balance, showed promise of further development toward the management of its problems and the achievement of its goals.

The student-physician's next step was even more directly fitted to Mrs. Tomasetti's background. Again, his own reasons for visiting her home were, as far as he was aware, according to the logic of the case. It was in the home that her difficulties with the diet occurred, and therefore he wanted to observe for himself what happened in that setting. From the patient's point of view, however, her home and family were above everything else her commitment in life. Virtually all her social relationships were influenced by this "collateral" orientation. By his visit to her family, the student-physician added another important building block to his relationship with Mrs. Tomasetti.

When the student-physician brought the family into active responsibility for Mrs. Tomasetti's treatment, he was implementing the patient's collateral orientation even further. Again, one is struck by the contrast. The first physician made this patient individually responsible for her own treatment. From his point of view and the more familiar cultural background of most of his patients, this request to "go-it-alone" was a reasonable and appropriate decision. In Mrs. Tomasetti's case, however, individualistic behavior was not only unfamiliar, it was in competition with the realities of her family life. Only by giving the special dietary requirements of her illness a place and meaning within the Tomasetti family did it become possible for her to accept it. Their mother's special diet, in other words, became psychologically "ours" for the whole Tomasetti family and not just "mine," in an isolated sense, for Mrs. Tomasetti.

It should be noted that the student-physician found it difficult himself to "go-it-alone" in this case. In the new traditions of "team" and comprehensive medicine, his decision to consult with the social worker and the public health nurse was correct and proved to be important in the final resolution of the patient's major problem. Medical social work, like nursing and other occupations in the health team, is in a very active developmental stage professionally, and therefore is still used less commonly by physicians than other forms of consultation.[15] Most important to this case is the fact that the social work consultant was used selectively and with purpose, and not as a last resort. The consultation was based on the physician's judgment that social and emotional factors were the important determining variables. Such factors are too often seen as "residual" or, as in so much research on therapy, as "contaminating" influences.[16]

A very similar experience to that described in the Tomasetti case has been reported by Spiegel and Kluckhohn from their work with Irish patients. They, too, found it necessary to shift the standard gears of the doctor-patient relationship in order to break an impasse created between a therapist and his patient by conflicting cultural values.[17]

The Irish have been observed to emphasize "lineal" relations between the individual and other men. This is explained as an emphasis upon a vertical hierarchy. In family terms, individualistic values are expressed in "mine" and "thine" attitudes toward property; lineal refers to "father's," "the eldest son's," and so forth; and the collateral orientation speaks of "ours."

Describing the American family, Spiegel says: "In American families the Individualistic orientation is in first position, the Collateral second, while the Lineal is the least favored. Thus, there is a certain amount of resentment felt toward any hierarchy and toward anyone who acts too 'bossy.' Husbands share authority, as well as other domestic roles, with their wives. Parents hope that their children will voluntarily manifest correct behavior so that the issue of discipline and authoritarian controls can be avoided. Every attempt is made to foster the autonomy of the individual family member and to allow children to make their own decisions. Thus independence and self-reliance form an important part of the egalitarian ethos. However, if group loyalty is to be invoked [as in organized games and sports] or when the family is to be represented in the community, then it is the collateral, groupwide emphasis that comes to the fore."[18]

"In the Irish-American family," Spiegel continues, "the lineal principle holds first rank; collaterality is second and individualism is in the third order position. The group, whether the family, a bureaucratic organization, or the church, always comes ahead of the individual. The ordered succession to hierarchical positions over time is constantly emphasized. For example, the father is very much the head of the family and never hesitates to express his authority over the wife and children. But if his own father is still alive, he owes him the same kind of respect and obedience which he showed as a child. In contrast to the American family, the Irish family trains its children for dependent behavior which is expected to remain a constant throughout life. This tends to backfire in a certain amount of hostility to authority, of which the political rebel in Irish history is a good example. Nevertheless, dependency training is on the whole thoroughly accepted, and is well reinforced through the mutual care and aid offered by the extended family, religious and community networks."[19]

With these cultural data in mind, Spiegel reports that his therapeutic team took an approach to their Irish-American patients "which emphasized the importance of the extended family and the community to the functioning of the individual. Although therapy concentrates mainly on the mother, father and child," Spiegel wrote, "we [the therapeutic team] attempt to see and make ourselves known to a wide assortment of relatives. This means that we become assimilated, to a certain extent, to the lineal chains of influence which bear upon the pathologic deviations in the family members. In addition, members of the therapeutic team become known, not simply as individuals, but also as members of a readily identifiable organization. This approximation of individuals and organizations reduces the fear of the strange, unknown group and, simultaneously, raises its prestige. At the same time, we have shown our willingness to depart from the routine of regular office appointments whenever this is necessary. Seeing family members when and where they are available is closer to the Present Time and Being orientations. Therefore, it is more apt to be perceived as a valid act of attention than strict adherence to a Future-oriented appointment book, and other bureaucratic routines."[20]

The results of these experimental attempts to use cultural data in direct aid to the therapeutic task, though modest, have been encouraging. In Spiegel's own words: "The results of [these modifications] are not spectacular. They have not led to dramatic relief of symptoms . . . but we have gained the conviction that we have been able to establish and maintain therapeutic contact with patients who would otherwise have been rejected or would have dropped out of treatment. We have been able to produce small increases in insight in individual family members. We have been impressed with the fact that a small gain in one or two family members is registered as a large gain in the total functioning of the family."[21]

The more traditional approach in psychiatry is to explain this type of situation with an emphasis upon psychological determinants. Hollender's discussion of the basic problem in diabetes is an example. The reader will recall Hollender's three models of the doctor-relationship quoted in Chapter 1 of this report from an article he wrote jointly with T. S. Szasz: (a) activity-passivity, (b) guidance cooperation, and (c) mutual participation. In a later publication Hollender has this to say:

> In each model the participation of doctor and patient is complementary. The stability of this paired system must be temporary since the physician strives to alter the patient's condition. The comatose patient will either recover [become conscious] or die. If he improves, the doctor-patient relationship must change. It is at this point that the physician's inner [usually unacknowledged] needs are most apt to interfere with what is "best" for the patient. At this juncture he either changes his attitude [not a consciously or deliberately assumed role] to complement the patient's emergent needs, or he foists upon the patient the very role of helpless passivity from which he [allegedly] tried to rescue him in the first place. The process of change which the physician undergoes to have a mutually constructive experience with the patient is similar to the change a parent must undergo to behave *ever differently* toward his growing child.
>
> This thesis can be illustrated by the following example. When a patient with diabetes mellitus is brought to the hospital in coma, the relationship must be based on the activity-passivity model. The

physician must *do* something to the patient who is completely helpless [unconscious]. Later the patient has to be educated [guided] and during this stage he must cooperate. Finally, ideally, he is treated as a full-fledged partner in the management of his own health [mutual participation].

Confronted by a problem of this type, the physician is called upon to change through a corresponding spectrum of attitudes. If he cannot make these changes, the patient regards him as unsympathetic and lacking in an understanding of his personally unique needs, while he regards the patient as uncooperative and difficult. Both are right. Both are confronted by the wish to induce changes in the other. Since this is no easy task, the dilemma is usually resolved in one of two ways. The patient attempts to conform to the physician's "requirements." Periods of rebellion [resulting in "poor" management] may then occur from time to time. The other, and more frequent, result is that the patient seeks another physician, one who is more attuned to his current "needs."[22]

We will take issue with this interpretation only to point out that it assumes that the doctor and the patient begin from a common cultural frame of reference. There is no question that personality is a factor in such relationships, that some physicians are more comfortable (out of their inner individual needs) when they are *doing to* a patient rather than when *guiding* or *participating with* a patient in treatment. Thus one must consider the possibility that Mrs. Tomasetti's second physician was more successful than the first because he was less rigid as a person and therefore more able to change his own approach in tune with her changing psychological needs and the changing requirements that follow from the development of the illness. Nevertheless, we believe it is equally true that cultural differences have a comparable power to influence the relationship. In this conclusion we join Spiegel's assessment of his experimental use of cultural variables in psychotherapy. Spiegel takes care to make clear that the modifications in approach which he describes are not to be considered general prescriptions for the field of psychotherapy as a whole. He argues only that modifications in technique should be rationally adapted to the varieties of cultural value-orientations that exist among patients. He proposes, as we do, that problems of cultural dynamics deserve similar consideration to that given in the past to purely psychologic processes.

Because of the unique history of immigrant populations in the United States, problems of intercultural communication like those presented by the Italian-American or Irish-American retain more than academic interest. In spite of the fact that large-scale immigration was stopped after World War I, a significant number of Americans continue a deep ethnic identification with other still-living cultural groups. For the physician this is part of reality. In the eastern part of the United States his patients are likely to include Puerto-Ricans and various European-Americans. In the Southwest, a large Spanish-speaking minority exists. In other places, one deals with people of Slavic, Scandinavian, and Oriental origins.

On the other hand, time has neutralized many of these ethnic differences, and the amalgamation of its many types of immigrants into a general American type has proceeded steadily. Does this mean that the variable represented by culture will become gradually insignificant for the physician? This is not likely because of the phenomenon that is called "subculture."

Modern society, as Saunders has pointed out, is too complex for an individual to encompass all of the culture of the society in which he is born. Consequently, subcultural groups emerge; that is, ". . . aggregations of people who have in common some, but not all, of the elements of a given culture."[23] Such groups form on the basis of region, race, and social class. In modern society, occupation has become increasingly important in determining the community of one's close associates. Thus one's sense of identity and the source of reference for values and norms have become more and more conditioned by one's work or way of life. For the professions, this is even more true, so that the medical profession is an example of an important subcultural group.

The approach to culture as a variable in the doctor-patient relationship is valid, we believe, for subcultural variables. In our presentation of the Q- family in Chapter 5, for example, social class was a major factor in the problem of determining effective medical care. The value-orientations of social class were analogous in their form to cultural value-orientations.

In the study of small groups, culture represents that class of variables which is part of the group's external environment. In the Q- family we traced first the influences that came from the American culture and its class system; then we turned to what were called the internal social dynamics of the group. Our analysis of the doctor-patient relationship as a social system proceeds in a similar way from emphasis on the external to a consideration of its internal environment.

The Internal Social Dynamics of the Doctor-Patient Relationship

Cultural factors provide a constant external field in which the doctor-patient relationship exists as a social unit. Internal to the group, patterns of interaction develop according to its own particular dynamics. Nothing is static in this situation. Cultural and subcultural forces set the baseline of expectations about the behavior of self and others, but elements of culture are either invoked or dormant, depending upon cues in the immediate ongoing relationship. Similarly, stable patterns of behavior are formed to manage the social-emotional problems indigenous to the group, but as in any system, they are largely quiescent, in the group's "memory," until aroused by their appropriate cues. Moreover, the internal and external fields overlap, acting upon each other. Because of the complexity of this system, it is, in an important sense, artificial to separate these intricately interwoven factors into two "fields" of influence. Nevertheless, it is a logical separation that, for purposes of analysis, is well justified.[24]

It will be recalled that in an earlier graphic representation of the doctor-patient relationship (see Figure 3, page 63) the doctor (A) and his patient (B) are shown interacting in two dimensions: (x) in processes of communication that emphasize the "human," or social-emotional problems, and (y) in ways that are focused on the main task of the relationship. Research in small group dynamics has called attention to these two types of "interaction process" as being typical of all small groups. They speak of the former (x) as *expressive* interaction, and the task-oriented category (y) as *instrumental*.[25] All social interaction, they assert, can be categorized according to its emphasis as either expressive or instrumental.

These same terms have been applied to the analysis of social roles in small groups. The conception of role here is dynamic, portraying patterns of the adjustment of role behavior according to their function for the establishment and maintenance of the group as a social system. Spiegel has developed this approach with particular reference to the doctor-patient relationship in a form that we believe merits the detailed attention of this discussion. As an introduction to Spiegel's method, his description of a "clinical fragment" from a relationship between a psychiatrist and his patient is inserted here.

THE CASE OF THE INTELLECTUAL WOMAN[26]

Spiegel describes a twenty-three-year-old, highly intelligent girl (a Ph.D. in mathematics) who came to him for psychiatric treatment most specifically because of a sense of poor adjustment to her chosen career. She was, by his description, "haunted by a deep and abiding sense of shame, on which account she was extremely shy and retiring in all her social relationships." The sample which Spiegel extracts from this relationship for the exposition of his method is from one of the regular therapeutic interviews. These interviews had been going on for some time, so that we may assume that the special "rules of the game" associated with this type of doctor-patient situation were well established for the patient.

On the occasion described, the relationship began according to its major working purpose, that is, the patient began discussing her "problem" by speaking of her abilities and career. Suddenly, however, the discussion shifted when the patient asked the doctor if he had seen a recent performance of a play, "Don Juan in Hell." The doctor did not respond to the question. After a pause, the patient continued, delivering a "highly perceptive account of Shaw's intention in the Don Juan interlude, of the actor's interpretation, and her reactions."

The doctor, after listening for some time, interrupted to ask if the patient knew why she wanted to tell him all this. She responded by saying she was "just chattering because she felt like it and that there was no particular reason for her talking about the play."

"I now told the patient," Spiegel states, "that I thought she must be feeling disappointed because she had hoped to interest me in the quality of her grasp of aesthetics. To this description of what I assumed had taken place between us, the patient had an intense reaction. She immediately covered her face with her hands and declared herself to be horribly embarrassed. Her face felt hot and red, the whole room felt hot—so intense was her feeling of shame. She felt that I had reprimanded her, as if she were a child."

How may the analysis of this interaction as a system of social roles help the doctor understand his patient? What, if any, contribution does a role analysis make to the therapy of this patient?

In his answer to these questions, Spiegel states: "It seems clear that if two people relate to each other at all, they become involved in a system of transaction characterized by mutually regulative processes which we ordinarily term adaptation or adjustment." The term "transaction" is preferred to "interaction" by Spiegel because it contains a specific connotation of mutual interrelationship and interdependence, attributes that are important to the conception of social system. "Transaction," he writes, "is a term introduced . . . to describe reciprocal, reverberating processes which occur in any system of action or behavior. In such a system, especially if it is in equilibrium, there occur two-way, phasic and cyclical exchanges which are largely self-regulating and self-correcting—that is, they keep the system going. A key example of transactional processes at the somatic level is the neural and hormonal exchanges which keep the body at a constant temperature."

In relationships between two or more people, Spiegel continues, ". . . these [transactional] processes are mediated by the exchange of information which is called communication. Thus, if we want to describe the doctor-patient situation as systematically as possible, we will study the flow of communication—verbal and nonverbal—that occurs in the system of transactions as it becomes established by the incorporation of the doctor and the patient within it. If such a study is to be successful, we should be able to name and describe the mechanisms which disturb the equilibrium in the system as well as those which restore it. Furthermore, we should be able to assign responsibility for perturbations in the equilibrium of the system to either doctor or patient, as the case might be."[27]

In the scene described above, the major item of communication is the patient's discussion of the play, "Don Juan in Hell." When the patient in this case introduced her elaborate drama criticism into the interview with the doctor, she was introducing new elements into the social situation. Immediately prior, the patient was discussing her "problem," accepting the patient role that was most customary. She was, in other words, behaving as a patient is expected to by discussing the symptoms of her disturbance (illness). We might say that she was accepting her *explicit, assigned role*. She was, at the same time, acting toward the doctor according to his customary role. The system of roles, between the doctor and the patient, was *complementary* and apparently well integrated. By introducing the discussion of "Don Juan in Hell," the patient was *implicitly* changing the role-structure of the relationship. Explaining his behavior at this point, Spiegel writes: "The question seemed a simple enough request for information regarding my play-going habits. But since I did not know what role I was being invited to take, because I suspected that behind whatever explicit role this might turn out to be there lurked a more important implicit one, I did not answer the question."

As the relationship continued, however, the intentions of the patient became more clear. "I became aware," Spiegel writes, "that my new role was an expressive one—to play the appreciative audience to her role as a gifted art and drama critic." At this point, he faced what must certainly be a common alternative in any doctor-patient relationship, and particularly in psychotherapy: he could have accepted the patient's implicit definition of the situation by taking the assigned role (appreciative audience), and supporting the patient with praise for a brilliant art criticism or, at least, with discussion of the intellectual content of her statement. Thus the complementarity and equilibrium of the relationship would be preserved, but on terms assigned by the patient. On the other hand, to do so, Spiegel believed, "would have meant passing up the opportunity to get more information regarding the hidden, implicit role buried in this transaction and thus to learn more about her motivation for shifting out of her initial instrumental [goal-directed] role in which she had started the interview."

Under these conditions, the doctor made his choice according to the long-term goals of the relationship. He rejected the role his patient was assigning to him, and interrupted the equilibrium of the transaction. The patient's response was to shift from brilliant art critic to "idle gossip and chatterer." Such a radical shift, however, raised further questions. "If she was not the gossip," the doctor reasoned, "it must have been that I thought her so. In other words, she must have interpreted my question as indicating I did not appreciate her talents and that I thought she was just chattering. In identifying with my assumed view of her, she was able to control her intense disappointment and thus to maintain the feeling of closeness to me which was being threatened."

Again, the doctor was faced with an alternative. Should he go along with the patient's redefinition of the situation, thereby protecting her feelings of comfort by not challenging what is obviously a defensive maneuver? Or should he make explicit his interpretation of what is happening, again interrupting the equilibrium of the transaction? When he chose the latter alternative, the patient was emotionally shattered, an indication that an extremely significant area of life experience had been uncovered. *"She felt that I had reprimanded her, as if she were a child."* This emotional reaction by the patient, in turn, became the basis of another restructuring of the relationship. As described by Spiegel, this occurred as follows:

> Because of the intensity of her reaction, I waited some moments until she became calmer. Then I speculated aloud that her expectation that I would accept the role of appreciator—of one who puts great emphasis on artistic achievements—must have been learned in some previous experience. In response she told me that her father was greatly interested in intellectual and artistic pursuits and could seldom make contact with anyone except at this level. When she was a child, dinner-table conversations used to consist of long orations by her father on some intellectual topic-conversations which she was

hardly ever allowed to enter, on the ground that she was not qualified.

As she spoke, the similarity of the role relations that she thought she had experienced with me to the role she felt she had occupied in relation to her father became clear to both of us. She felt that she had tried to master with me a situation which she had never mastered at home, had failed, and had then felt presumptuous, exposed and ashamed—just as she had all her life. Thus, the implicit role which guided her in talking to me about the play had finally become explicit and clear.

Reviewing briefly the role concept that has been applied to this case, there are first two general categories of social role: *instrumental* and *expressive*. "Instrumental roles are designed for solving problems, and emotion has little place in them. Expressive roles are patterned for the expression of feeling or emotion and are not concerned with getting anything done." Roles, furthermore, may be *implicit* or *explicit*. In all human relationships, roles are being consciously or unconsciously *assumed, assigned, accepted,* or *declined*.

The complementarity of the roles is, according to Spiegel, "the chief homeostatic or regulative mechanism in the system. . . . Roles are culturally patterned to dovetail or integrate with each other by means of reciprocal actions, verbal communications or symbolic gestures. A question calls forth an answer, and the answer maintains equilibrium in the system." If one refuses to answer a question, or answers in unexpected ways, tension is introduced in the system.

The doctor in the case just described is shown in the act of applying the analysis of a transactional system to achieve a therapeutic purpose. He deliberately interrupted the equilibrium of the relationship to gain information about the implicit content of his patient's behavior. By knowing what he was doing, his control of the situation was increased, and consequently his power to use the psychosocial elements of the situation to help the patient was increased. If he had refused to play a complementary role in this situation *without* conscious and purposeful intent, he would have produced anger or anxiety in both his patient and himself. This is what usually occurs when a doctor refuses to pay attention to a patient's complaints, or when a patient does not follow the doctor's orders.

Of course, this is a special type of doctor-patient relationship for which the analogy with other types of medical relationships must be carefully qualified. The doctor, in a relationship of this type, expects and deliberately encourages the patient to use him as an object that symbolizes other significant people in the patient's life experience. By the disciplined understanding of such a situation, the doctor is able to utilize the doctor-patient relationship as the major instrument of therapy. In most doctor-patient relationships, on the other hand, the major goal of the relationship between doctor and patient is not psychological therapy; it is the diagnosis and effective management of somatic complaints. This difference between the cases is significant particularly for the handling of the acceptance and rejection by the physician of the role-assignments made by the patient.

In the case of Spiegel's intellectual woman, the doctor manipulated the transactional aspects of the relationship, interrupting the complementarity of roles in order to *uncover* the hidden implication of the patient's behavior. Although this disturbed the patient's feelings, the doctor controlled the situation, restoring the balance of complementarity when he judged that the patient could no longer tolerate this type of treatment.

This degree of knowledge about a patient, however, takes more time than a doctor is ordinarily allowed. Time is also required to establish the kind of "rules of the game" Spiegel was able to use as cues for judging shifts in his patient's behavior.

The limitations of a busy medical practice are not so great, however, that they must prevent the doctor from being sensitive to the transactional aspects of his relationships with patients. In the case of Mrs. Tomasetti, for example, this type of awareness might have served a critically useful purpose. The relationship with her first physician was disturbed, but the doctor did not conceive of it as a two-way system. He focused instead upon what he saw as the patient's noncooperative behavior. Instead of this serving as a cue to the need for a change in his approach to the patient, he reacted with frustration and anger, after "reasoning" with the patient.

Following Spiegel's method, what can be added to our view of the Tomasetti case? First, in terms of the processes of interaction —or, as Spiegel prefers, *transaction*—the first physician treated the relationship with an intense focus upon the instrumental, or task-oriented, processes. He was highly conscientious in his own utilization of the technological skills of his profession. He expected the patient to respond with a similar dedication to the main purpose of the relationship. With a different type of patient this approach would be appropriate, but not with Mrs. Tomasetti. She was not prepared by her cultural background to deal with illness—or with anything else—in such organized rational terms. She was emotional; she lacked the same faith in science that the physician had; she was not trained for the special kind of sacrifices he demanded, and the reward he offered, "health," did not have the same meaning for her that it had for him.

Her next step was to reject implicitly the role assignments of the physician. This he interpreted, with rage, as duplicity—as lying or subterfuge. Actually, such contradiction between explicit and implicit role behavior is not unusual; to judge it, under these circumstances, as a *moral infraction*, misses entirely— indeed obscures—what is its most probable meaning. This becomes clear in Spiegel's discussion of the interplay between explicit and implicit roles:

> If one focuses a high-power microscope—so to speak—on the processes inherent in role systems, it becomes plain that any two-person system is characterized by multiple, simultaneously enacted roles. Everyone wears many hats at the same time. . . . This multiple, layered structure of roles is arranged in an order of nearness and remoteness from the surface aspect of the social situation. The *explicit* roles are those that are closest to the surface and therefore closest to the observation and awareness of the participants. In addition, they are oriented to the most highly structured and therefore the most stable aspects of the social situation. *Implicit* roles, on the other hand, are thus more subtle, complicated, and variable. Associated with their remote position in the role-structuring of human relations is the fact that the implicit roles are the seat of the chief emotional currents and dynamic trends in the social situation. It is the configuration of

implicit roles assumed by a person that constitutes his "character." The life, the color, the vividness of any human situation is given by the interplay among explicit and implicit roles.[28]

What this means in application to Mrs. Tomasetti is that her apparent duplicity was more accurately a reflection of deep-seated motives that prevented her from cooperating with the doctor even though she quite honestly, on the manifest conscious level of behavior, wanted to cooperate.

It will be recognized that the conception of implicit roles is very close to psychological theories of the unconscious. Indeed, Spiegel intends it as a bridge concept between sociology and psychoanalysis. Therefore, it does not violate this method to include psychological factors in the explanation of behavior together with the dissection of social role dynamics.

The Full Context of the Doctor-Patient Relationship

The schema of social system analysis is not limited to an isolated view of the doctor-patient relationship as a two-person group. If it were, it would not be adaptable to the modern medical situation, in which the doctor's role has been, to a significant extent, assigned to a medical team and in which the relationship has moved largely out of the home and the private office to the hospital. We have done no more than introduce the potential applications of research in group dynamics and organizational analysis to the doctor-patient analysis seen in its full context.

Our sketch, at this point, may be redrawn as shown in Figure 4. Graphically, this represents the doctor and the patient, acting in their respective roles (A and B) in a transactional social system $(x + y)$. The internal environment of the relationship is contained within these four elements, $A + B$ and $x + y$; however, the interpretation of roles A and B is initially dependent upon a series of social forces. For the doctor, the major source of reference for his behavior as a physician is the medical profession (A'); for the patient, it is the family (B'). Both A' and B', however, are based in the dominant culture (C), and together these three $(A' + B' + C)$ form the comprehensive external environment in which the group itself $(A + B)$ exists. Further subdivision of the

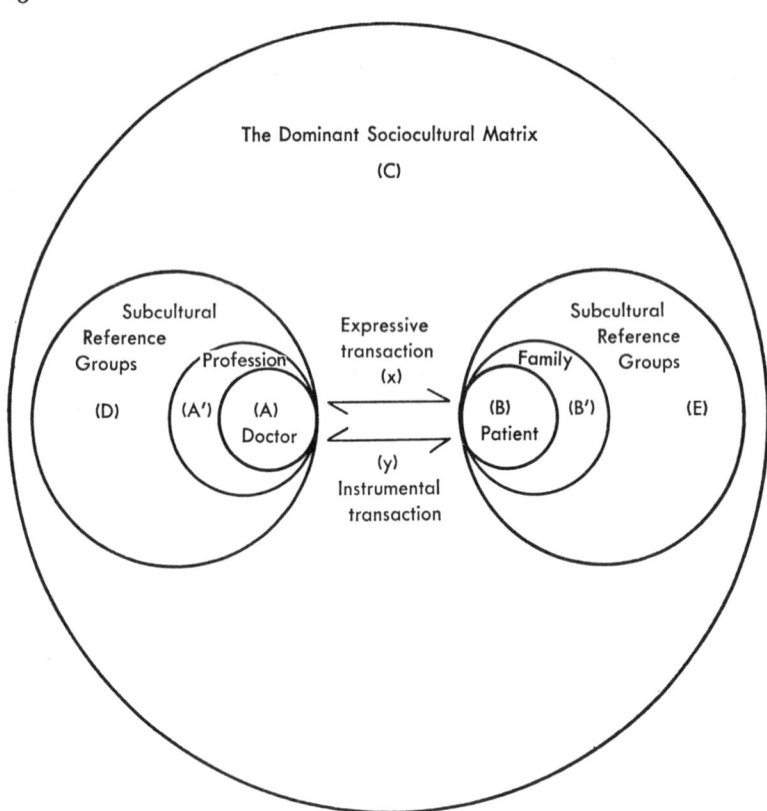

FIGURE 4. THE TOTAL TRANSACTIONAL SYSTEM

cultural factor is included as "subcultural reference groups." These refer to such factors as class, race, region, and ethnicity which function in particular cases as the significant sources of value-orientation for either or both the doctor and his patient.

Not included in this sketch is the hospital, but one can easily visualize its place as a major institution of the dominant sociocultural matrix, encompassing all of the classes of individual shown here, and adding the hospital "team."

Conclusions

An outline of the contents of these pages can be summarized in the following three propositions: (1) social and emotional factors are important in many medical problems and crucial in some;

(2) the scientific method is applicable to the study of such factors; and (3) a conceptual frame of reference that is both logically and empirically derived is valuable for the discernment of psychosocial factors and for the differential judgment of their significance. Our emphasis has been upon the formulation of an approach that would be compatible both to the established practices of the social sciences and to the special situation of medical students. In the process, time was not taken for the description of much that is already available in the content of the sciences of behavior which is relevant to medicine.

This choice was deliberate not only because this is a period in social science more of rapid development than of stable theory and well-established knowledge, but also because it is with the approach of method and a focus upon process that we believe education best serves the needs of students to proceed on their own. Nevertheless, it should be noted that the past two decades have witnessed important achievements in these fields.

During this period attention has been directed by social scientists to varied types of social phenomena in medicine. Some examples which we have discussed at least partially here include: (1) the growing place of medicine and medical practice in the western world; (2) the different attitudes and values which various subcultural and other subgroups of the population have toward health, illness, and medical care; (3) the social structure and functioning of hospitals; and (4) the social roles played by patients and health personnel as they interact in different settings.

Other areas of study are only barely mentioned here, including two that have been particularly active. The first is the education of doctors and other health personnel. As these studies seek to show, the conception of such education should weight the learning of attitudes and values with at least equal importance to skills and knowledge. The second type of investigation to which we have not been able to give the attention it ordinarily would deserve is concerned with how various social and psychological factors relate to different kinds of disease in patients and in the course of certain diseases.[29]

As recent books demonstrate,[30] full descriptions of all these areas are becoming increasingly available, and the hope is thereby encouraged that both education and research in the social science of medicine will be facilitated.

Finally, let us say that no more than a working model is intended in the sketch which has been presented of the sociological processes basic to the doctor-patient relationship. Its purpose is to formulate some of the problems inherent in medicine that require attention to their psychosocial aspects before comprehensive solutions are possible. In this purpose we seek not to deflect or replace the contributions of other disciplines, but to join them in the common task of seeking deeper and more comprehensive knowledge, and thereby to serve more effectively in those situations of immediate and practical need, such as illness, where all possible skill must be mustered, to help humanity in trouble.

NOTES TO CHAPTER 10

1. See Hollender, Marc H., *The Psychology of Medical Practice*, W. B. Saunders Co., Philadelphia, 1958, pp. 5–6 and 213.

2. Kluckhohn, Florence R., "Dominant and Substitute Profiles of Cultural Orientations: Their Significance for the Analysis of Social Stratification," *Social Forces*, vol. 28, May, 1950, pp. 376–394. Also, by the same author, "Variations in the Basic Values of Family Systems," *Social Casework*, vol. 39, February, 1958, pp. 63–72.

3. Kluckhohn, Florence R., and John P. Spiegel, *Integration and Conflict in Family Behavior*. Group for the Advancement of Psychiatry (Report No. 27), Topeka, Kans., August, 1954.

4. Spiegel, John P., and Florence R. Kluckhohn, "The Influence of the Family and Cultural Values on the Mental Health and Illness of an Individual." Review of Work in Progress on M-971. Unpublished manuscript, p. 12.

5. *Ibid.*, p. 16.

6. See Williams, Robin M., Jr., *American Society:* A Sociological Interpretation, 2d ed., rev., Alfred A. Knopf, Inc., New York, 1961, p. 24.

7. *Ibid.*, pp. 397–400.

8. *Ibid.*, chaps. 3 and 11. See also Kluckhohn, Florence R., and Fred L. Strodtbeck, *Variations in Value Orientations*. Row, Peterson and Co., Evanston, Ill., 1961, chap. 1.

9. Williams, Robin M., *op. cit.*, p. 402.

10. Myrdal, Gunnar, with the assistance of Richard Sterner and Arnold Rose, *An American Dilemma*. Harper and Bros., New York, 1944, 2 vols.

11. Cited as the source of this definition is Clyde Kluckhohn's "Values and Value-Orientations in the Theory of Action" in Parsons, Talcott, Edward A. Shils, and others, *Toward a General Theory of Action*. Harvard University Press, Cambridge, Mass., 1951, pp. 411 ff.

12. Kluckhohn, Florence R., and Fred L. Strodtbeck, *op. cit.*, 1961, p. 11.

13. *Ibid.*, p. 3.

14. This example is used by Kluckhohn and Spiegel in *Integration and Conflict in Family Behavior* to describe the meaning of "interaction" as compared to "transaction."

15. King, Stanley H., *Perceptions of Illness and Medical Practice*. Russell Sage Foundation, New York, 1962, p. 281.

16. See Hollender, Marc H., *op. cit.*, pp. 5-6, and p. 213.

17. Spiegel, John, "Some Cultural Aspects of Transference and Countertransference" in Masserman, Jules H., editor, *Individual and Familial Dynamics*. Grune and Stratton, Inc., New York, 1959, pp. 160-182.

18. *Ibid.*, pp. 168-169.

19. *Ibid.*

20. *Ibid.*, p. 180.

21. *Ibid.*, p. 181.

22. Hollender, Marc H., *op. cit.*, pp. 7-8.

23. Saunders, Lyle, *Cultural Difference and Medical Care*. Russell Sage Foundation, New York, 1954, p. 8.

24. Those familiar with the work of Homans will recognize his strong influence on this discussion. See Homans, George C., *The Human Group*, Harcourt, Brace and Co., New York, 1950.

25. Bales, Robert F., *Interaction Process Analysis*. Addison-Wesley Press, Cambridge, 1950. This is a classic early statement of a research approach to the study of small groups. For a more recent review, see Olmstead, Michael S., *The Small Group*, Random House, New York, 1959.

26. Spiegel, John P., "The Social Role of Doctor and Patient in Psychoanalysis and Psychotherapy," *Psychiatry*, vol. 17, November, 1954, pp. 369-376. This article is the source from which all the data of what we call "The Case of the Intellectual Woman" are taken. Unless otherwise indicated, quotations are from this article.

27. Kluckhohn, Florence R., and John P. Spiegel, *Integration and Conflict in Family Behavior*, pp. 21-22.

28. Spiegel, John P., "The Social Role of Doctor and Patient in Psychoanalysis and Psychotherapy," p. 373.

29. We are indebted for this sixfold classification of medical sociology to George G. Reader and Mary E. W. Goss, "The Sociology of Medicine" in Merton, Robert K., Leonard Broom, and Leonard S. Cottrell, Jr., editors, *Sociology Today: Problems and Prospects*, Basic Books, Inc., New York, 1959, pp. 229-246. They include a bibliography for each classification.

30. A selected list of these books appears on page 51, note 18.

INDEX

ACKERKNECHT, Erwin H., 50, 84, 96, 97
American Medical Association, 77, 78
American Psychiatric Association, Report of the 1951 Conference on Psychiatric Education, 28
Anderson, J. K., 29, 208
Anthropology: conception of culture, 63–64; medical education, 11; physical, 64; primitive medicine, studies of, 79–84. *See also* Behavioral science; Social science
Antibiotic drugs, 17–18
Aprilton, a case example of role conflict in the hospital, 176–181. *See also* Hospitals
Argyris, Chris, 50
Arieti, Sylvano, 201, 208
Asch, Solomon E., 53–58, 60, 72, 73
Association of American Medical Colleges, 15

BACHMEYER, Arthur C., 159
Bacon, Francis, 36
Badgley, Rodger, 27
Bales, Robert F., 259
Barg, Irwin, 26
Barrabee, Paul S., 209, 230
Baylor University College of Medicine, 11–14, 15, 25–26
Becker, Howard S., 28
Beers, Clifford W., 185–194, 198, 205, 207, 209, 211, 231
Behavioral science: attitudes toward department of, 12, 28; in departments of preventive medicine and public health, 12, 28; origins and history, 17; in psychiatric education, 11–16, 22, 23–25; University of Kentucky Department of, 12, 28. *See also* Social science; Sociology

Belknap, Ivan, 211, 212, 220–221, 230, 231, 232
Bell, Norman W., 140
Bendix, Reinhold, 118
Benedict, Ruth, 79, 96, 97
Berg, Roland H., 141, 159
Bernard, Claude, 69
Bernstein, Marcella, 26
Berry, George Packer, 15–16, 29, 140
Biological sciences: emphasis in medical education, 13, 19; in history of medicine, 33–37; relationship to behavioral science, 17. *See also* Medical education
Biological systems. *See* Physicochemical systems
Bleuler, Eugen, 206
Bloom, Jonathan, 26
Bloom, Samuel W., 8, 9, 28, 29
Bock, Arlie V., 69, 74
Bockoven, J. Sanbourne, 194, 196, 207
Boston Psychopathic Hospital. *See* Massachusetts Mental Health Center
Brill, H., 232
British Medical Association, 92
Brody, E. B., 207, 231
Brooks, George W., 232
Broom, Leonard, 28, 182, 259
Brown, Esther Lucile, 25, 29, 51, 97, 183, 207, 208, 211, 228, 231, 232
Burch, Neil, 26
Bureaucracy, 160, 167–181. *See* Hospitals
Burling, Temple, 152, 159, 163, 165, 168, 173, 175–176, 182, 183
Burlingham, Dorothy T., 29

CAMERON, Norman, 15
Caplovitz, David, 26
Carnegie Foundation, 16
Carr-Saunders, A. M., 87, 97
Cartwright, D., 182

Caudill, William, 28, 96, 193, 207, 210, 212–213, 215–219, 221, 231
Centers, Richard, 118
Cherokee Indians, 81
Cheyenne Indians, 81–82
Christie, Richard, 51
Churchill, Edward D., 145, 147, 150, 154, 159
Ciocco, Antonio, 118
Clausen, John A., 28, 117, 118
Cloward, Richard A., 222, 232
Columbia University, Bureau of Applied Social Research, 26, 159
Committee on Medical Care Teaching of the Association of Teachers of Preventive Medicine, 51
Commonwealth Fund, The, 26, 159
Comprehensive medicine, 9–10, 157
Comte, August, 167
Copernican hypothesis, 34
Cornell Comprehensive Care and Teaching Program, 27
Cornell University, 26
Cornish, Mary Jean Huntington, 26
Cottrell, Leonard S., Jr., 25, 28, 182, 259
Council of Nicaea, and early hospitals, 148
Crutchfield, Richard S., 57–58, 73
Cultural value-orientation, 236–247; American middle-class, 236–239, 242–243; defined, 238–239; Irish, 242–244; Italian, 236–242
Culture, 24, 72; beliefs and attitudes about illness, 99–111; defined, 63–67, 236; and doctor-patient relationship, 8, 42–43, 48, 236–242, 254; and family relationships, 121–139; in Irish family, 242–244; in Italian family, 42–43, 236–242; in middle-class American family, 121–127; primitive medicine, 79–84; the significant sociological unit, 79–81 and social role, 68–69. *See also* Cultural value-orientation; Family
Cumming, Elaine, 101–105, 117, 232
Cumming, John, 101–105, 117, 232
Custodial function of hospitals, 184, 186, 193–194, 197, 205–206, 211, 219–229

Davis, Kingsley, 140
Death: beliefs and attitudes about, 8, 157–158; effects on attitudes toward patient, 8
Descartes, René, 34

Devereux, George, 230
Diabetes: organic symptoms and behavioral implications, 39–40; socioemotional aspects of, a case example, 37–50. *See also* Doctor-patient relationship; Illness
Dickens, Charles, 195, 196, 208
Disease: conceptions of, 7–8, 35–36; the disease-entity concept, 59–60, 198; primitive medicine and, 79–84. *See also* Illness
Dobuan culture, 81, 82–84
Doctor-patient relationship: analogy to perception theory, 52, 63; in ancient Greece, 85–88; basic models of, 40–41, 244–245; beliefs and attitudes about, 7–9, 34–37; conceived as social interaction, 52–53, 247–248; culture, influence on, 8, 42–44, 121–127, 236–247; ethnic factors, 43, 246; in the hospital, 156, 200; in medical education, 8, 16; internal social dynamics, 247–255; as a social system, 8–9, 50, 70–72, 235–258
Doctor's role, 24; change to team practice, 8, 161, 165, 172, 176–181, 203–204, 228–229, 242; changes caused by bureaucratization of hospitals, 170–172, 176–181; defined as a profession, 87–96, 165–166; and the hospital, 145–147, 150, 151–153, 160–181; management of time, 47–48; in modern family, 119–121, 139–140; origins in Greek and medieval medicine, 85–88; relationships to the community, 164–165; responsibility when a consultant is called, 47–48; values and norms in education of, 60. *See also* Physician; Social role
Dunham, H. Warren, 208

Earle, Pliny, 198
Eaton, Joseph W., 117
Ebaugh, Franklin G., 14, 28
Eberhart, John, 26
Edelstein, Ludwig, 86
Eliot, T. S., 119, 140
Empey, Lamar T., 232
Erasistratus, 85
Eron, Leonard D., 51
Etzioni, Amitai, 231
Euthanasia, 94
Evans, Lester J., 10, 26

INDEX

FABIAN Society, 92
Family: authority relationships, 122–123; conjugal type, 121; cross-cultural study of, 237–247; effects of industrialization and urbanization, 62, 119–120, 122–123; familistic type, 122–123; individualistic type, 122; major social roles, 124–127; in medical education, 120; Negro, 123, 136–137; nuclear type, 121–123, 136; of orientation, 121; of procreation, 121; of psychiatric patients, 237; and the sick role, 24, 62–63, 72, 116–117, 119–140; social organization of, 122–123; urban middle-class type, 123–127, 135–136, 236, 242–243; working-class, 136–137
Faxon, Nathaniel, 159
Field: disturbances in the mental hospital, 213–219; of doctor-patient relationship, 24, 58–63; social, concept of, 24, 53–58
Flexner, Abraham, 15, 16, 28, 90, 97
Fox, Renée C., 26, 125, 140, 141, 182
Frame, Janet, 207
Franz, Sheppard Ivory, 27
Freeman, Howard E., 28
Freidson, Eliot, 51
Freud, Anna, 29
Freud, Sigmund, 200, 201, 206

GALEN, Claudius, 34, 86
Galilei, Galileo, 34, 35
Garceau, Oliver, 96
Gee, Helen Hofer, 51
Geer, Blanche, 28
Gerth, Hans H., 159
Gestalt psychology, 52–53
Gibbs, Willard, 70, 72
Gilmore, H. R., 207–231
Ginsburg, Sol W., 29, 208
Ginzberg, Eli, 29, 208
Glaser, Robert J., 51
Glick, P. C., 141
Goffman, Erving, 211, 219–222, 231, 232
Goldwater, S. S., 159
Goode, William J., 88–89, 97
Gordon, Milton M., 118
Goss, Mary E. W., 26, 28, 259
Gouldner, Alvin W., 182
Graham, Saxon, 118
Greenblatt, Milton, 141, 194, 196, 207, 208, 211, 228, 231, 232
Group for the Advancement of Psychiatry (GAP), 12, 14–15, 27, 28

HAGERSTOWN survey, 110–111
Hall, Oswald, 118
Harcourt-Reilly, Sir Henry, 119
Hartley, Eugene, 73
Hartman, Gerhard, 159
Health as a social value, 7
Henderson, Lawrence J., 51, 59, 62, 69–72, 73, 74
Henry, Jules, 141
Hering, Karl Ewald Konstantin, 52–53
Herma, John L., 29, 208
Herophilus, 85
Hippocrates, 85
Hiroshima, 19
Hollender, Marc H., 41, 49, 51, 182, 244, 258, 259
Hollingshead, August B., 112, 118, 208
Homans, George C., 74, 141, 259
Homeostasis: in hospital social systems, 219; in social systems, 8–9, 70–72, 249–255; in theories of physicochemical systems, 70–71
Hospital administrator, 161, 162–167; conflict with physicians, 176–181; as a professional, 165–166; relationships to medical staff, 162–167, 173–176
Hospitals, 145–230; administration, 162, 173–176; authority relationships, 160, 162–167, 173–176; board of trustees, 162, 164–165, 173–176; bureaucracy, 160, 167–181; changes in patient care, 157–158, 184–185; charity and almsgiving, concept of, 148, 151, 156; communication problems, 160; custody-therapy dichotomy, 184–185; effects of changing technology, 145–147, 151–155, 156, 168; history of, 147–159; hospitalism, 150–151; influence of Christian religion, 146, 147–151, 155; influence on the sick role, 116–117, 184–185; and modern family, 124, 126–127, 140; and modern medicine, 72, 120, 151, 184–185; patient role in, 151, 157–158, 161, 184–185; philanthropy and humanitarianism, 149, 150; public attitudes about, 156–157; Reformation and Henry VIII, 149; relationship to medical education, 153–155, 173–176; relationship to medical profession, 145, 150–155; relationship to society, 145–146, 150; research function of, 155, 162; role of the doctor in, 145–147, 150, 151–153, 160–181; role of natural sciences in, 153–157, 158;

role of nurse in, 146-147, 151, 161, 171-172; Roman and medieval period, 148-149; social system of, 161, 166; status hierarchy in, 165-167, 170-171. *See also* Bureaucracy; Hospital administrator
Hughes, Everett C., 28
Human behavior, the study of: basic preparation for medicine, 15, 18, 48-50; psychosocial aspects, 18, 19, 23, 49-50; science of, 34, 49
Hume, David, 149
Huntington, Mary Jean, 28
Hutterites, 100-101, 105

IATREION, 85
Illness: behavioral implications of organic symptoms, 39-40; chronic, special requirements of, 41, 42, 161-162, 185, 224-229; definition, across cultures, 99-105; definition, subcultural differences, 105-111; and the family, 120, 123-127; patient beliefs and attitudes about, 98-112, 158; and normality, 99-100; in primitive cultures, 80-84; and role requirements of the doctor-patient relationship, 40-42; and social class, 106-112; as social deviance, 113-116, 135; socioemotional factors, 157-158. *See also* Disease; Sick role
Incantation, 82-84
Ithaca Conference on Psychiatric Education, 14-15, 28. *See also* American Psychiatric Association

JACO, E. Gartly, 27, 51, 117, 118, 140, 182
Janowitz, Morris, 29
Jones, Maxwell, 202-203, 206, 208

KAPLAN, Howard B., 26
Kendall, Patricia Lazarsfeld, 26, 27, 28, 29, 140, 141
Kennard, Edward A., 225-226, 232
Kennedy, President John F., 182
Kentucky, University of, 12, 28
Kerkhoff, J. D., 207
King, Stanley H., 27, 51, 211, 224, 226-227, 231, 232
Klerman, Gerald L., 232
Kluckhohn, Clyde B., 63, 73, 259

Kluckhohn, Florence R., 237-239, 241-242, 258, 259
Knutson, Andie L., 28
Koffka, Kurt, 72, 80
Koos, Earl Lomon, 107-110, 117, 118
Korean War, 23
Kraepelin, Emil, 200, 206
Kramer, Morton, 232
Kroeber, A. L., 28
Kuba of Sumatra, 99
Kubie, Lawrence S., 100, 117
Kutner, Bernard, 27, 28

LAWRENCE, P. S., 118
Leacock, Eleanor, 118
Leeuwenhoek, Antonj van, 35
"Legend of Chronicity," 211, 227, 230
Leibnitz, Gottfried Wilhelm, 34
Leighton, Alexander H., 117, 118
Lentz, Edith M., 152, 159, 163, 165, 168, 173, 176, 182, 183
Levine, Gene N., 26
Levinson, Daniel J., 141, 207, 232
Lewin, Kurt, 210
Lhamon, William T., 12, 26
Life expectancy, 7-8, 18, 158
Linton, Ralph, 67-69, 74
Lipset, S. M., 118
Lister, Baron Joseph, 151
Locke, John, 34, 149
Lynd, Helen M., 118
Lynd, Robert S., 118

MACCOBY, Eleanor E., 73
Macgregor, Frances Cooke, 27, 51
Magic, 79-84
Malev, Jonathan, 25
Malinowski, Bronislaw, 64, 73
Manitoba Provincial Legislature, 100
Maranos, 220, 232
Margolis, Max L., 232
Marti-Ibanez, Felix, 96
Martin, Russell, 25
Martin, William, 26
Marx, Alexander, 232
Massachusetts Mental Health Center, 228-229
Masserman, Jules H., 259
Medical care: home care, 127; in the hospital, 157-158, 184-185; socioemotional factors in, 157-158, 256-257

INDEX

Medical education: behavioral sciences in, 7–10, 11–12, 13, 15, 23–25, 50, 257–258; biological sciences in, 13, 15–16; commitment to scientific method, 16–17; doctor-patient relationship in, 8–10, 14, 16; effects of atomic science, 19, 22–23; experimental programs, 15–16, 120; and the hospital, 153–155; in Middle Ages, 85; new trends in, 7–10, 11–14, 16–17, 157; relationship to the university, 13–14, 16, 153

Medical profession: attitudes toward family, 119–123; history of, 24, 77–90; reference group of doctor's role, 72, 140; as a social institution, 78; social organization of, 24. *See also* Medicine

Medicine: in ancient Greece, 84–88; art-science dualism, 33–34; behavioral sciences in, 7, 12, 27; beliefs and attitudes about, 35–37; in Civil War, 35; life expectancy and attitudes toward, 7–8, 18, 158; in Middle Ages, 86–88; modern, special requirements of, 7, 119–120; origins of modern, 84–87; primitive, 79–84; science, role in, 7, 33–37, 205–207; as a social institution, 63–64, 66–67, 78; social organization as a profession, 77–96; socioemotional factors in, 18, 33–34, 256–257; team medicine, development of, 91, 161; technology of, 8, 119–120

Melanesian society. *See* Dobuan culture

Mental hospitals: attendant's role, 193, 198, 203, 220–221, 229; attitudes toward patients, 197–199, 211–213, 224–230; authority relationships, 210–211, 219–224, 229–230; custody-therapy dichotomy, 211, 224–230; doctor-patient relationship in, 212–213, 218–219, 225–226; "Moral Treatment," history of, 194–201; nurse's role in, 203; patient feelings and reactions, 211, 213, 215–224; patient-patient relationships, 186–193, 198, 201–205, 213, 216–219, 220–224, 226; patient role in, 191, 203–205, 224; problems of communication, 210–219, 229–230; psychoanalysis, influence of, 200–201, 206–207; public attitudes toward, 104, 209; racial factors in, 217–218; social organization, analogy to industrial research, 210; sociological research in, 193, 194, 201–202, 204–205, 209–229; "Thera-

peutic Community" movement, 185, 193–194, 201–205, 206; World War II, influence of, 202–204

Mental illness: conceptions of, 20–21, 193–194, 198–199, 200–207; among Hutterites, 100–101; psychosocial factors in, 201–205, 213–219; public beliefs and attitudes about, 102–105, 193–194, 200, 223–224; public education in, 101–105; and social class, 111–112, 197–198; wartime, incidence and treatment, 19–21

Merton, Robert K., 16, 26, 27, 28, 29, 51, 74, 140, 141, 182, 259
Messinger, Sheldon, 232
Meyer, Adolph, 200, 206
Meyer, Alan, 26
Mills, C. Wright, 159, 182
Mills, T. M., 182
Miner, J. B., 29, 208
Mitchell, John McK., 26
Moore, George Foot, 50
Murray, Henry, 74
Myers, Jerome K., 111–112, 118, 141
Myrdal, Gunnar, 238, 258

NAGAN, Peter S., 96
Nasiter, David, 26
Navahos, 81
New York Academy of Medicine, 18, 29
New York State Committee on Medical Education, 10
Newcomb, Theodore M., 73
Newton, Sir Isaac, 149
Nichols, William, 26
Nightingale, Florence, 151
Normality, concept of, 99–100, 102–105
Norms: cognitive, 65–66; cultural, 65, 67; defined, 65–66, 238; institutional, 66–67, 78; moral, 66
Nursing: as a profession, 91–92; public health, 45–47; role in the general hospital, 146–147, 151, 161, 184; role in mental hospital, 184. *See also* Hospitals

OBESITY, 49–50
Ohlin, Lloyd E., 222, 232
Olmstead, Michael S., 259
Olson, Stanley W., 26
Organizational analysis, 160–181. *See also* Hospitals

PACKARD, Mrs. E. P. W., 207
Pain, 39–40
Palmer, Margot, 26
Parsons, Talcott, 51, 74, 92–94, 97, 117, 118, 125, 140, 141, 259
Participant-observation, 204–205, 212–222
Pasteur, Louis, 151
Patient: beliefs and attitudes about, 36–37; conceptions of, 34–37; cultural expectations of, 61–62; as disease entity, 59–60; in family, 119; social role of, 24, 67, 70–72; as a whole person, 9, 60
Patton, R. E., 232
Paul, Benjamin D., 27, 51, 117
Payne Whitney Psychiatric Clinic, Cornell Medical Center, 26
Penal institutions, 222–224
Pennsylvania, University of, 26
Perception: the magico-religious frame of reference, 80–84; theories and the doctor-patient relationship, 52–63
Physician: in ancient Greece, 85–88; in Middle Ages, 85–88; moralistic attitudes toward patients, 36–37, 48–49; perception of patients, 60–63; social role of the, 8, 67, 70–72, 91–96; values of, 111–112. *See also* Doctor's role
Physicochemical systems: analogy to social systems, 8–9; Gibbs model, 69–72
Physiological systems. *See* Physicochemical systems
Pinel, Philippe, 194, 200
Plains Indian Tribes. *See* Cheyenne Indians
Prairie Town, 101–105
Preventive medicine and public health, 12, 28
Profession: defined, 87–91; law and medicine compared, 87–88; medicine as a, 78; medicine and pharmacy compared, 90; status of the professional in the hospital, 165–166
Professional, professionalism, professionalization. *See* Profession
Pritchett, Henry S., 16
Psychiatry: approach to patients, 244–245; collaboration with social sciences, 15, 21–23; influence of values in treatment of patients, 111–112; preclinical education, 12; preventive, 20–21; psychodynamics and psychoanalysis in, 14; psychology in, 14; wartime, 19–23
Psychoanalysis. *See* Freud; Mental illness; Mental hospitals; Psychiatry
Psychology. *See* Behavioral science; Psychiatry
Ptolemaic theory, 34
Public health nurse. *See* Nurse

RABOR, Jerome, 232
Ramsoy, Natalie Rogoff, 26, 118
Reader, George G., 26, 27, 28, 29, 140, 141, 259
Redlich, Frederick C., 100, 112, 117, 118, 207, 208, 231
Reeder, Leo G., 28
Reference groups, 24: family as, 72; medical profession as, 72; patient as, 161
Regionville, 107–110
Rennie, Thomas A. C., 112
Richardson, Henry Barber, 127, 131–132, 141
Rivers, W. H. R., 66, 73
Roberts, Bertram H., 141
Roemer, Milton I., 117
Rogoff, Natalie, 28, 118
Rose, Arnold M., 117, 118, 208, 258
Rose, Marianne, 26
Rossman, I. J., 51
Rowland, Howard, 204, 208, 211, 212, 230, 231
Russell Sage Foundation, 25, 26, 51
Rymer, Charles A., 14, 28

SAINT-SIMON, Henri de, 167, 169
Saunders, Lyle, 27, 28, 51, 246, 259
Schaffer, Leslie, 111–112, 118
Schwartz, Doris R., 51
Schwartz, Morris S., 193, 207, 209, 210, 212–216, 218–219, 221, 230, 231
Seabrook, William, 207
Shaw, George Bernard, 248
Sheldon, Eleanor Bernert, 25
Shils, Edward A., 29, 74, 259
Shryock, Richard H., 50, 208
Sick role: cultural variations, 100–105; definition, 112–116; the family as context of, 116–117, 125–127, 140; social class influences, 106–112; social norms of, 62–63, 112–117; subcultural differences, 105–112; variations by

INDEX

age, 116, 126; variations by sex, 113–114, 126; variations according to social situation, 116
Sigerist, Henry E., 77, 85, 96, 97, 98, 117
Simmel, George, 182
Simmons, Leo W., 27, 51
Small group research, 22–23, 247–248, 255–256
Smith, Harvey L., 163–164, 182
Social class, 106–112, 136–137, 246–247
Social equilibrium. *See* Homeostasis
Social institution, 72; defined, 66–67, 79; familial and kinship, 62–63; hospital as, 72; medicine as a, 63, 66, 78, 79; political, 66
Social interaction. *See* Social role; Social system
Social psychology. *See* Social science
"Social remotivation," 211, 224–230
Social role: defined, 67–69; of patient, 67, 98–117, 255–256; normative, 67; in social systems, 70–72, 247–256; of physician, 67–68, 91–96, 255–256. *See also* Doctor-patient relationship; Social system
Social science: medical education, 50; in medicine, 11–12, 17, 23–25, 33–34, 36, 257; mental hospitals, research in, 204–205; origins in medicine, 14–23. *See also* Behavioral science; Sociology; Medical education
Social system, 24, 50; defined, 69–72; doctor-patient relationship as a, 63, 235–258; the family as a, 122–123, 127, 138–140; and the human group, 48–50; psychoanalysis and, 255
Social worker, 45, 47, 132, 161, 241–242
Socialization: becoming a professional, 89–90; the family as a socializing agency, 121, 135; of mental patient, 216–219; process of, 65; in the sick role, 116–117
Sociocultural matrix. *See* Culture
Sociology: conception of culture, 63–64; in medical education, 10, 12–13, 23–25; research in medicine, 14, 28; sources of convergence with medicine, 16–17
Spencer, Herbert, 81
Spiegel, John P., 141, 237, 242–245, 248–255, 258, 259
Srole, Leo, 118
Stainbrook, Edward, 28
Stanton, Alfred H., 193, 207, 209, 210, 212–216, 218–219, 221, 230, 231

Starr, Isaac, 159
Status, 68–69. *See also* Social role
Sterner, Richard, 258
Stiles, Charles Wardwell, 117
Stine, Leonard A., 51
Stouffer, Samuel A., 29
Straus, Robert, 27, 28, 118
Strauss, Anselm L., 28
Strodtbeck, Fred L., 258, 259
Subcultural groups and influences, 246, 247, 256. *See also* Culture
Sullivan, Harry Stack, 185, 186, 201–202, 206, 207, 230
Summy, Carol, 26
Sydenstricker, Edgar, 110, 118
Sykes, Gresham M., 232
Szasz, T. S., 41, 51, 182, 244

Therapeutic functions of hospitals, 184, 191, 193, 200–205, 211, 224–225, 226–230
Tomasetti case, 37–50, 68, 70–71, 235–242, 245, 253–255
Tranquilizers, 228
Transaction, 249–255

Values, 34–37, 60, 105, 238
Vesalius, Andreas, 34
Veterans Administration Hospital, 20, 217–218, 225–226, 228
Vogel, Ezra F., 140
Von Mering, Otto, 211, 224, 226–227, 231, 232

War Department, Research Branch, Information and Education Division, 21–32
Ward, Mary Jane, 207
Warner, Lloyd W., 118
Warren, Charles, 26
Warson, Samuel, 141
Watson, John B., 27
Weber, Max, 155, 159, 170, 172
Weil, Robert J., 117
Weiner, Herbert, 27
Wessen, Albert F., 161, 170, 182, 183
West, Louis Jolyon, 17, 29
Western Reserve University, 15
Wexler, Murray, 28
White, William Alanson, 206
Whyte, William H., Jr., 182

Williams, Richard H., 141, 207, 232
Williams, Robin M., Jr., 65–66, 73, 258
Wilson, P. A., 87, 97
Wilson, Robert N., 117, 118, 152, 159, 163, 165, 168, 170, 173, 176, 180, 182, 183
Witkin, H. A., 53, 73
Wolf, Katherine M., 29
Wolff, Harold G., 27, 51
Wolff, Kurt, 182
Worcester State Hospital, 197–198
World War I, 18, 204, 246
World War II: children, emotional effects on, 19; medical education, 11, 15, 17; medicine, influence on, 17–25; mental hospitals, influence on, 202–207, 228; social-psychological research, 21–23

York, Richard H., 207, 208, 211, 231, 232
Young, Donald, 25

Zander, A., 182
Zborowski, Mark, 51, 117
Zimmern, Sir Arthur, 181, 183